ANATOMY &

Golf Academy of America ®

PHYSIOLOGY

FOR **PE 251**

ANATOMY, EXERCISE, AND BIOMECHANICS

With Select Material from

Anatomy & Physiology with Integrated Study Guide

Fifth Edition

Stanley E. Gunstream
Pasadena City College

Exercise Physiology
Theory and Application to Fitness and Performance

Eighth Edition

Scott K. Powers
University of Florida

Edward T. Howley
University of Tennessee, Knoxville

 **Learning Solutions**

Boston   Burr Ridge, IL Dubuque, IA New York San Francisco St. Louis
Bangkok Bogotá Caracas Lisbon London Madrid
Mexico City Milan New Delhi Seoul Singapore Sydney Taipei Toronto

Anatomy & Physiology for PE 251
Anatomy, Exercise, and Biomechanics

This book is a McGraw-Hill Learning Solutions textbook and contains select material from the following sources:
Anatomy & Physiology with Integrated Study Guide, Fifth Edition by Stanley E. Gunstream. Copyright © 2013, 2010, 2006, 2000 by The McGraw-Hill Companies, Inc.
Exercise Physiology: Theory and Application to Fitness and Performance, Eighth Edition by Scott K. Powers and Edward T. Howley. Copyright © 2012, 2009, 2007, 2004, 2001, 1997, 1994, 1990 by The McGraw-Hill Companies, Inc.
Reprinted with permission of the publisher. Many custom published texts are modified versions or adaptations of our best-selling textbooks. Some adaptations are printed in black and white to keep prices at a minimum, while others are in color.

3 4 5 6 7 8 9 0   DOH DOH   18 17 16

ISBN-13: 978-0-697-81513-2
ISBN-10: 0-697-81513-7

Learning Solutions Consultant: Heidi Freund Degheri
Learning Solutions Representative: Nada Mraovic
Project Manager: Nina Meyer
Printer/Binder: R.R. Donnelley
Cover Photo Credits: ShutterStock

Contents

Credits

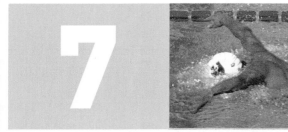

7

The Nervous System: Structure and Control of Movement

■ Objectives

By studying this chapter, you should be able to do the following:

1. Discuss the general organization of the nervous system.
2. Describe the structure and function of a nerve.
3. Draw and label the pathways involved in a withdrawal reflex.
4. Define depolarization, action potential, and repolarization.
5. Discuss the role of position receptors in the control of movement.
6. Describe the role of the vestibular apparatus in maintaining equilibrium.
7. Discuss the brain centers involved in voluntary control of movement.
8. Describe the structure and function of the autonomic nervous system.

■ Outline

■ Key Terms

action potential
afferent fibers
autonomic nervous system
axon
brain stem
cell body
central nervous system (CNS)
cerebellum
cerebrum
conductivity
dendrites
efferent fibers
excitatory postsynaptic potentials (EPSPs)
Golgi tendon organs (GTOs)
homeostasis
inhibitory postsynaptic potentials (IPSPs)
irritability
kinesthesia
motor cortex
motor neuron
motor unit
muscle spindle
neuron
parasympathetic nervous system
peripheral nervous system (PNS)
proprioceptors
reciprocal inhibition
resting membrane potential
Schwann cell
size principle
spatial summation
sympathetic nervous system
synapses
temporal summation
vestibular apparatus

The nervous system provides the body with a rapid means of internal communication that allows us to move about, talk, and coordinate the activity of billions of cells. Thus, neural activity is critically important in the body's ability to maintain homeostasis. The purpose of this chapter is to present an overview of the nervous system, with emphasis on neural control of voluntary movement. We will begin with a brief discussion of the general function of the nervous system.

GENERAL NERVOUS SYSTEM FUNCTIONS

The nervous system is the body's means of perceiving and responding to events in the internal and external environments. Receptors capable of sensing touch, pain, temperature changes, and chemical stimuli send information to the **central nervous system (CNS)** concerning changes in our environment. The CNS can respond to these stimuli in several ways. The response may be involuntary movement (e.g., rapid removal of a hand from a hot surface) or alteration in the rate of release of some hormone from the endocrine system (see chapter 5). In addition to integrating body activities and controlling voluntary movement, the nervous system is responsible for storing experiences (memory) and establishing patterns of response based on previous experiences (learning). The four major functions of the nervous system that will be discussed in this chapter are as follows (5):

1. Control of the internal environment (nervous system works with endocrine system)
2. Voluntary control of movement
3. Programming of spinal reflexes
4. Assimilation of experiences necessary for memory and learning

ORGANIZATION OF THE NERVOUS SYSTEM

Anatomically, the nervous system can be divided into two main parts: the CNS and the **peripheral nervous system (PNS).** The CNS is the portion of the nervous system contained in the skull (brain) and the spinal cord; the PNS consists of nerve cells (neurons) outside the CNS (see figure 7.1). Recall from your previous courses in physiology that the term *innervation* refers to the supply of nerves to a particular organ (e.g., skeletal muscle). In other words, the term innervation means that nerves are connected to a particular organ.

The PNS can be further subdivided into two sections: (1) the sensory portion and (2) the motor portion.

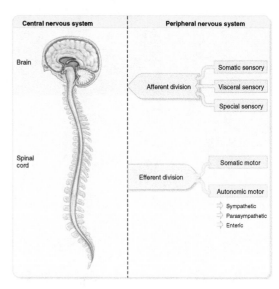

Figure 7.1 Overview of the anatomical divisions of the nervous system.

The sensory division is responsible for transmission of neuron impulses from sense organs (receptors) to the CNS. These sensory nerve fibers, which conduct information toward the CNS, are called **afferent fibers.** The motor portion of the PNS can be further subdivided into the somatic motor division (which innervates skeletal muscle) and autonomic motor division (which innervates involuntary effector organs like smooth muscle in the gut, cardiac muscle, and glands). Motor nerve fibers, which conduct impulses away from the CNS, are referred to as **efferent fibers.** The relationships between the CNS and the PNS are visualized in figure 7.2.

IN SUMMARY

- The nervous system is the body's means of perceiving and responding to events in the internal and external environments. Receptors capable of sensing touch, pain, temperature, and chemical stimuli send information to the CNS concerning changes in our environment. The CNS responds by either voluntary movement or a change in the rate of release of some hormone from the endocrine system, depending on which response is appropriate.
- The nervous system is divided into two major divisions: (1) the central nervous system and (2) the peripheral nervous system. The central nervous system includes the brain and the spinal cord, whereas the peripheral nervous system includes the nerves outside the central nervous system.

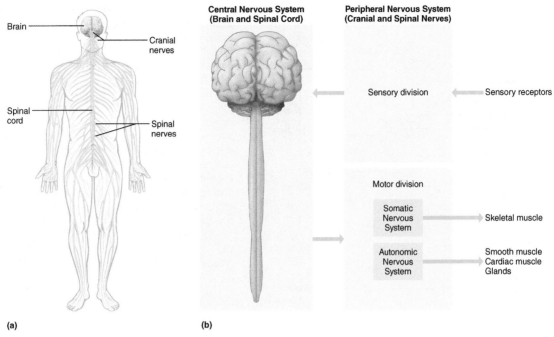

Central Nervous System (Brain and Spinal Cord)

Peripheral Nervous System (Cranial and Spinal Nerves)

Brain

Cranial nerves

Spinal cord

Spinal nerves

Sensory division

Sensory receptors

Motor division

Somatic Nervous System

Skeletal muscle

Autonomic Nervous System

Smooth muscle
Cardiac muscle
Glands

(a)

(b)

Figure 7.2 The relationship between the motor and sensory fibers of the peripheral nervous system (PNS) and the central nervous system (CNS).

Structure of the Neuron

The functional unit of the nervous system is the **neuron.** Anatomically, neurons are cells that can be divided into three regions: (1) **cell body,** (2) **dendrites,** and (3) **axon** (see figure 7.3). The center of operation for the neuron is the cell body, or soma, which contains the nucleus. Narrow, cytoplasmic attachments extend from the cell body and are called dendrites. **Dendrites** serve as a receptive area that can conduct electrical impulses toward the cell body. The **axon** (also called the nerve fiber) carries the electrical message away from the cell body toward another neuron or effector organ. Axons vary in length from a few millimeters to a meter (14). Each neuron has only one axon; however, the axon can divide into several collateral branches that terminate at other neurons, muscle cells, or glands (figure 7.3). Contact points between an axon of one neuron and the dendrite of another neuron are called **synapses** (see figure 7.4).

In large nerve fibers like those innervating skeletal muscle, the axons are covered with an insulating layer of cells called **Schwann cells.** The membranes of Schwann cells contain a large amount of a lipid-protein substance called myelin, which forms a discontinuous sheath that covers the outside of the axon. The gaps or spaces between the myelin segments along the axon are called nodes of Ranvier and play an important role in neural transmission. In general, the larger the diameter of the axon, the greater the speed

of neural transmission (14). Thus, those axons with large myelin sheaths conduct impulses more rapidly than small, nonmyelinated fibers. Damage or destruction of myelin along myelinated nerve fibers results in nervous system dysfunction. Indeed, damage to myelin is the basis for the neurological disease multiple sclerosis (see Clinical Applications 7.1 for more information about multiple sclerosis).

Electrical Activity in Neurons

Neurons are considered "excitable tissue" because of their specialized properties of irritability and conductivity. **Irritability** is the ability of the dendrites and neuron cell body to respond to a stimulus and convert it to a neural impulse. **Conductivity** refers to the transmission of the impulse along the axon. In simple terms, a nerve impulse is an electrical signal carried the length of the axon. This electrical signal is initiated by a stimulus that causes a change in the electrical charge of the neuron. Let's begin our discussion with a definition of the resting membrane potential.

Resting Membrane Potential At rest, all cells (including neurons) are negatively charged on the inside of the cell with respect to the charge that exists outside the cell. This negative charge is the result of an unequal distribution of charged ions (ions are elements with a positive or negative charge) across the cell membrane. Thus, a neuron is polarized, and this

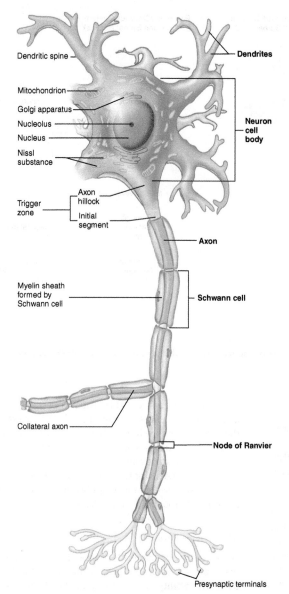

Figure 7.3 The parts of a neuron.

electrical charge difference is called the **resting membrane potential.** The magnitude of the resting membrane potential varies from −5 to −100 mv depending upon the cell type. The resting membrane potential of neurons is generally in the range of −40 mv to −75 mv (58) (figure 7.5).

Let's discuss the resting membrane potential in more detail. Cellular proteins, phosphate groups, and other nucleotides are negatively charged (anions) and are fixed inside the cell because they cannot cross the cell membrane. Because these negatively charged molecules are unable to leave the cell, they attract positively charged ions (cations) from the extracellular fluid. This results in an accumulation of a net positive charge on the outside surface of the membrane and a net negative charge on the inside surface of the membrane.

The magnitude of the resting membrane potential is primarily determined by two factors: (1) the permeability of the plasma membrane to different ion

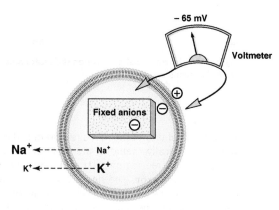

Figure 7.5 Illustration of the resting membrane potential in cells. Compared to the outside of the cell, more negatively charged (fixed) ions exist inside the cell; this results in a negative resting membrane potential. Also, notice that both sodium and potassium can diffuse across the plasma member with potassium diffusing from the inside of the cell to the extracellular fluid, whereas sodium diffuses into the cell from the extracellular fluid.

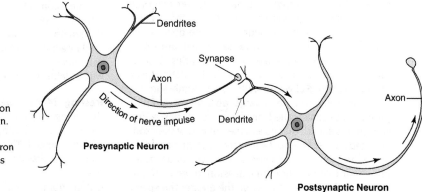

Figure 7.4 An illustration of synaptic transmission. For a nerve impulse to continue from one neuron to another, it must cross the synaptic cleft at a synapse.

CLINICAL APPLICATIONS 7.1

Multiple Sclerosis and Nervous System Function

Multiple sclerosis (MS) is a neurological disease that progressively destroys the myelin sheaths of axons in multiple areas of the central nervous system. Although the exact cause of MS is not known, the MS-mediated destruction of myelin has an inherited (i.e., genetic) component and is due to an immune system attack on myelin. Destruction of the myelin sheath prohibits the normal conduction of nerve impulses, resulting in a progressive loss of nervous system function. The pathology of MS is

characterized by general fatigue, muscle weakness, poor motor control, loss of balance, and mental depression (62). Therefore, patients with MS often have difficulties in performing activities of daily living and suffer from a low quality of life.

Although there is no known cure for MS, growing evidence indicates that regular exercise, including both endurance and resistance exercise, can improve the functional capacity of patients suffering from this neurologi-

cal disorder (60–63). For example, recent studies reveal that MS patients engaging in a regular exercise program exhibit increased muscular strength and endurance resulting in an improved quality of life (9, 60). Importantly, regular exercise may also reduce the mental depression associated with MS (60, 62). However, because of limited research, the amount and types of exercise that provide the optimum benefit for MS remains unknown (1).

species and (2) the difference in ion concentrations between the intracellular and extracellular fluids (64). Although numerous intracellular and extracellular ions exist, sodium, potassium, and chloride ions are present in the greatest concentrations and therefore play the most important role in generating the resting membrane potential (64). The concentrations of sodium, potassium, chloride, and calcium are illustrated in figure 7.6. Notice that the concentration of sodium is much greater on the outside of the cell, whereas the concentration of potassium is much greater on the inside of the cell. For comparative purposes, the intracellular and extracellular concentra-

tions of calcium and chloride are also illustrated (figure 7.6).

The permeability of the neuron membrane to potassium, sodium, and other ions is regulated by proteins within the membrane that function as channels that can be opened or closed by "gates" within the channel. This concept is illustrated in figure 7.7. Notice that ions can move freely across the cell

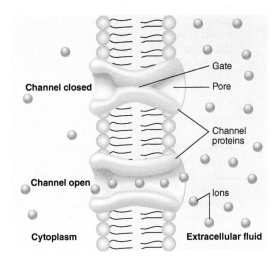

Figure 7.7 Illustration of channels that regulate ion passage across the plasma membrane. Ion channels are composed of proteins that span the entire membrane from the inside to the outer surface. Ion passage through the channels is regulated by the opening or closing of "gates" that serve as doors in the middle of the channel. For example, when channels are open (i.e., gate is open) ions are free to pass through the channel (lower portion of figure). In contrast, when the channel gate is closed, ions' movement through the channel is halted (upper portion of figure).

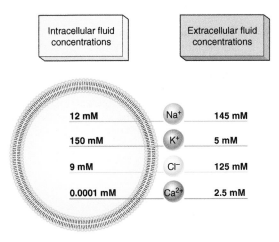

Figure 7.6 Concentrations of ions across a typical cell membrane. Although the body contains many different ions, sodium, potassium, and chloride ions exist in the largest concentrations and therefore play the most important roles in determining the resting membrane potential in cells.

membrane when the channel is open, whereas closure of the channel gate prevents ion movement. Because the concentration of potassium (+ charge) is high inside the cell and the concentration of sodium (+ charge) is high outside the cell, a change in the membrane's permeability to either potassium or sodium would result in a movement of these charged ions down their concentration gradients. That is, sodium would enter the cell, and potassium would leave the cell. At rest, almost all the sodium channels are closed, whereas a few potassium channels are open. This means that there are more potassium ions leaving the cell than sodium ions "leaking" into the cell. This results in a net loss of positive charges from the inside of the membrane, thus making the resting membrane potential negative. In short, the negative membrane potential in a resting neuron is due primarily to the diffusion of potassium out of the cell, caused by (1) the higher permeability of the membrane for potassium than sodium and (2) the concentration gradient for potassium from inside to outside the cell.

As mentioned previously, a small number of ions are always moving across the cell membrane. If potassium ions continued to diffuse out of the cell and the sodium ions continued to diffuse into the cell, the concentration gradients for these ions would decrease. This would result in a loss of the negative membrane potential. What prevents this from happening? The cell membrane has a sodium/potassium pump that uses energy from ATP to maintain the intracellular/extracellular concentrations by pumping sodium out of the cell and potassium into the cell. Interestingly, this pump not only maintains the concentration gradients that are needed to maintain the resting membrane potential, but it also helps to generate the potential because it exchanges three sodium ions for every two potassium ions (5, 62) (figure 7.8).

Action Potential   Research that explained how neurons transmit impulses from the periphery to the brain was completed in England more than 50 years ago. A neural message is generated when a stimulus of sufficient strength reaches the neuron membrane and opens sodium gates, which allows sodium ions to diffuse into the neuron, making the inside more and more positive (depolarizing the cell). When depolarization reaches a critical value called "threshold," the sodium gates open and an **action potential,** or nerve impulse, is formed (see figures 7.9 and 7.10b). After an action potential has been generated, a sequence of ionic exchanges occurs along the axon to propagate the nerve impulse. This ionic exchange along the neuron occurs in a sequential fashion at the nodes of Ranvier (figure 7.3).

Repolarization occurs immediately following depolarization, resulting in a return of the resting membrane potential with the nerve ready to be stimulated again (figures 7.9 and 7.10). How does repolarization occur? Depolarization, with a slight time delay, causes a brief increase in membrane permeability to potassium. As a result, potassium leaves the cell rapidly, making the inside of the membrane more negative (see figure 7.10c). Further, after the depolarization stimulus is removed, the sodium gates within the cell membrane close, and sodium entry into the cell is slowed (therefore, few positive charges are entering the cell). The combined result of these activities quickly restores the resting membrane potential to the original negative charge. To summarize, the events leading to neuron depolarization and repolarization are illustrated step-by-step in figure 7.10a–c. That is, the resting membrane potential is illustrated in figure 7.10a, whereas the events that lead to an action potential are highlighted in figure 7.10b. Finally, the ionic movements that lead to repolarization of the neuron are illustrated in figure 7.10c.

All-or-None Law   The development of a nerve impulse is considered to be an "all-or-none" response and is referred to as the "all-or-none" law of action potentials. This means that if a nerve impulse is initiated, the impulse will travel the entire length of the axon without a decrease in voltage. In other words, the neural impulse is just as strong after traveling the length of the axon as it was at the initial point of stimulation.

A mechanical analogy of the all-or-none law is the firing of a gun (62). That is, the speed of the bullet leaving the gun does not depend upon how hard you pulled the trigger. Indeed, firing a gun is all or none; you cannot fire a gun halfway.

Neurotransmitters and Synaptic Transmission
As mentioned previously, neurons communicate with other neurons at junctions called synapses. A **synapse** is a small gap (20–30 nanometers) between the synaptic endfoot of the presynaptic neuron and a dendrite of a postsynaptic neuron (see figure 7.11).

Communication between neurons occurs via a process called synaptic transmission. Synaptic transmission occurs when sufficient amounts of a specific neurotransmitter (a neurotransmitter is a chemical messenger that neurons use to communicate with each other) are released from synaptic vesicles contained in the presynaptic neuron (figure 7.11). The nerve impulse results in the synaptic vesicles releasing stored neurotransmitter into the synaptic cleft (space between presynaptic neuron and postsynaptic membrane; see figure 7.11). Neurotransmitters that cause the depolarization of membranes are termed excitatory transmitters. After release into the synaptic cleft, these neurotransmitters bind to "receptors" on the target membrane, which produces a series of

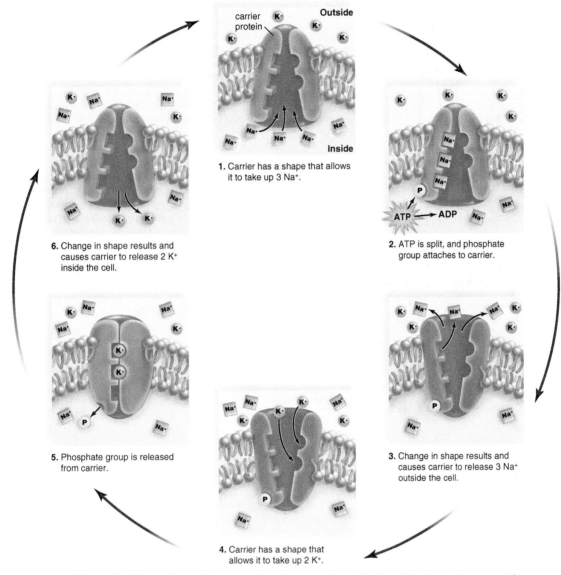

carrier
protein

Outside

Inside

1. Carrier has a shape that allows it to take up 3 Na⁺.

ATP → ADP

2. ATP is split, and phosphate group attaches to carrier.

3. Change in shape results and causes carrier to release 3 Na⁺ outside the cell.

4. Carrier has a shape that allows it to take up 2 K⁺.

5. Phosphate group is released from carrier.

6. Change in shape results and causes carrier to release 2 K⁺ inside the cell.

Figure 7.8 Exchange of sodium and potassium across the plasma membrane by the sodium/potassium pump. The sodium/potassium pump requires energy (ATP) and is therefore an active transport pump that moves three molecules of sodium out of the cell and returns two molecules of potassium into the cell. The sodium/potassium pump process is summarized by steps 1 through 6.

graded depolarizations in the dendrites and cell body (3, 4, 25, 30, 39, 53). These graded depolarizations are known as **excitatory postsynaptic potentials (EPSPs).** If sufficient amounts of the neurotransmitter are released, the postsynaptic neuron is depolarized to threshold and an action potential is generated.

EPSPs can bring the postsynaptic neuron to threshold in two ways: (1) temporal summation and (2) spatial summation. The summing of several EPSPs from a single presynaptic neuron over a short time period is termed **temporal summation** ("temporal" refers to time). The number of EPSPs required to bring the postsynaptic neuron to threshold varies, but it is estimated that the addition of up to fifty EPSPs might be required to produce an action potential within some neurons. Nonetheless, one means by which an action potential can be generated is through rapid, repetitive excitation from a single excitatory presynaptic neuron.

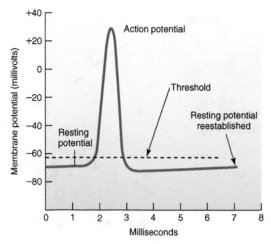

Figure 7.9 An action potential is produced by an increase in sodium conductance into the neuron. As sodium enters the neuron, the charge becomes more and more positive, and an action potential is generated.

A second means of achieving an action potential at the postsynaptic membrane is to sum EPSPs from several different presynaptic inputs (i.e., several different axons), known as spatial summation. In **spatial summation,** concurrent EPSPs come into a postsynaptic neuron from numerous different excitatory inputs. As with temporal summation, up to fifty EPSPs arriving simultaneously on the postsynaptic membrane may be required to produce an action potential (5).

A common neurotransmitter, which also happens to be the transmitter at the nerve/muscle junction, is acetylcholine. Upon release into the synaptic cleft, acetylcholine binds to receptors on the postsynaptic membrane and opens "channels" that permit sodium to enter the nerve or muscle cell. As discussed above, when enough sodium enters the postsynaptic membrane of a neuron or muscle, depolarization results. To prevent chronic depolarization of the postsynaptic neuron, the neurotransmitter must be broken down into less-active molecules via enzymes located within

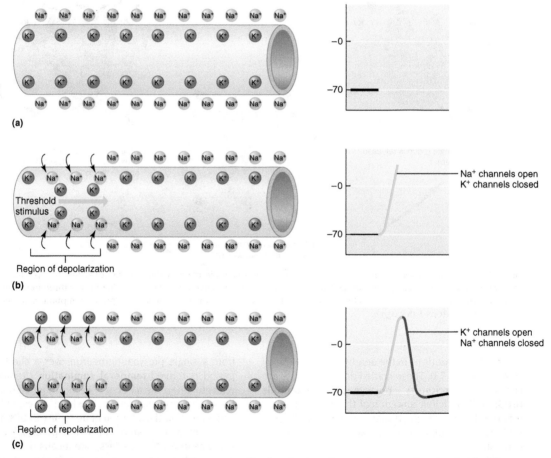

Figure 7.10 (a) At rest, the membrane is about −70 millivolts. (b) When the membrane reaches threshold, sodium channels open, some sodium ions diffuse inward, and the membrane is depolarized. (c) When the potassium channels open, potassium channels diffuse outward, and the membrane is repolarized.

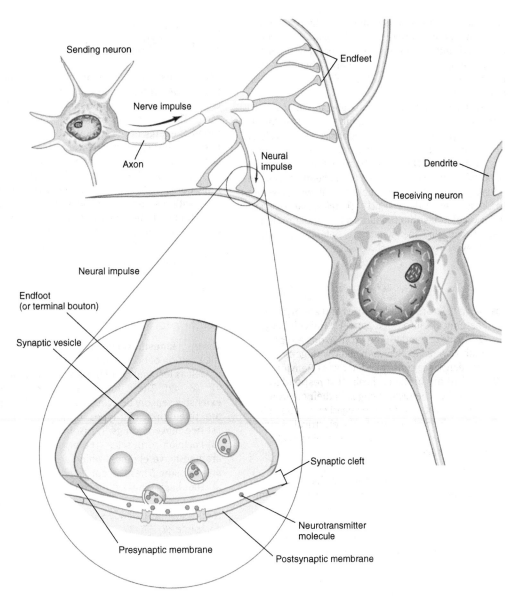

Figure 7.11 The basic structure of a chemical synapse. In this idealized drawing, the basic elements of the synapse can be seen: the terminal of the presynaptic axon containing synaptic vesicles, the synaptic cleft, and the postsynaptic membrane. From A. J. Vander et al., *Human Physiology: The Mechanisms of Body Function*, 8th edition. Copyright 2001 McGraw-Hill, Inc., New York. Reprinted by permission.

the synaptic cleft. In the case of acetylcholine, the degrading enzyme is called acetylcholinesterase. This enzyme breaks down acetylcholine into acetyl and choline and thus removes the stimulus for depolarization (14). Following breakdown of the neurotransmitter, the post synaptic membrane repolarizes and is prepared to receive additional neurotransmitters and generate a new action potential. Note that not all neurotransmitters are excitatory. In fact, some neurotransmitters have just the opposite effect of excitatory

transmitters (5). These inhibitory transmitters cause a hyperpolarization (increased negativity) of the postsynaptic membrane. This hyperpolarization of the membrane is called an **inhibitory postsynaptic potential, or IPSP.** The end result of an IPSP is that the neuron develops a more negative resting membrane potential, is pushed further from threshold, and thus resists depolarization. In general, whether a neuron reaches threshold or not is dependent on the ratio of the number of EPSPs to the number of IPSPs. For example, a neuron that is simultaneously bombarded by an equal number of EPSPs and IPSPs will not reach threshold and generate an action potential. On the other hand, if the EPSPs outnumber the IPSPs, the neuron is moved toward threshold and an action potential may be generated.

Acetylcholine is an interesting example of a neurotransmitter that can be both inhibitory and excitatory. While acetylcholine produces depolarization of skeletal muscle, it causes a hyperpolarization of the heart, slowing the heart rate. This occurs because the combination of acetylcholine with receptors in the heart causes the opening of membrane channels that allow potassium to diffuse out of the cell (21). Therefore, an outward diffusion of potassium produces a hyperpolarization of heart tissue, and the membrane potential is moved further away from the threshold valve.

IN SUMMARY

- Nerve cells are called neurons and are divided anatomically into three parts: (1) the cell body, (2) dendrites, and (3) the axon. Axons are generally covered by Schwann cells, with gaps between these cells called nodes of Ranvier.
- Neurons are specialized cells that respond to physical or chemical changes in their environment. At rest, neurons are negatively charged in the interior with respect to the electrical charge outside the cell. This difference in electrical charge is called the resting membrane potential.
- A neuron "fires" when a stimulus changes the permeability of the membrane, allowing sodium to enter at a high rate, which depolarizes the cell. When the depolarization reaches threshold, an action potential or nerve impulse is initiated. Repolarization occurs immediately following depolarization due to an increase in membrane permeability to potassium and a decreased permeability to sodium.
- Neurons communicate with other neurons at junctions called synapses. Synaptic transmission occurs when sufficient amounts of a specific neurotransmitter are released from the presynaptic neuron. Upon release, the neurotransmitter binds to a receptor on the post synaptic membrane.
- Neurotransmitters can be excitatory or inhibitory. An excitatory transmitter increases neuronal permeability to sodium and results in excitatory postsynaptic potentials (EPSPs). Inhibitory neurotransmitters cause the neuron to become more negative (hyperpolarized). This hyperpolarization of the membrane is called an inhibitory postsynaptic potential (IPSP).

SENSORY INFORMATION AND REFLEXES

The CNS receives a constant bombardment of messages from receptors throughout the body about changes in both the internal and external environment. These receptors are sense organs that change forms of energy in the "real world" into the energy of nerve impulses, which are conducted to the CNS by sensory neurons. A complete discussion of sense organs is beyond the scope of this chapter, so we will limit our discussion to those receptors responsible for position sense and muscle chemoreceptors (i.e., receptors that are sensitive to changes in the chemical environment of muscles). Receptors that provide the CNS with information about body position are called **proprioceptors,** or kinesthetic receptors, and include muscle spindles, Golgi tendon organs, and joint receptors.

Joint Proprioceptors

The term **kinesthesia** means conscious recognition of the position of body parts with respect to one another as well as recognition of limb-movement rates (32, 33, 42, 48, 49). These functions are accomplished by extensive sensory devices in and around joints. There are three principal types of joint proprioceptors: (1) free nerve endings, (2) Golgi-type receptors, and (3) Pacinian corpuscles. The most abundant of these are free nerve endings, which are sensitive to touch and pressure. These receptors are stimulated strongly at the beginning of movement; they adapt (i.e., become less sensitive to stimuli) slightly at first, but then transmit a steady signal until the movement is complete (7, 17, 29, 48). A second type of position receptor, Golgi-type receptors (not to be confused with Golgi tendon organs found in muscle tendons), are found in ligaments around joints. These receptors are not as abundant as free nerve endings, but they work in a similar manner. Pacinian corpuscles are found in the tissues around joints and adapt rapidly following the initiation of movement. This rapid adaptation presumably helps detect the rate of joint rotation (29). To summarize, the joint receptors work together to provide the body with a conscious means of recognition of the orientation of body parts as well as feedback about the rates of limb movement.

Muscle Proprioceptors

Skeletal muscle contains several types of sensory receptors. These include chemoreceptors, muscle spindles, and Golgi tendon organs (29, 34, 49). Chemoreceptors are specialized free nerve endings that send information to the central nervous system in

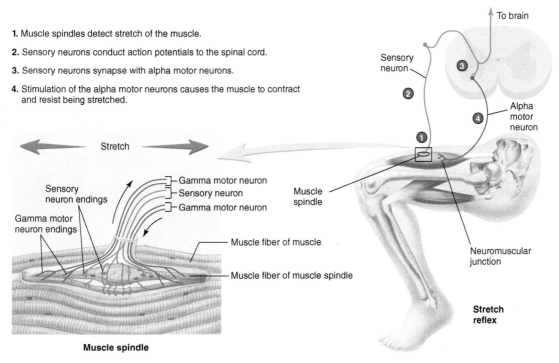

1. Muscle spindles detect stretch of the muscle.

2. Sensory neurons conduct action potentials to the spinal cord.

3. Sensory neurons synapse with alpha motor neurons.

4. Stimulation of the alpha motor neurons causes the muscle to contract and resist being stretched.

Figure 7.12   The structure of muscle spindles and their location in skeletal muscle.

response to changes in muscle pH, concentrations of extracellular potassium, and changes in O_2 and CO_2 tensions. Chemoreceptors may play a role in cardiopulmonary regulation during exercise and will be discussed in more detail in chapters 9 and 10.

For the nervous system to properly control skeletal muscle movements, it must receive continuous sensory feedback from the contracting muscle. This sensory feedback includes (1) information concerning the tension developed by a muscle and (2) an account of the muscle length. Golgi tendon organs (GTOs) provide the central nervous system with feedback concerning the tension developed by the muscle, whereas the muscle spindle provides sensory information concerning the relative muscle length (8, 34, 49). A discussion of each sensory organ follows.

Muscle Spindle   As previously stated, the **muscle spindle** functions as a length detector. Muscle spindles are found in large numbers in most human locomotor muscles (24, 49). Muscles that require the finest degree of control, such as the muscles of the hands, have the highest density of spindles. In contrast, muscles that are responsible for gross movements (e.g., quadriceps) contain relatively few spindles.

The muscle spindle is composed of several thin muscle cells (called intrafusal fibers) that are surrounded by a connective tissue sheath. Like normal

skeletal muscle fibers (called extrafusal fibers), muscle spindles insert into connective tissue within the muscle. Therefore, muscle spindles run parallel with muscle fibers (see figure 7.12).

Muscle spindles contain two types of sensory nerve endings. The primary endings respond to dynamic changes in muscle length. The second type of sensory ending is called the secondary ending, and it does not respond to rapid changes in muscle length, but provides the central nervous system with continuous information concerning static muscle length.

In addition to the sensory neurons, muscle spindles are innervated by gamma motor neurons, which stimulate the intrafusal fibers to contract simultaneously along with extrafusal fibers. Gamma motor neuron stimulation causes the central region of the intrafusal fibers to shorten, which serves to tighten the spindle. The need for contraction of the intrafusal fibers can be explained as follows: When skeletal muscles are shortened by motor neuron stimulation, muscle spindles are passively shortened along with the skeletal muscle fibers. If the intrafusal fibers did not compensate accordingly, this shortening would result in "slack" in the spindle and make them less sensitive. Therefore, their function as length detectors would be compromised.

Muscle spindles are responsible for the observation that rapid stretching of skeletal muscles results in a reflex contraction. This is called the stretch reflex

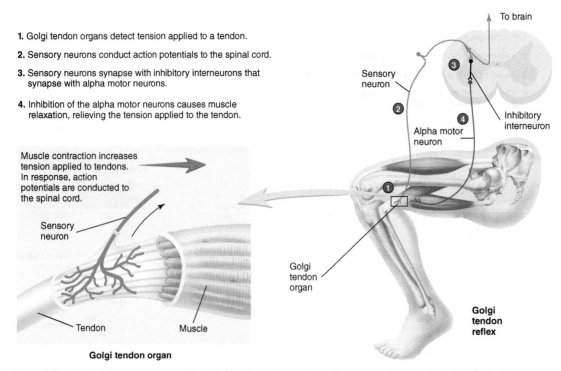

1. Golgi tendon organs detect tension applied to a tendon.

2. Sensory neurons conduct action potentials to the spinal cord.

3. Sensory neurons synapse with inhibitory interneurons that synapse with alpha motor neurons.

4. Inhibition of the alpha motor neurons causes muscle relaxation, relieving the tension applied to the tendon.

Muscle contraction increases tension applied to tendons. In response, action potentials are conducted to the spinal cord.

Sensory neuron

Tendon   Muscle

Golgi tendon organ

To brain

Sensory neuron

Inhibitory interneuron

Alpha motor neuron

Golgi tendon organ

Golgi tendon reflex

Figure 7.13 The Golgi tendon organ is located in series with muscle and serves as a "tension monitor" that acts as a protective device for muscle. See text for details.

or myotatic reflex; it is present in all muscles but is most dramatic in the extensor muscles of the limbs. The so-called knee-jerk reflex is often evaluated by the physician by tapping the patellar tendon with a rubber mallet. The blow by the mallet stretches the entire muscle and thus "excites" the primary nerve endings located in muscle spindles. The neural impulse from the muscle spindle synapses at the spinal cord level with a motor neuron, which then stimulates the extrafusal fibers of the extensor muscle, resulting in an isotonic contraction.

The function of the muscle spindle is to assist in the regulation of movement and to maintain posture. This is accomplished by the muscle spindle's ability to detect and cause the central nervous system (CNS) to respond to changes in the length of skeletal muscle fibers. The following practical example shows how the muscle spindle assists in the control of movement. Suppose a student is holding a single book in front of him or her with the arm extended. This type of load poses a tonic stretch on the muscle spindle, which sends information to the CNS concerning the final length of the extrafusal muscle fibers. If a second book is suddenly placed upon the first book, the muscles would be suddenly stretched (arm would drop) and a burst of impulses from the muscle spindle would alert the CNS about the change in muscle length due to the increased load. The ensuing reflex

would recruit additional motor units to raise the arm back to the original position. Generally, this type of reflex action results in an overcompensation. That is, more motor units are recruited than are needed to bring the arm back to the original position. However, immediately following the overcompensation movement, an additional adjustment rapidly occurs and the arm is quickly returned to the original position.

Golgi Tendon Organs The **Golgi tendon organs (GTOs)** continuously monitor the tension produced by muscle contraction. Golgi tendon organs are located within the tendon and thus are in series with the extrafusal fibers (figure 7.13). In essence, GTOs serve as "safety devices" that help prevent excessive force during muscle contraction. When activated, GTOs send information to the spinal cord via sensory neurons, which in turn excite inhibitory neurons (i.e., send IPSPs). This inhibitory reflex prevents motor neurons from firing, reduces muscle force production, and therefore protects the muscle against contraction-induced injury. This process is pictured in figure 7.13.

It seems possible that GTOs play an important role in the performance of strength activities. For instance, the amount of force that can be produced by a muscle group may be dependent on the ability of the individual to voluntarily oppose the inhibition of the GTO. It seems possible that the inhibitory influences of the GTO could be gradually reduced in response to strength training (20). This would allow an individual to produce a greater amount of muscle force and, in many cases, improve sport performance.

Finally, the GTO is also responsible for a reflex known as the inverse stretch reflex (also called inverse myotatic reflex). As the name implies, the inverse stretch reflex is the opposite of the stretch reflex and results in decreased muscle tension by GTO-mediated inhibition of motor neurons in the spinal cord supplying the muscle. Here's how the inverse stretch reflex works. A vigorous contraction of a muscle group activates the GTO. The GTO responds by sending a message to the spinal cord to inhibit motor neuron firing and reduce the amount of force generated by the muscle. Interestingly, passive stretching of a muscle also activates the GTO and results in relaxation of the stretched muscle.

Muscle Chemoreceptors

Skeletal muscles contain chemoreceptors that respond to chemical changes in the muscle (26–28, 35). Specifically, these receptors are a type of free nerve ending and are sensitive to changes in the chemical environment surrounding muscle; they send information to the CNS via slow conducting fibers classified as group III (myelinated) and group IV (unmyelinated) fibers. Scientific debate continues about the complete list of factors that stimulate muscle chemoreceptors. However, changes in the concentration of hydrogen ions, carbon dioxide, and/or potassium around muscle are known to be potent stimulators of these receptors. The physiological role of muscle chemoreceptors is to provide the CNS with information about the metabolic rate of muscular activity. This information may be important in the regulation of the cardiovascular and pulmonary responses to exercise (6, 28, 35) and is discussed in chapters 9 and 10.

Withdrawal Reflex

A reflex arc is the nerve pathway from the receptor to the CNS and from the CNS along a motor pathway back to the effector organ. Reflex contraction of skeletal muscles can occur in response to sensory input and is not dependent on the activation of higher brain centers. One purpose of a reflex is to provide a rapid means of removing a limb from a source of pain. Consider the case of a person touching a sharp object. The obvious reaction to this painful stimulus is to quickly remove the hand from the source of pain. This rapid removal is accomplished via reflex action. Again, the pathways for this neural reflex are as follows (21): (1) a sensory nerve (pain receptor) sends a nerve impulse to the spinal column; (2) interneurons

within the spinal cord are excited and in turn stimulate motor neurons; (3) the excited interneurons cause depolarization of specific motor neurons, which control the flexor muscles necessary to withdraw the limb from the point of injury. The antagonistic muscle group (e.g., extensors) is simultaneously inhibited via IPSPs. This simultaneous excitatory and inhibitory activity is known as **reciprocal inhibition** (see figure 7.14).

Another interesting feature of the withdrawal reflex is that the opposite limb is extended to support the body during the removal of the injured limb. This event is called the crossed-extensor reflex and is illustrated by the left portion of figure 7.14. Notice that the extensors are contracting as the flexors are inhibited.

IN SUMMARY

- Proprioceptors are position receptors located in joint capsules, ligaments, and muscles. The three most abundant joint and ligament receptors are free nerve endings, Golgi-type receptors, and Pacinian corpuscles. These receptors provide the body with a conscious means of recognizing the orientation of body parts as well as feedback about the rates of limb movement.
- Muscle chemoreceptors are sensitive to changes in the chemical environment surrounding muscle and send information back to the CNS about the metabolic rate of muscular activity.
- The muscle spindle functions as a length detector in muscle.
- Golgi tendon organs continuously monitor the tension developed during muscular contraction. In essence, Golgi tendon organs serve as safety devices that help prevent excessive force during muscle contractions.
- Reflexes provide the body with a rapid, unconscious means of reacting to some stimuli.

SOMATIC MOTOR FUNCTION AND MOTOR NEURONS

The term *somatic* refers to the outer (i.e., nonvisceral) regions of the body. The somatic motor portion of the peripheral nervous system is responsible for carrying neural messages from the spinal cord to skeletal muscle fibers. These neural messages are the signals for muscular contraction to occur. Muscular contraction will be discussed in detail in chapter 8.

The organization of the somatic motor nervous system is illustrated in figure 7.15. The somatic neuron

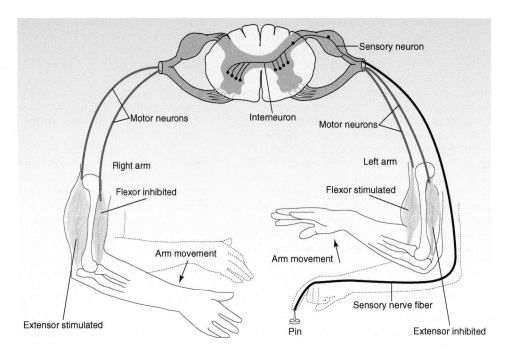

Figure 7.14 When the flexor muscle on one side of the body is stimulated to contract via a withdrawal reflex, the extensor on the opposite side also contracts.

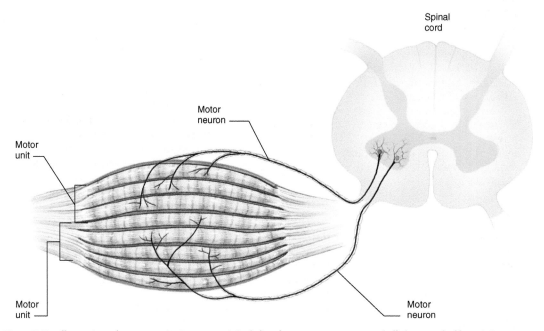

Figure 7.15 Illustration of a motor unit. A motor unit is defined as a motor neuron and all the muscle fibers it innervates.

that innervates skeletal muscle fibers is called a **motor neuron** (also called an alpha motor neuron). Note that the cell body of motor neurons is located within the spinal cord (figure 7.15). The axon of the

motor neuron leaves the spinal cord as a spinal nerve and extends to the muscle that it is responsible for innervating. After the axon reaches the muscle, the axon splits into collateral branches; each collateral

A CLOSER LOOK 7.1

Motor Unit Recruitment and the Size Principle

As introduced in the text, motor unit recruitment is the progressive activation of more and more muscle fibers by the successive recruitment of additional motor units. Recall that a motor unit consists of one motor neuron and all of the muscle fibers that it is responsible for activating. All muscles in the body contain many motor units, and the fibers belonging to a motor unit are spread out across the entire muscle. When a single motor unit is activated, all the muscle fibers innervated by the motor neuron are stimulated to contract. The activation of a single motor unit results in a weak muscle contraction (i.e., limited force production). To increase muscle force production, more motor units must be recruited. This process of motor unit recruitment occurs in an orderly fashion beginning with the smallest motor neurons and eventually activating larger and larger motor neurons (37). This concept was developed by Elwood Henneman and is known as the size principle.

Henneman proposed that the mechanism responsible for the size principle was that the smaller motor neurons had a smaller surface area and

would produce a larger EPSP, which would reach threshold sooner, resulting in an action potential. Further, he predicted that larger motor neurons (with a larger surface area) would produce smaller EPSPs; therefore, these motor neurons would be more difficult to depolarize and achieve an action potential. Taken together, the size principle predicts that motor unit recruitment will occur in order of their increasing size, with the smallest motor neurons firing first, followed by larger and larger motor neurons.

To better understand how the size principle works, let's discuss the three main types of motor units in the body:

1. Type S (slow)—These small motor neurons innervate the slow and high oxidative muscle fibers. These fibers are called type I muscle fibers; muscle fiber types are discussed in detail in chapter 8.

2. Type FR (fast, fatigue resistant)— These larger motor neurons innervate the "intermediate" muscle fibers (called type IIa fibers).

3. Type FF (fast, fatigable)—These are the largest motor neurons and

innervate the "fast" muscle fibers (called type IIx fibers).

An incremental exercise test is a good example to illustrate how the size principle works during exercise. Recall from chapter 4 that an incremental exercise test consists of numerous stages lasting 1–3 minutes per stage. The test begins at a low work rate and with each progressive stage, the work rate increases until the subject cannot maintain the desired power output. So, during the first stage of a graded exercise test, only a low level of muscle force production is required; therefore, you would recruit only the slow, type S motor units. As the test progresses, you will need to produce more muscular force and therefore you will recruit more and more of the type S motor units and eventually progress to the type FR motor units. As the exercise test becomes more difficult, any further increase in muscle force production would come from recruiting the type FF motor units. The size principle and its role in muscle force production is mentioned again in chapter 8.

branch innervates a single muscle fiber. Each motor neuron and all the muscle fibers that it innervates is known as a **motor unit.**

When a single motor neuron is activated, all of the muscle fibers that it innervates are stimulated to contract. However, note that the number of muscle fibers that a motor neuron innervates is not constant and varies from muscle to muscle. The number of muscle fibers innervated by a single motor neuron is called the innervation ratio (i.e., number of muscle fibers/motor neuron). In muscle groups that require fine motor control, the innervation ratio is low. For example, the innervation ratio of the extraocular muscles (i.e., muscles that regulate eye movement) is 23/1. In contrast, innervation ratios of large muscles that are not involved in fine motor control (e.g., leg muscles) may range from 1,000/1 to 2,000/1.

One of the ways that the central nervous system can increase the force of muscle contraction is by

increasing the number of motor units that are recruited. The term *motor unit recruitment* refers to the progressive activation of more and more motor neurons. Recruitment of additional motor units activates more muscle fibers, which increases the strength of a voluntary muscle contraction. In general, motor units are recruited in an orderly fashion as a function of their size. For example, when a muscle is initially activated to lift a light weight, the first motor units to fire are small in size; this results in a limited amount of force generation. However, when more force is required (i.e., lifting a heavy weight), there is a progressive increase in the recruitment of more large motor neurons to increase muscle force production. This orderly and sequential recruitment of larger motor units is called the **size principle** (37). For more details on the size principle see A Closer Look 7.1, and for information on the scientist that discovered this important principle of neurophysiology, see Important People in Science.

A LOOK BACK—IMPORTANT PEOPLE IN SCIENCE

Elwood Henneman Discovered the Size Principle of Motor Neuron Recruitment

Elwood Henneman (1915–1995) was an American scientist who was interested in understanding how the nervous system controls the actions of skeletal muscles. Dr. Henneman completed his medical education at McGill University, and following his postdoctoral training at Johns Hopkins he became a faculty member at Harvard.

Although Dr. Henneman's research advanced our understanding of many aspects of the nervous system, one of his most important discoveries was that the susceptibility of a motor neuron to "fire" is a function of its size.

That is, the smallest motor neurons are the most easily excited, whereas large motor neurons are the least susceptible to excitation. This important discovery is referred to as the *size principle* (also called the *Henneman size principle*) and is discussed in A Closer Look 7.1.

Dr. Henneman's research interest in skeletal muscles developed from his lifelong pursuit of sports and physical activity. During his undergraduate studies, Henneman was a star on the Harvard tennis team. Dr. Henneman was also an excellent downhill skier, and he remained physically active throughout his life. In fact, his strong physique is credited with allowing him to survive a series of major operations,

including installation of an artificial aortic valve, coronary bypass surgery, and an aortic aneurysm (i.e., tear in the aorta). The latter operation was described as "colorful" because the aneurysm occurred when Dr. Henneman was delivering a lecture to Harvard medical students. He diagnosed the problem himself from behind the speakers' podium and ordered a student in the front row to call the hospital and alert the surgery department that Professor Henneman would be arriving to the emergency room with an aortic aneurysm. Although this was a close call, Dr. Henneman survived the surgery and remained active in science until his death.

IN SUMMARY

- The somatic motor portion of the peripheral nervous system is responsible for carrying neural messages from the spinal cord to skeletal muscle fibers.
- A motor neuron and all the muscle fibers that it innervates are known as a motor unit.
- The number of muscle fibers innervated by a single motor neuron is called the innervation ratio (i.e., number of muscle fibers/motor neuron).
- The size principle is defined as the progressive recruitment of motor units beginning with the smallest motor neurons and progressing to larger and larger motor neurons.

VESTIBULAR APPARATUS AND EQUILIBRIUM

Before we begin a discussion of how the brain controls motor functions, it is important to appreciate how the body maintains balance (i.e., equilibrium). The **vestibular apparatus,** an organ located in the inner ear, is responsible for maintaining general equilibrium. Although a detailed discussion of the anatomy of the vestibular apparatus will not be presented here, a brief discussion of the function of the vestibular apparatus is appropriate. The receptors contained within the vestibular apparatus are sensitive to any change in head

position or movement direction (5, 25, 47). Movement of the head excites these receptors, and nerve impulses are sent to the CNS regarding this change in position. Specifically, these receptors provide information about linear acceleration and angular acceleration. This mechanism allows us to have a sense of acceleration or deceleration when running or traveling by car. Further, a sense of angular acceleration helps us maintain balance when the head is turning or spinning (e.g., performing gymnastics or diving).

The neural pathways involved in the control of equilibrium are outlined in figure 7.16. Any head movement results in the stimulation of receptors in

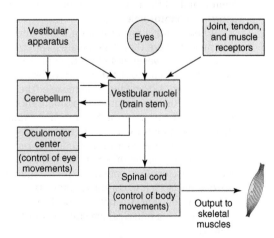

Figure 7.16 The role of the vestibular apparatus in the maintenance of equilibrium and balance.

the vestibular apparatus, which transmits neural information to the cerebellum and the vestibular nuclei located in the brain stem. Further, the vestibular nuclei relay a message to the oculomotor center (controls eye movement) and to neurons in the spinal cord that control movements of the head and limbs. Thus, the vestibular apparatus controls head and eye movement during physical activity, which serves to maintain balance and visually track the events of movement. In summary, the vestibular apparatus is sensitive to the position of the head in space and to sudden changes in the direction of body movement. Its primary function is to maintain equilibrium and preserve a constant plane of head position. Failure of the vestibular apparatus to function properly would prevent the accurate performance of any athletic task that requires head movement. Since most sporting events require at least some head movement, the importance of the vestibular apparatus is obvious.

IN SUMMARY

■ The vestibular apparatus is responsible for maintaining general equilibrium and is located in the inner ear. Specifically, these receptors provide information about linear and angular acceleration.

MOTOR CONTROL FUNCTIONS OF THE BRAIN

The brain can be conveniently subdivided into three parts: the brain stem, cerebrum, and cerebellum. Figure 7.17 demonstrates the anatomical relationship of these components. Each of these structures makes important contributions to the regulation of movement. The next several paragraphs will outline the brain's role in regulating the performance of sports skills.

Brain Stem

The **brain stem** is located inside the base of the skull just above the spinal cord. It consists of a complicated series of nerve tracts and nuclei (clusters of neurons) and is responsible for many metabolic functions, cardiorespiratory control, and some highly complex reflexes. The major structures of the brain stem are the medulla, pons, and midbrain. In addition, there is a series of complex neurons scattered throughout the brain stem that is collectively called the reticular formation. The reticular formation receives and integrates information from all regions of the CNS and works with higher brain centers in controlling muscular activity (5).

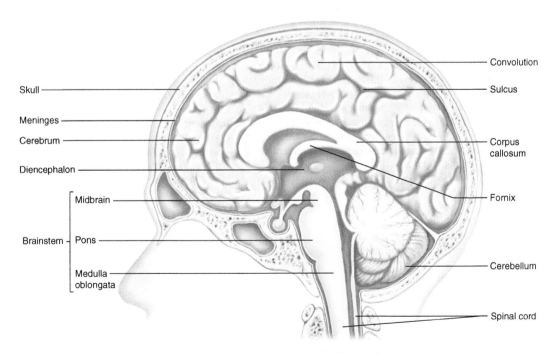

Figure 7.17 The anatomical relationship among the cerebrum, the cerebellum, and the brain stem.

In general, the neuronal circuits in the brain stem are thought to be responsible for the control of eye movement and muscle tone, equilibrium, support of the body against gravity, and many special reflexes. One of the most important roles of the brain stem in control of locomotion is that of maintaining postural tone. That is, centers in the brain stem provide the nervous activity necessary to maintain normal upright posture and therefore support the body against gravity. It is clear that the maintenance of upright posture requires that the brain stem receive information from several sensory modalities (e.g., vestibular receptors, pressure receptors of the skin, vision). Damage to any portion of the brain stem results in impaired movement control(5, 13, 25).

Cerebrum

The **cerebrum** is the large dome of the brain that is divided into right and left cerebral hemispheres. The outermost layer of the cerebrum is called the cerebral cortex and is composed of tightly arranged neurons. Although the cortex is only about one-fourth of an inch thick, it contains over eight million neurons. The cortex performs three very important motor behavior functions (14): (1) the organization of complex movement, (2) the storage of learned experiences, and (3) the reception of sensory information. We will limit our discussion to the role of the cortex in the organization of movement. The portion of the cerebral cortex that is most concerned with voluntary movement is the motor cortex. Although the motor cortex plays a significant role in motor control, it appears that input to the motor cortex from subcortical structures (i.e., cerebellum, etc.) is absolutely essential for coordinated movement to occur (14, 23, 55). Thus, the **motor cortex** can be described as the final relay point upon which subcortical inputs are focused. After the motor cortex sums these inputs, the final movement plan is formulated and the motor commands are sent to the spinal cord. This "movement plan" can be modified by both subcortical and spinal centers, which supervise the fine details of the movement.

Cerebellum

The **cerebellum** lies behind the pons and medulla (figure 7.17). Although complete knowledge about cerebellar function is not currently available, much is known about the role of this structure in movement control. It is clear that the cerebellum plays an important role in coordinating and monitoring complex movement. This work is accomplished via connections leading from the cerebellum to the motor cortex, the brain stem, and the spinal cord. Evidence exists to suggest that the primary role of the cerebellum is to aid in the control of movement in response to feedback from proprioceptors (29, 55). Further, the cerebellum may initiate fast, ballistic movements via its connection with the motor cortex (5). Damage to the cerebellum results in poor movement control and muscular tremor that is most severe during rapid movement. Head injuries due to sport-related injuries can lead to damage and dysfunction in both the cerebrum and/or cerebellum. For an overview of sport-related concussions, see Clinical Applications 7.2.

Role of the Brain in Exercise-Induced Fatigue

Everyone has experienced fatigue during an exercise training session. Indeed, prolonged or high intensity exercise results in fatigue, which limits human performance. In theory, exercise-induced fatigue can be due to central factors (e.g., higher brain centers and/or motor neurons) or peripheral factors (fatigue within skeletal muscle fibers). Let's discuss the possible role of the brain in exercise-induced fatigue in more detail.

In regard to fatigue within the exercising muscle fibers, it is clear that prolonged or intense contractions can disturb muscle homeostasis and impair the ability of muscle fibers to generate force (45, 46). However, it is also possible that exercise-induced fatigue could result from dysfunction of the central nervous system (i.e., central fatigue) resulting in a reduced motor output to the exercising skeletal muscles (43, 52, 56). This type of central fatigue could occur during prolonged endurance exercise due to the depletion of excitatory neurotransmitters in the motor cortex. This depletion of excitatory neurotransmitters would limit the activation of motor neurons and the muscle fibers that they innervate. In fact, some investigators have proposed that higher brain centers act as a "governor" to control exercise tolerance (40, 41). This "central governor" theory of fatigue proposes that exercise-induced fatigue is regulated by the action of a central (brain) control center that regulates exercise performance (40). It is proposed that this type of control system would limit muscle activation during exercise by reducing motor output from higher brain centers. A theorized advantage of the central governor theory of exercise fatigue is that this system would protect the body against catastrophic disturbances in homeostasis by promoting fatigue and the cessation of exercise before damage occurs.

So, is exercise-induced fatigue controlled solely by the brain, as predicted by the central governor theory? Unfortunately, the answer to this question remains unknown. Nonetheless, current evidence suggests that both central and peripheral factors can contribute to exercise-induced fatigue, and that the

CLINICAL APPLICATIONS 7.2

Sport-Related Concussions

Although head injuries can occur in many activities, sports with the greatest risk of head injury include football, gymnastics, ice hockey, wrestling, and boxing. Other sporting activities that pose a significant risk for head injury include horse racing, motorcycle and automobile racing, martial arts, soccer, and rugby.

A forceful blow to the head during sports (e.g., a football collision) can result in a brain injury that is classified by the amount of damage to brain tissue. One of the most common brain injuries in sports is the concussion, and it is estimated that approximately 3.8 million sports-related concussions occur each year in the U.S. (22, 51). A concussion is defined as a complex brain injury resulting from a traumatic force to the head, neck, or body (36). Concussions differ in their degree of severity, but most concussions share several common features (see table 7.1). Note that a concussion does not always result in a loss of consciousness. Indeed, only 10% of athletes who suffer a sport-related concussion are rendered unconscious (2).

Interestingly, girls appear to have a higher rate of concussion than boys in the same sport (e.g., basketball) (11, 22). The reason for this difference is unknown, but some experts suggest that gender differences exist in the

ability to withstand equivalent blows to the head and neck (11, 22). It is also possible that, compared to female athletes, some male athletes may be reluctant to report their head injuries to coaches or parents for fear of being removed from athletic competition (22). Therefore, the incidence of concussion in male athletes may be underestimated (22). If this is the case, the occurrence of concussions may not differ between girls and boys.

What health risks are associated with sustaining a concussion? In general, most concussions result in a short-lived impairment of brain function that typically resolves naturally within a few days (36). Nonetheless, there are some atypical outcomes of a concussion that present serious health risks. These major health risks associated with a concussion include (51): (1) permanent brain damage or death associated with delayed brain swelling; (2) second-impact syndrome; (3) same season repeat concussion; and (4) late-life consequences of repeated concussions. A brief discussion of these concussion-related risks follows.

The risk of permanent brain damage or death in most sports is low. For example, although American football is considered a high risk sport for head injury, it is estimated that only 1 out of every 20,500 football players

develop a permanent brain injury each year (51). The second-impact syndrome occurs when an athlete who has sustained an initial concussion suffers a second head injury before the first injury has healed. This second-impact syndrome promotes brain vascular congestion, which can progress to cerebral swelling and death. Also, after sustaining a concussion, the brain is in a state of vulnerability for an extended period. Therefore, an additional risk of a sports-related concussion is the increased vulnerability to a second concussion within the same season (51). This concussion-related health risk is often called the *same-season repeat concussion*. A final health risk of suffering a concussion is the possibility that a brain injury early in life increases the risk of late-life degenerative brain disorders (e.g., Alzheimer's disease) (51). Indeed, one study suggests that retired professional American football players are at a higher risk for early onset of Alzheimer's disease than a nonathletic population (19). Therefore, although the typical concussion does not pose an acute life-threatening injury, several post-concussion health risks exist. For more details on sports-related concussions, see Halstead and Walter (2010) in the Suggested Readings.

TABLE 7.1	Signs and Symptoms of a Concussion		
Physical	**Cognitive**	**Emotional**	**Sleep**
Headache	Difficulty remembering	Irritability	Drowsiness
Nausea	Difficulty concentrating	Sadness	Sleeping more than usual
Vomiting	Feeling mentally "foggy"	Emotional	Sleeping less than usual
Visual problems	Answers questions slowly	Nervousness	Difficulty falling asleep

---

relative contribution of central or peripheral factors may depend upon the environmental conditions and the type of exercise (e.g., intensity and duration) performed to induce fatigue. Therefore, the "central governor" theory of exercise-induced fatigue remains a theory, and future research will be required to support or reject this concept (57). More will be said about muscle fatigue in chapter 8.

IN SUMMARY

- The brain can be subdivided into three parts: (1) the brain stem, (2) the cerebrum, and (3) the cerebellum.
- The motor cortex controls motor activity with the aid of input from subcortical areas.
- Prolonged endurance exercise can deplete excitatory neurotransmitters in higher brain centers (i.e., motor cortex) and reduce motor neuron activation. This type of exercise-induced fatigue (i.e., central fatigue) results from a reduced activation of motor neurons and the muscle fibers that they innervate.

MOTOR FUNCTIONS OF THE SPINAL CORD

One motor function of the spinal cord has already been discussed (withdrawal reflex). The precise role of spinal reflexes in the control of movement is still being debated. However, there is increasing evidence that normal motor function is influenced by spinal reflexes. In fact, some authors claim that reflexes play a major role in the control of voluntary movements. These investigators believe that the events that underlie volitional movement are built on a variety of spinal reflexes (5, 23, 59). Support for this idea comes from the demonstration that spinal reflex neurons are directly affected by descending neural traffic from the brain stem and cortical centers.

The spinal cord makes a major contribution to the control of movement by the preparation of spinal centers to perform the desired movement. The spinal mechanism by which a voluntary movement is translated into appropriate muscle action is termed *spinal tuning*. Spinal tuning appears to operate in the following way: Higher brain centers of the motor system are concerned with only the general parameters of movement. The specific details of the movement are refined at the spinal cord level via interaction of spinal cord neurons and higher brain centers. In other words, although the general pattern of the anticipated movement is controlled by higher motor centers, additional refinement of this movement may occur by a complex interaction of spinal cord neurons and higher centers (5). Thus, it appears that spinal centers play an important role in volitional movement.

IN SUMMARY

- Evidence exists that the spinal cord plays an important role in voluntary movement with groups of neurons controlling certain aspects of motor activity.
- The spinal mechanism by which a voluntary movement is translated into appropriate muscle action is termed *spinal tuning*.

CONTROL OF MOTOR FUNCTIONS

Watching a highly skilled athlete perform a sports skill is exciting, but it really does not help us to appreciate the complex integration of the many parts of the nervous system required to perform this act. A pitcher throwing a baseball seems to the observer to be accomplishing a simple act, but in reality this movement consists of a complex interaction of higher brain centers with spinal reflexes performed together with precise timing. How the nervous system produces a coordinated movement has been one of the major unresolved mysteries facing neurophysiologists for many decades. Although progress has been made toward answering the basic question of "How do humans control voluntary movement?," much is still unknown about this process. Our purpose here will be to provide the reader with a simplistic overview of the brain and the control of movement.

Traditionally, it was believed that the motor cortex controlled voluntary movement with little input from subcortical areas. However, evidence suggests that this is not the case (23, 55). Although the motor cortex is the final executor of movement programs, it appears that the motor cortex does not give the initial signal to move, but rather is at the end of the chain of neurophysiological events involved in volitional movement (44). The first step in performing a voluntary movement occurs in subcortical and cortical motivational areas, which play a key role in consciousness. This conscious "prime drive" sends signals to the so-called association areas of the cortex (different from the motor cortex), which forms a "rough draft" of the planned movement from a stock of stored subroutines (12, 38). Information concerning the nature of the plan of movement is then sent to both the cerebellum and the basal nuclei (clusters of neurons located in the cerebral hemispheres) (see figure 7.18). These structures cooperate to convert the "rough draft" into precise temporal and spatial excitation programs (23). The cerebellum is possibly more important for making fast movements, whereas the basal nuclei are more responsible for slow or deliberate movements. From the cerebellum and basal nuclei, the precise program is sent through the thalamus to the motor cortex, which forwards the message down to spinal neurons for "spinal tuning" and finally to skeletal muscle (16, 18). Feedback to the CNS from muscle receptors and proprioceptors allows for modification of motor programs if necessary. The ability to change movement patterns allows the individual to correct "errors" in the original movement plan.

To summarize, the control of voluntary movement is complex and requires the cooperation of many areas of the brain as well as several subcortical areas.

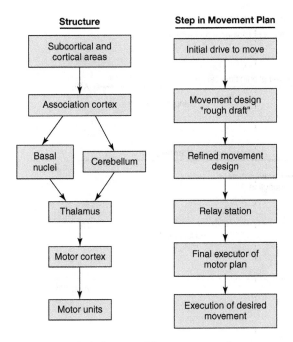

Structure	Step in Movement Plan
Subcortical and cortical areas	Initial drive to move
Association cortex	Movement design "rough draft"
Basal nuclei / Cerebellum	Refined movement design
Thalamus	Relay station
Motor cortex	Final executor of motor plan
Motor units	Execution of desired movement

Figure 7.18   Block diagram of the structures and processes leading to voluntary movement.

Recent evidence suggests that the motor cortex does not by itself formulate the signals required to initiate voluntary movement. Instead, the motor cortex receives input from a variety of cortical and subcortical structures. Feedback to the CNS from muscle and joint receptors allows for adjustments to improve the movement pattern. Much is still unknown about the details of the control of complex movement, and this topic provides an exciting frontier for future research.

IN SUMMARY

- Control of voluntary movement is complex and requires the cooperation of many areas of the brain as well as several subcortical areas.
- The first step in performing a voluntary movement occurs in subcortical and cortical motivational areas, which send signals to the association cortex, which forms a "rough draft" of the planned movement.
- The movement plan is then sent to both the cerebellum and the basal nuclei. These structures cooperate to convert the "rough draft" into precise temporal and spatial excitation programs.
- The cerebellum is important for making fast movements, whereas the basal nuclei are more responsible for slow or deliberate movements.

- From the cerebellum and basal nuclei, the precise program is sent through the thalamus to the motor cortex, which forwards the message down to spinal neurons for "spinal tuning" and finally to skeletal muscle.
- Feedback to the CNS from muscle receptors and proprioceptors allows for the modification of motor programs if necessary.

AUTONOMIC NERVOUS SYSTEM

The **autonomic nervous system** plays an important role in maintaining **homeostasis.** In contrast to somatic motor nerves, autonomic motor nerves innervate effector organs (e.g., smooth muscle, cardiac muscle), which are not usually under voluntary control. Autonomic motor nerves innervate cardiac muscle, glands, and smooth muscle found in airways, the gut, and blood vessels. In general, the autonomic nervous system operates below the conscious level, although some individuals apparently can learn to control some portions of this system. Although involuntary, it appears that the function of the autonomic nervous system is closely linked to emotion. For example, all of us have experienced an increase in heart rate following extreme excitement or fear. Further, the secretions from the digestive glands and sweat glands are affected by periods of excitement. It should not be surprising that participation in intense exercise results in an increase in autonomic activity.

The autonomic nervous system can be separated both functionally and anatomically into two divisions: (1) **sympathetic division** and (2) **parasympathetic division** (see figure 7.19). Most organs receive dual innervation by both the parasympathetic and sympathetic branches of the autonomic nervous system (62). In general, the sympathetic portion of the autonomic nervous system tends to activate an organ (e.g., increases heart rate), whereas parasympathetic impulses tend to inhibit it (e.g., slows heart rate). Therefore, the activity of a particular organ can be regulated according to the ratio of sympathetic/parasympathetic impulses to the tissue. In this way, the autonomic nervous system may regulate the activities of involuntary muscles (i.e., smooth muscle) and glands in accordance with the needs of the body (see chapter 5).

The sympathetic division of the autonomic nervous system has its cell bodies of the preganglionic neurons in the thoracic and lumbar regions of the spinal cord. These fibers leave the spinal cord and enter the sympathetic ganglia (figure 7.19). The neurotransmitter between the preganglionic neurons and postganglionic

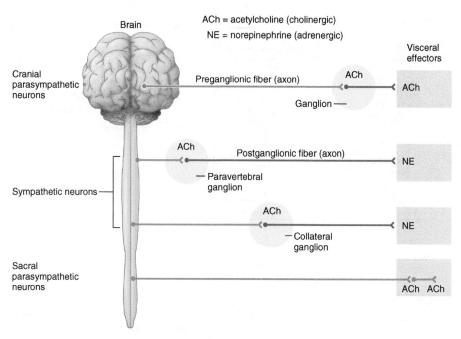

Figure 7.19   A simple schematic demonstrating the neurotransmitters of the autonomic nervous system.

neurons is acetylcholine. Postganglionic sympathetic fibers leave these sympathetic ganglia and innervate a wide variety of tissues. The neurotransmitter released at the effector organ is primarily norepinephrine. Recall from chapter 5 that norepinephrine exerts its action on the effector organ by binding to either an alpha or a beta receptor on the membrane of the target organ (21). Following sympathetic stimulation, norepinephrine is removed in two ways: (1) reuptake into the postganglionic fiber; and/or (2) broken down into nonactive by-products (21).

The parasympathetic division of the autonomic nervous system has its cell bodies located within the brain stem and the sacral portion of the spinal cord. Parasympathetic fibers leave the brain stem and the spinal cord and converge on ganglia in a wide variety of anatomical areas. Acetylcholine is the neurotransmitter in both preganglionic and postganglionic fibers. After parasympathetic nerve stimulation, acetylcholine is released and rapidly degraded by the enzyme acetyl-cholinesterase.

At rest, the activities of the sympathetic and parasympathetic divisions of the autonomic nervous system are in balance. However, during a bout of exercise, the activity of the parasympathetic nervous system decreases and activation of the sympathetic nervous system increases. A major role of the sympathetic nervous system during exercise is to regulate blood flow to the working muscles (54). This is achieved by

increasing cardiac output and a redistribution of blood flow toward the contracting muscles (discussed in chapter 9). At the cessation of exercise, sympathetic activity decreases and parasympathetic activity increases, allowing the body to return to a resting state (15).

IN SUMMARY

- The autonomic nervous system is responsible for maintaining the constancy of the body's internal environment.
- Anatomically and functionally, the autonomic nervous system can be divided into two divisions: (1) the sympathetic division and (2) the parasympathetic division.
- In general, the sympathetic portion (releasing norepinephrine) tends to excite an organ, whereas the parasympathetic portion (releasing acetylcholine) tends to inhibit the same organ.

EXERCISE ENHANCES BRAIN HEALTH

Although it is well known that regular exercise can benefit overall health, research now indicates that exercise can also improve brain (cognitive) function, particularly in later life. Maintaining brain health

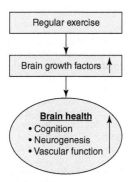

Figure 7.20 Regular exercise targets many aspects of brain function and has broad positive benefits on overall brain health. Specifically, exercise promotes an increase in several brain growth factors that lead to improved brain health by improving cognition, neurogenesis, and vascular function.

throughout life is an important goal, and both mental stimulation (e.g., reading) and exercise are interventions that can contribute to good brain health. Therefore, daily exercise is a simple and inexpensive way to help maintain the health of the central nervous system.

How strong is the evidence that regular exercise improves brain function and protects against age-related deterioration? In short, the evidence is extremely strong. Specifically, numerous studies reveal that exercise targets many aspects of brain

function and has broad effects on overall brain health, learning, memory, and depression, particularly in older populations (8). Moreover, regular exercise can protect against several types of dementia (e.g., Alzheimer's disease) and certain types of brain injury (e.g., stroke) (8, 50). Therefore, exercise increases brain health, just as it improves body health, and thus represents an important lifestyle intervention to improve brain function and resistance to neurodegenerative diseases (10, 31).

How does exercise enhance brain health? Regular aerobic exercise promotes a cascade of brain growth factor signaling that (1) enhances learning and memory; (2) stimulates neurogenesis (i.e., formation of new neurons); (3) improves brain vascular function and blood flow; and (4) attenuates the mechanisms driving depression (7). In addition to these central mechanisms, exercise also reduces several peripheral risk factors for cognitive decline, including inflammation, hypertension, and insulin resistance (8). Figure 7.20 summarizes the exercise-induced cascade of events that lead to improved brain function and health.

IN SUMMARY

- Research indicates that exercise can improve brain (cognitive) function, particularly in older individuals.

STUDY QUESTIONS

1. Identify the location and functions of the central nervous system.
2. Draw a simple chart illustrating the organization of the nervous system.
3. Define *synapses*.
4. Define *membrane potential* and *action potential*.
5. Discuss an IPSP and an EPSP. How do they differ?
6. What are proprioceptors? Give some examples.
7. Describe the location and function of the vestibular apparatus.
8. What is meant by the term *spinal tuning*?
9. List the possible motor functions played by the brain stem, the motor cortex, and the cerebellum.
10. Describe the divisions and functions of the autonomic nervous system.
11. Define the terms *motor unit* and *innervation ratio*.
12. Briefly describe the positive benefits of exercise on brain function.
13. How does regular exercise maintain neuronal health?
14. Describe the withdrawal reflex.
15. Outline the functions of both muscle spindles and the Golgi tendon organ.
16. Describe the general anatomical design of a muscle spindle and discuss its physiological function.
17. Discuss the function of Golgi tendon organs in monitoring muscle tension.

SUGGESTED READINGS

Colcombe, S. J. et al. 2006. Aerobic exercise training increases brain volume in aging humans. *The Journals of Gerontology. Series A, Biological Sciences and Medical Sciences* 61:1166–70.

Cotman, C. W., N. Berchtold, and L. Christie. 2007. Exercise builds brain health: Key roles of growth factor cascades and inflammation. *Trends in Neuroscience* 30: 464–72.

Fox, S. 2009. *Human Physiology*. New York, NY: McGraw-Hill Companies.

Halstead, M. E., and Walter, K. D. 2010. American Academy of Pediatrics. Clinical report—sport-related concussion in children and adolescents. *Pediatrics* 126: 597–615.

Roatta, S., and Farina, D. 2010. Sympathetic actions on the skeletal muscle. *Exercise and Sports Science Review* 38: 31–35.

REFERENCES

1. **Asano M, Dawes DJ, Arafah A, Moriello C, and Mayo NE.** What does a structured review of the effectiveness of exercise interventions for persons with multiple sclerosis tell us about the challenges of designing trials? *Multiple Sclerosis* (Houndmills, Basingstoke, England) 15: 412–421, 2009.

2. **Bailes J.** Sports-related concussion: what we know in 2009—a neurosurgeon's perspective. *Journal of the International Neuropsychological Society* 15: 509–511, 2009.

3. **Barchas JD, Akil H, Elliott GR, Holman RB, and Watson SJ.** Behavioral neurochemistry: neuroregulators and behavioral states. *Science* 200: 964–973, 1978.

4. **Barde YA, Edgar D, and Thoenen H.** New neurotrophic factors. *Annu Rev Physiol* 45: 601–612, 1983.

5. **Brodal P.** *Central Nervous System.* New York: Oxford University Press, 2010.

6. **Busse MW, Maassen N, and Konrad H.** Relation between plasma K+ and ventilation during incremental exercise after glycogen depletion and repletion in man. *The Journal of Physiology* 443: 469–476, 1991.

7. **Clark FJ, and Burgess PR.** Slowly adapting receptors in cat knee joint: can they signal joint angle? *Journal of Neurophysiology* 38: 1448–1463, 1975.

8. **Cotman CW, Berchtold NC, and Christie LA.** Exercise builds brain health: key roles of growth factor cascades and inflammation. *Trends Neurosci* 30: 464–472, 2007.

9. **De Souza-Teixeira F, Costilla S, Ayan C, Garcia-Lopez D, Gonzalez-Gallego J, and de Paz JA.** Effects of resistance training in multiple sclerosis. *International Journal of Sports Medicine* 30: 245–250, 2009.

10. **Desai AK, Grossberg GT, and Chibnall JT.** Healthy brain aging: a road map. *Clinics in Geriatric Medicine* 26: 1–16, 2010.

11. **Dick RW.** Is there a gender difference in concussion incidence and outcomes? *British Journal of Sports Medicine* 43 Suppl 1: i46–50, 2009.

12. **Dietz V.** Human neuronal control of automatic functional movements: interaction between central programs and afferent input. *Physiological Reviews* 72: 33–69, 1992.

13. **Eccles JC.** *The Understanding of the Brain.* New York: McGraw-Hill, 1977.

14. **Fox S.** *Human Physiology.* New York: McGraw-Hill, 2009.

15. **Freeman JV, Dewey FE, Hadley DM, Myers J, and Froelicher VF.** Autonomic nervous system interaction with the cardiovascular system during exercise. *Prog Cardiovasc Dis* 48: 342–362, 2006.

16. **Fregni F, and Pascual-Leone A.** Hand motor recovery after stroke: tuning the orchestra to improve hand motor function. *Cogn Behav Neurol* 19: 21–33, 2006.

17. **Goodwin GM, McCloskey DI, and Matthews PB.** The contribution of muscle afferents to kinaesthesia shown by vibration induced illusions of movement and by the effects of paralysing joint afferents. *Brain* 95: 705–748, 1972.

18. **Grillner S.** Control of locomotion in bipeds, tetrapods, and fish. In: *Handbook of Physiology: The Nervous System Motor Control.* Washington, DC: American Physiological Society, 1981, p. 1179–1236.

19. **Guskiewicz KM, Marshall SW, Bailes J, McCrea M, Cantu RC, Randolph C, and Jordan BD.** Association between recurrent concussion and late-life cognitive impairment in retired professional football players. *Neurosurgery* 57: 719–726; discussion 719–726, 2005.

20. **Hakkinen K, Pakarinen A, Kyrolainen H, Cheng S, Kim DH, and Komi PV.** Neuromuscular adaptations and serum hormones in females during prolonged power training. *International Journal of Sports Medicine* 11: 91–98, 1990.

21. **Hall J.** *Guyton and Hall: Textbook of Medical Physiology.* Philadelphia: Saunders, 2011.

22. **Halstead ME, and Walter KD.** American Academy of Pediatrics. Clinical report—sport-related concussion in children and adolescents. *Pediatrics* 126: 597–615, 2010.

23. **Henatsch HD, and Langer HH.** Basic neurophysiology of motor skills in sport: a review. *International Journal of Sports Medicine* 6: 2–14, 1985.

24. **Hunt CC.** Mammalian muscle spindle: peripheral mechanisms. *Physiological Reviews* 70: 643–663, 1990.

25. **Kandel E, Schwartz J, and Jessell D.** *Principles of Neural Science.* Stamford: Appleton & Lange, 2000.

26. **Kaufman MP, Rybicki KJ, Waldrop TG, and Ordway GA.** Effect of ischemia on responses of group III and IV afferents to contraction. *J Appl Physiol* 57: 644–650, 1984.

27. **Kaufman MP, Waldrop TG, Rybicki KJ, Ordway GA, and Mitchell JH.** Effects of static and rhythmic twitch contractions on the discharge of group III and IV muscle afferents. *Cardiovasc Res* 18: 663–668, 1984.

28. **Kniffki K, Mense S, and Schmidt R.** Muscle receptors with fine afferent fibers which may evoke circulatory reflexes. *Circulation Research* 48 (Suppl.): 25–31, 1981.

29. **Konczak J, Corcos DM, Horak F, Poizner H, Shapiro M, Tuite P, Volkmann J, and Maschke M.** Proprioception and motor control in Parkinson's disease. *Journal of Motor Behavior* 41: 543–552, 2009.

30. **Krieger DT, and Martin JB.** Brain peptides (first of two parts). *N Engl J Med* 304: 876–885, 1981.

31. **Marks BL, Katz LM, and Smith JK.** Exercise and the aging mind: buffing the baby boomer's body and brain. *The Physician and Sportsmedicine* 37: 119–125, 2009.

32. **Matthews PB.** Muscle afferents and kinaesthesia. *Br Med Bull* 33: 137–142, 1977.

33. **McAuley E, Kramer AF, and Colcombe SJ.** Where does Sherrington's muscle sense originate? *Annual Review of Neuroscience* 5: 189–218, 1982.

34. **McCloskey D.** Sensing position and movements of the fingers. *News in Physiological Sciences* 2: 226–230, 1987.

35. **McCloskey DI, and Mitchell JH.** Reflex cardiovascular and respiratory responses originating in exercising muscle. *The Journal of Physiology* 224: 173–186, 1972.

36. **McCrory P, Meeuwisse W, Johnston K, Dvorak J, Aubry M, Molloy M, and Cantu R.** Consensus statement on concussion in sport—the Third International Conference on Concussion in Sport held in Zurich, November 2008. *The Physician and Sportsmedicine* 37: 141–159, 2009.

37. **Mendell LM.** The size principle: a rule describing the recruitment of motoneurons. *Journal of Neurophysiology* 93: 3024–3026, 2005.

38. **Morton SM, and Bastian AJ.** Cerebellar contributions to locomotor adaptations during splitbelt treadmill walking. *J Neurosci* 26: 9107–9116, 2006.

39. **Nicoll RA, Malenka RC, and Kauer JA.** Functional comparison of neurotransmitter receptor subtypes in mammalian central nervous system. *Physiological Reviews* 70: 513–565, 1990.

40. **Noakes TD.** The central governor model of exercise regulation applied to the marathon. *Sports Medicine (Auckland, NZ)* 37: 374–377, 2007.

41. **Noakes TD, St Clair Gibson A, and Lambert EV.** From catastrophe to complexity: a novel model of integrative central neural regulation of effort and fatigue during exercise in humans: summary and conclusions. *British Journal of Sports Medicine* 39: 120–124, 2005.

42. **O'Donovan MJ.** Developmental regulation of motor function: an uncharted sea. *Med Sci Sports Exerc* 17: 35–43, 1985.

43. **Ogoh S, and Ainslie PN.** Cerebral blood flow during exercise: mechanisms of regulation. *J Appl Physiol* 107: 1370–1380, 2009.

44. **Petersen TH, Rosenberg K, Petersen NC, and Nielsen JB.** Cortical involvement in anticipatory postural reactions in man. *Experimental Brain Research Experimentelle Hirnforschung* 193: 161–171, 2009.

45. **Place N, Bruton JD, and Westerblad H.** Mechanisms of fatigue induced by isometric contractions in exercising humans and in mouse isolated single muscle fibres. *Clinical and Experimental Pharmacology & Physiology* 36: 334–339, 2009.

46. **Powers SK, and Jackson MJ.** Exercise-induced oxidative stress: cellular mechanisms and impact on muscle force production. *Physiological Reviews* 88: 1243–1276, 2008.

47. **Pozzo T, Berthoz A, Lefort L, and Vitte E.** Head stabilization during various locomotor tasks in humans. II. Patients with bilateral peripheral vestibular deficits. *Experimental Brain Research Experimentelle Hirnforschung* 85: 208–217, 1991.

48. **Proske U.** Kinesthesia: the role of muscle receptors. *Muscle & Nerve* 34: 545–558, 2006.

49. **Proske U, and Gandevia SC.** The kinaesthetic senses. *The Journal of Physiology* 587: 4139–4146, 2009.

50. **Radak Z, Hart N, Sarga L, Koltai E, Atalay M, Ohno H, and Boldogh I.** Exercise plays a preventive role against Alzheimer's disease. *J Alzheimers Dis* 20: 777–783, 2010.

51. **Randolph C, and Kirkwood MW.** What are the real risks of sport-related concussion, and are they modifiable? *J Int Neuropsychol Soc* 15: 512–520, 2009.

52. **Rasmussen P, Nielsen J, Overgaard M, Krogh-Madsen R, Gjedde A, Secher NH, and Petersen NC.** Reduced muscle activation during exercise related to brain oxygenation and metabolism in humans. *The Journal of Physiology* 588: 1985–1995.

53. **Redman S.** Monosynaptic transmission in the spinal cord. *News in Physiological Sciences* 1: 171–174, 1986.

54. **Roatta S, and Farina D.** Sympathetic actions on the skeletal muscle. *Exerc Sport Sci Rev* 38: 31–35, 2010.

55. **Sage GH.** *Motor Learning and Control: A Neuropsychological Approach.* New York: McGraw-Hill, 1984.

56. **Saldanha A, Nordlund Ekblom MM, and Thorstensson A.** Central fatigue affects plantar flexor strength after prolonged running. *Scandinavian Journal of Medicine & Science in Sports* 18: 383–388, 2008.

57. **Shephard RJ.** Is it time to retire the "central governor"? *Sports Medicine (Auckland, NZ)* 39: 709–721, 2009.

58. **Shier D, Butler J, and Lewis R.** *Hole's Human Anatomy and Physiology.* New York: McGraw-Hill, 2007.

59. **Soechting J, and Flanders M.** Arm movements in three-dimensional space: computation, theory, and observation. In: *Exercise and Sport Science Reviews*, edited by Holloszy J. Baltimore: Lippincott Williams & Wilkins, 1991, p. 389–418.

60. **Stroud NM, and Minahan CL.** The impact of regular physical activity on fatigue, depression and quality of life in persons with multiple sclerosis. *Health and Quality of Life Outcomes* 7: 68, 2009.

61. **White LJ, and Castellano V.** Exercise and brain health—implications for multiple sclerosis: part 1—neuronal growth factors. *Sports Medicine (Auckland, NZ)* 38: 91–100, 2008.

62. **White LJ, and Dressendorfer RH.** Exercise and multiple sclerosis. *Sports Medicine (Auckland, NZ)* 34: 1077–1100, 2004.

63. **White LJ, McCoy SC, Castellano V, Gutierrez G, Stevens JE, Walter GA, and Vandenborne K.** Resistance training improves strength and functional capacity in persons with multiple sclerosis. *Multiple Sclerosis (Houndmills, Basingstoke, England)* 10: 668–674, 2004.

64. **Widmaier E, Raff H, and Strang K.** *Vander's Human Physiology.* New York: McGraw-Hill, 2006.

CHAPTER 6

Skeletal System

Chapter Preview & Learning Objectives

Functions of the Skeletal System
1. Describe the basic functions of the skeletal system.

Bone Structure
2. Describe the structure of a long bone.
3. Describe the microscopic structure of compact bone.

Bone Formation
4. Compare intramembranous and endochondral ossification.
5. Compare the functions of osteoblasts and osteoclasts.

Divisions of the Skeleton
6. Name the two divisions of the skeleton.
7. Describe the major surface features of bones.

Axial Skeleton
8. Identify the bones of the axial skeleton.
9. Compare the skull of an infant and an adult.
10. Compare cervical, thoracic, lumbar, and sacral vertebrae.

Appendicular Skeleton
11. Identify the bones of the appendicular skeleton.

Articulations
12. Compare immovable, slightly movable, and freely movable joints.

Disorders of the Skeletal System
13. Describe common disorders of bones.
14. Describe common disorders of joints.

Chapter Summary
Building My Vocabulary
Self-Review
Critical Thinking

Anatomy & Physiology REVEALED®
aprevealed.com

Module 05
Skeletal System

SELECTED KEY TERMS

Articular cartilage Cartilage covering the ends of bones forming a joint.

Articulation (articul = joint) A joint formed between two bones.

Compact bone Dense bone tissue formed of numerous tightly packed osteons.

Diaphysis (dia = through, apart; physis = to grow) The shaft of a long bone.

Endochondral ossification (endo = inside; chondr = cartilage; oss = bone) The formation of bone tissue within a cartilage.

Epiphysis (epi = upon) The enlarged ends of a long bone.

Intramembranous ossification (intra = inside) The formation of bone tissue within a fibrous membrane.

Ligament A band or cord of fibrous connective tissue that joins bones together at movable joints.

Medullary cavity (medulla = marrow) The cavity within the shaft of a long bone that is filled with yellow marrow.

Osteoblast (osteo = bone; blast = bud) A bone cell that deposits matrix.

Osteoclast (clast = break) A bone cell that breaks down bone matrix.

Osteocyte (cyt = cell) A bone cell occupying a lacuna.

Paranasal sinus (para = beside) An air-filled cavity in a bone located near the nasal cavity.

Periosteum (peri = around; os = bone) The fibrous membrane that covers bones.

Spongy bone Bone tissue that contains numerous spaces filled with red marrow.

The skeletal system serves as the supporting framework of the body, and it performs several other important functions as well. The body shape, mechanisms of movement, and erect posture observed in humans would be impossible without the skeletal system. Two very strong tissues, bones and cartilages, compose the skeletal system.

6.1 Functions of the Skeletal System

The skeletal system performs five major functions:

1. **Support.** The skeleton serves as a rigid supporting framework for the soft tissues of the body.
2. **Protection.** The arrangement of bones in the skeleton provides protection for many internal organs. The thoracic cage provides protection for the internal thoracic organs including the heart and lungs; the cranial bones form a protective case around the brain, ears, and all but the anterior portion of the eyes; vertebrae protect the spinal cord; and the pelvic girdle protects reproductive, urinary, and digestive organs.
3. **Attachment sites for skeletal muscles.** Skeletal muscles are attached to bones and span across joints between bones. Bones function as levers, enabling movement at joints when skeletal muscles contract.
4. **Blood cell production.** The red marrow in spongy bone forms red blood cells, white blood cells, and platelets.
5. **Mineral storage.** The matrix of bones serves as a storage area for large amounts of calcium phosphate, which may be removed for use in other parts of the body when needed.

6.2 Bone Structure

Each bone is an organ composed of a number of tissues. Bone tissue forms the bulk of each bone and consists of both living cells and a nonliving matrix formed primarily of calcium salts. Other tissues include cartilage, blood, nerve, and fibrous connective tissue.

There are four basic types of bones based on their shapes: *long bones* (e.g., thigh bone); *short bones* (e.g., wrist bones); *flat bones* (e.g., most skull bones); and *irregular bones* (e.g., bones of the spine).

Structure of a Long Bone

The femur, the bone of the thigh, will be used as an example in considering the structure of a long bone. Refer to figure 6.1 as you study the following section.

At each end of the bone, there is an enlarged portion called an **epiphysis** (ē-pif′-e-sis). The *epiphyses* (plural) articulate with adjacent bones to form joints. The articular surface of each epiphysis is covered by an **articular** (hyaline) **cartilage** that protects and cushions the end of the bone and provides a smooth surface for movement. The long shaft of bone that extends between the two epiphyses is the **diaphysis** (dī-af′-e-sis). Each epiphysis is joined to the diaphysis by an **epiphyseal plate** of hyaline cartilage in immature bones or by an **epiphyseal line,** a line of fusion, in mature bones.

Except for the region covered by articular cartilages, the entire bone is covered by the **periosteum**

Chapter 6   Skeletal System

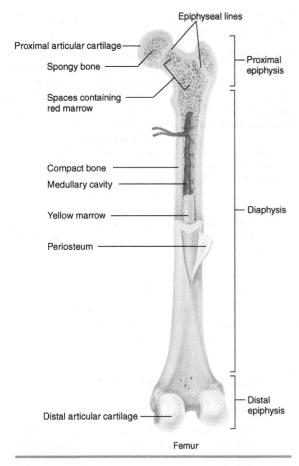

Epiphyseal lines

Proximal articular cartilage

Spongy bone

Proximal epiphysis

Spaces containing red marrow

Compact bone

Medullary cavity

Yellow marrow

Periosteum

Diaphysis

Distal articular cartilage

Distal epiphysis

Femur

Figure 6.1   Major parts of a long bone.   AP|R

(per-ē-os´-tē-um), a fibrous connective tissue membrane that is firmly attached to the underlying bone. The periosteum provides protection and also is involved in the formation and repair of bone tissue. Tiny blood vessels from the periosteum help to nourish the bone tissue.

The interior structure of a long bone is revealed by a longitudinal section. **Spongy** or **cancellous bone** forms the interior of small bones, skull bones, and the epiphyses in long bones. It consists of thin rods or plates called *trabeculae* (trah-bek´-u-lē) that form a meshlike framework containing numerous spaces. Spongy bone reduces the weight of a bone without reducing its supportive strength. The numerous spaces in spongy bone are filled with **red marrow.**

Compact bone forms the wall of the diaphysis and a thin surface layer over the epiphyses. As the name implies, compact bone is formed of tightly

packed bone tissue that lacks the spaces found in spongy bone. Compact bone is very strong, and it provides the supportive strength of long bones. The cavity that extends the length of the diaphysis is the **medullary cavity.** It is lined by a thin membrane, the **endosteum** (en-dos´-tē-um), and it is filled with fatty **yellow marrow.**

Microscopic Structure

As noted earlier, there are two types of bone tissue: compact bone and spongy or cancellous bone. When viewed microscopically, compact bone is formed of a number of subunits called osteons. An **osteon** (os´-tē-on) is composed of an **osteonic** or **central canal** containing blood vessels and nerves, surrounded by the **lamellae** (lah-mel´-lē), concentric layers of bone matrix. Bone cells, the **osteocytes** (os´-tē-ō-sītz), are arranged in concentric rings between the lamellae and occupy tiny spaces in the bone matrix called **lacunae** (lah-kū´-nē). Extensions of the osteocytes extend into tiny channels, the **canaliculi** (kan-ah-lik´-ū-lī), that extend between lacunae and between the innermost lacunae and the osteonic canal.

Blood vessels and nerves enter a bone through a **foramen** (fō-rā´-men; plural, *foramina*), a channel entering or passing through a bone. The blood vessels form branches that pass through communicating canals and enter the osteonic canals to supply nutrients to the bone cells. Materials are exchanged between bone cells and the blood vessels via numerous canaliculi (figure 6.2).

The bony plates of spongy bone lack osteons, so bone cells receive nutrients by diffusion of materials through canaliculi from blood vessels in the red marrow surrounding the bony plates.

Check My Understanding

1. What are the general functions of the skeletal system?
2. What is the basic structure of a long bone?

6.3 Bone Formation

The process of bone formation is called **ossification** (os-i-fi-kā´-shun). It begins during the sixth or seventh week of embryonic life. Bones are formed by the replacement of existing connective tissues with bone tissue (figure 6.3). There are two types of bone formation: intramembranous ossification and endochondral ossification. Table 6.1 summarizes these processes.

Part 2 **Covering, Support, and Movement of the Body**

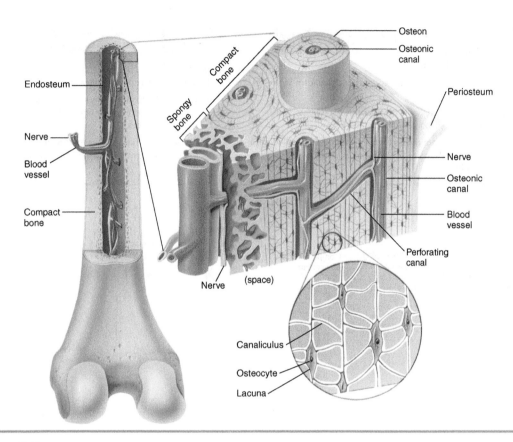

Figure 6.2 Compact bone is composed of osteons cemented together.

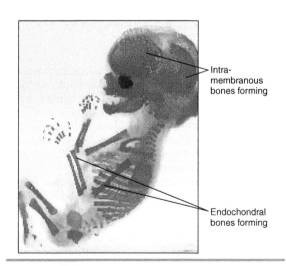

Figure 6.3 Note the stained, developing bones of this 14-week fetus.

In both types of ossification, some primitive connective tissue cells are changed to become bone-forming cells called **osteoblasts** (os´-tē-ō-blasts). Osteoblasts deposit bone matrix around themselves and soon become imprisoned in lacunae. Once this occurs, they are called osteocytes, or bone cells.

Intramembranous Ossification

Most skull bones are formed by **intramembranous ossification.** Connective tissue membranes form early in embryonic development at sites of future intramembranous bones. Later, some connective tissue cells become osteoblasts and deposit spongy bone within the membranes starting in the center of the bone. Osteoblasts from the covering membrane (periosteum) deposit a layer of compact bone over the spongy bone.

Some bone tissue must be removed and re-formed in order to produce the correct shape of the bone as it develops and grows. Cells that remove bone matrix are called **osteoclasts.** The opposing actions of osteoblasts

Chapter 6 **Skeletal System**

Table 6.1 Comparison of Intramembranous and Endochondral Ossification

Intramembranous	**Endochondral**
1. Membranes of embryonic connective tissue form at sites of future bones.	1. Bone is preformed in hyaline cartilage.
2. Some connective tissue cells become osteoblasts, which deposit spongy bone within the membrane.	2. Cartilage is calcified, and osteoblasts derived from the periosteum form spongy bone, which replaces cartilage in ossification centers.
3. Osteoblasts from the enclosing membrane, now called the periosteum, deposit a layer of compact bone over the spongy bone.	3. Osteoblasts of periosteum form a collar of compact bone that thickens and grows toward each end of the bone.

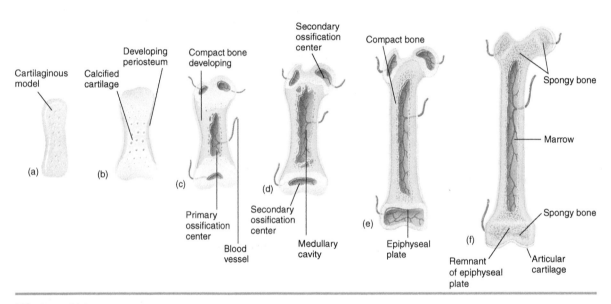

Figure 6.4 Major stages (*a–f*) in the development of an endochondral bone. (Bones are not shown to scale.)

and osteoclasts ultimately produce the shape of the mature bone.

Endochondral Ossification

Most bones of the body are formed by **endochondral** (en-dō-kon´-drul) **ossification.** Future endochondral bones are preformed in hyaline cartilage early in embryonic development. Figure 6.4 illustrates the ossification of a long bone.

In long bones, a *primary ossification center* forms in the middle of the bone, and osteoblasts from the periosteum form a collar of compact bone around the ossification center. Cartilage in the primary ossification center calcifies, and the chondrocytes die. Blood vessels and nerves penetrate into the primary ossification center carrying along osteoblasts from the periosteum, which form spongy bone. A *secondary ossification*

center forms in each epiphysis, and osteoclasts begin to remove spongy bone in the diaphysis to form the medullary cavity. The bone continues to grow as ossification progresses. As cartilage continues to be replaced, the cartilage between the primary and secondary ossification centers decreases until only a thin plate of cartilage, the *epiphyseal plate*, separates the epiphyses from the diaphysis.

Subsequent growth in diameter results from continued formation of compact bone by osteoblasts from the periosteum. Growth in length occurs as bone replaces cartilage on the diaphysis side of each epiphyseal plate while new cartilage is formed on the epiphysis side. The opposing actions of osteoblasts and osteoclasts continually reshape the bone as it grows.

Growth usually continues until about age 25, when the epiphyseal plates are completely replaced by bone tissue. After this, growth in the length of a bone is not possible. The visible lines of fusion between the epiphyses and the diaphysis are called *epiphyseal lines.*

Homeostasis of Bone

Bones are dynamic, living organs, and they are continually restructured throughout life. This occurs by the removal of calcium salts by osteoclasts and by the deposition of new bone matrix by osteoblasts. Physical activity causes the density and volume of bones to be maintained or increased, though inactivity results in a reduction in bone density and volume.

Calcium salts may be removed from bones to meet body needs when dietary calcium is inadequate. When dietary calcium salts return to a sufficient level, they are used to form new bone matrix.

Children have a relatively large amount of protein fibers in their bone matrix, which makes their bones somewhat flexible. But as people age, the amount of protein gradually decreases. This trend causes older people to have brittle bones that are prone to fractures. Older persons may also experience a gradual loss of calcium salts (osteoporosis), which reduces the strength of the bones.

Check My Understanding

3. How do intramembranous ossification and endochondral ossification differ?
4. How does physical activity affect the homeostasis of bones?

6.4 Divisions of the Skeleton

The human adult skeleton is composed of two distinct divisions: the axial skeleton and the appendicular skeleton. The **axial** (ak´-sē-al) **skeleton** consists of the bones along the longitudinal axis of the body that support the head, neck, and trunk. The **appendicular** (ap-en-dik´-ū-lar) **skeleton** consists of the bones of the upper extremities and pectoral girdle and of the lower extremities and pelvic girdle (figure 6.5).

A study of the skeleton includes the various surface features of bones, such as projections, depressions, ridges, grooves, and holes. Specific names are given to each type of surface feature. The names of the major surface features are listed in table 6.2 for easy reference as you study the bones of the skeleton.

6.5 Axial Skeleton

The major components of the axial skeleton are the skull, vertebral column, and thoracic cage. Bones of the axial skeleton are listed in table 6.3.

Skull AP|R

The **skull** is subdivided into the *cranium,* which is formed of eight fused bones encasing the brain, and the *facial bones,* which consist of 13 fused bones and the movable lower jaw. The fused bones are joined by immovable joints called **sutures** (sū´-churs) because they resemble stitches. Several bones in the skull contain air-filled spaces called **paranasal sinuses** that reduce the weight of the skull (table 6.4) and add resonance to a person's voice. The bones of the skull are shown in figures 6.6 to 6.10. Locate the bones on these figures as you study this section.

Cranium

The **cranium** is formed of the following bones: one frontal bone, two parietal bones, one sphenoid bone, two temporal bones, one occipital bone, and one ethmoid bone (figure 6.6).

The **frontal bone** forms the anterior part of the cranium, including the superior portion of the eye orbits (sockets), the forehead, and the roof of the nasal cavity. There are two large sinuses in the frontal bone, one located over each eye (figure 6.7).

The two **parietal** (pah-rī´-e-tal) **bones** form the sides and roof of the cranium. They are joined at the midline by the *sagittal suture* and to the frontal bone by the *coronal sutures* (figure 6.8).

The **occipital** (ok-sip´-i-tal) **bone** forms the posterior portion and floor of the cranium. It contains a large opening, the *foramen magnum,* through which the brain stem extends to join with the spinal cord. On each side of the foramen magnum are the *occipital condyles* (kon´-dīls), large knucklelike surfaces that articulate with the first vertebra of the vertebral column. The occipital bone is joined to the parietal bones by the *lambdoidal* (lam-doy´-dal) *sutures* (figures 6.9 and 6.10).

The **temporal bones** are located inferior to the parietal bones on each side of the cranium. They are joined to the parietal bones by *squamosal* (skwa-mō´-sal) *sutures* and to the occipital bone by the lambdoidal suture. In each temporal bone, an **external auditory canal** leads inward to the eardrum. Just anterior to the auditory canal is the *mandibular fossa,* a depression that receives the mandibular condyle to form the *temporomandibular joint.*

Three processes are located on each temporal bone. The *zygomatic* (zī-gō-mat´-ic) *process* projects

Chapter 6 **Skeletal System**

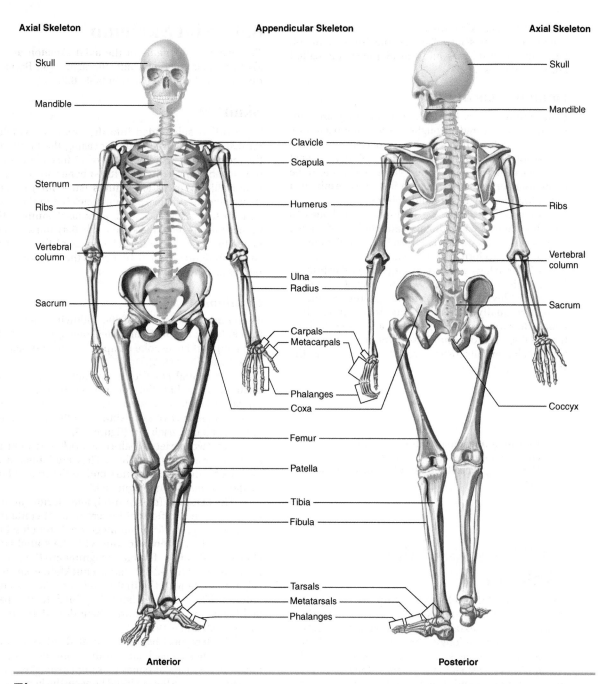

Figure 6.5 The human skeleton. Bones of the axial skeleton are colored ▪. Bones of the appendicular skeleton are colored gold. AP|R

anteriorly to join with the zygomatic bone. The *mastoid* (mas´-toyd) *process* is a large, rounded projection that is located inferior to the auditory canal. It contains small spaces called air cells and serves as

an attachment site for some neck muscles. The *styloid process* lies just medial to the mastoid process. It is a long, spikelike process to which muscles and ligaments of the tongue and neck are attached.

Part 2   Covering, Support, and Movement of the Body

Table 6.2   Surface Features of Bones

Feature	Description
Processes Forming Joints	
Condyle	A rounded or knucklelike process
Head	An enlarged, rounded end of a bone supported by a constricted neck
Facet	A smooth, nearly flat articulating surface
Processes for Attachment of Ligaments and Tendons	
Crest	A prominent ridge or border
Epicondyle	A prominence above a condyle
Trochanter	A very large process found only on the femur
Tubercle	A small, rounded process
Tuberosity	A large, roughened process
Depressions and Openings	
Alveolus	A deep pit or socket
Canal	A tubelike passageway into a bone
Foramen	An opening or passageway into or through a bone through which blood vessels or nerves pass
Fossa	A small depression
Groove	A furrowlike depression
Sinus	An air-filled cavity within a bone

Table 6.3   Bones of the Axial Skeleton

Region and Bones	Number of Bones	Region and Bones	Number of Bones
Skull		**Hyoid**	1
Cranium			1
Ethmoid	1	**Vertebral Column**	
Frontal	1	Cervical	7
Occipital	1	Thoracic	12
Parietal	2	Lumbar	5
Sphenoid	1	Sacrum	1
Temporal	2	Coccyx	1
	8		26
		Thoracic Cage	
Face		Ribs	24
Inferior nasal concha	2	Sternum	1
Lacrimal	2		25
Mandible	1		Total = 80
Maxilla	2		
Nasal	2		
Palatine	2		
Vomer	1		
Zygomatic	2		
	14		

Chapter 6 **Skeletal System**

Table 6.4 Skull Bones Containing Paranasal Sinuses	
Bone	**Number**
Ethmoid	2 groups
Frontal	2
Maxillae	I each
Sphenoid	2

The **sphenoid** (sfē´-noid) **bone** forms part of the floor of the cranium, the lateral posterior portions of the eye orbits, and the lateral portions of the cranium just anterior to the temporal bones. It articulates with all other cranial bones, so it is the "keystone" of the cranium. On its superior surface at the midline is a saddle-shaped structure called the *sella turcica* (ter´-si-ka), or Turk's saddle. It has a depression that contains the pituitary gland. Two sphenoidal sinuses are located just below the sella turcica.

The **ethmoid** (eth´-moid) **bone** forms the anterior portion of the cranium, including part of the medial surface of each eye orbit and part of the roof of the nasal cavity. The lateral portions contain several air-filled sinuses. The *perpendicular plate* extends downward to form most of the nasal septum, which separates the right and left portions of the nasal cavity. It joins the sphenoid and vomer bones posteriorly and the nasal and frontal bones anteriorly.

The superior and middle **nasal conchae** (kong´-kē) extend from the lateral portions of the ethmoid toward the perpendicular plate. These delicate, scroll-like bones support the mucous membrane and increase the surface area of the nasal wall. The roof of the nasal cavity is formed by the *cribriform plates* of the ethmoid. On the superior surface where these plates join at the midline is a prominent projection called the *crista galli,* or cock's comb. The meninges that envelop the brain are attached to the crista galli.

Facial Bones

The paired bones of the face are the maxillae, palatine bones, zygomatic bones, lacrimal bones, nasal bones, and inferior nasal conchae. The single bones are the vomer and mandible.

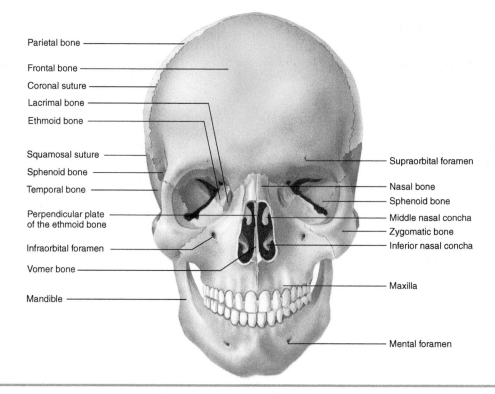

Figure 6.6 An anterior view of the skull. AP|R

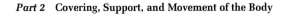

Part 2   Covering, Support, and Movement of the Body

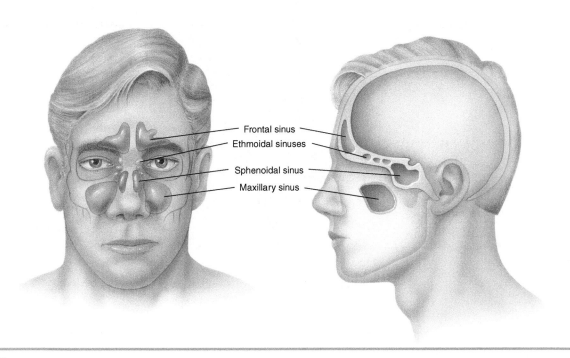

Frontal sinus
Ethmoidal sinuses
Sphenoidal sinus
Maxillary sinus

Figure 6.7   The locations of the paranasal sinuses.

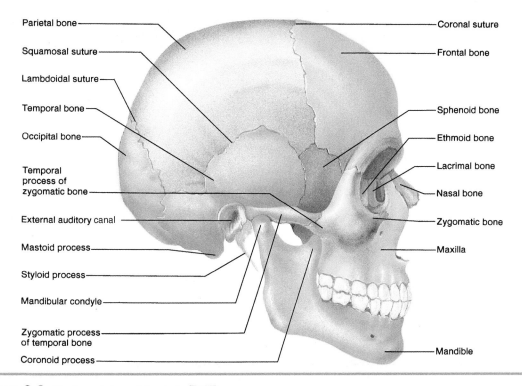

Parietal bone
Squamosal suture
Lambdoidal suture
Temporal bone
Occipital bone
Temporal process of zygomatic bone
External auditory canal
Mastoid process
Styloid process
Mandibular condyle
Zygomatic process of temporal bone
Coronoid process

Coronal suture
Frontal bone
Sphenoid bone
Ethmoid bone
Lacrimal bone
Nasal bone
Zygomatic bone
Maxilla
Mandible

Figure 6.8   The lateral view of the skull. AP|R

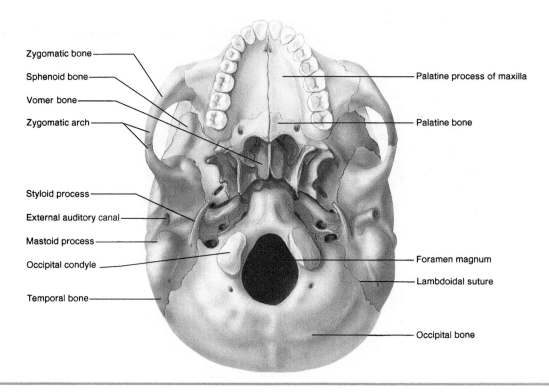

Zygomatic bone

Sphenoid bone

Vomer bone

Zygomatic arch

Styloid process

External auditory canal

Mastoid process

Occipital condyle

Temporal bone

Palatine process of maxilla

Palatine bone

Foramen magnum

Lambdoidal suture

Occipital bone

Figure 6.9 An inferior view of the skull. AP|R

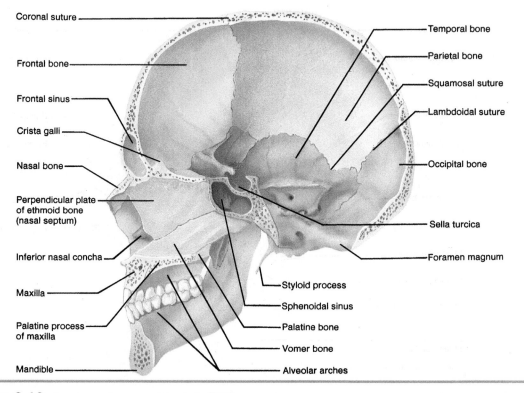

Coronal suture

Frontal bone

Frontal sinus

Crista galli

Nasal bone

Perpendicular plate
of ethmoid bone
(nasal septum)

Inferior nasal concha

Maxilla

Palatine process
of maxilla

Mandible

Temporal bone

Parietal bone

Squamosal suture

Lambdoidal suture

Occipital bone

Sella turcica

Foramen magnum

Styloid process

Sphenoidal sinus

Palatine bone

Vomer bone

Alveolar arches

Figure 6.10 A midsagittal section of the skull. AP|R

The **maxillae** (mak-sil´-ē) form the upper jaw. Each maxilla is formed separately, but they are joined at the midline during embryonic development. The maxillae articulate with all of the other facial bones except the mandible. The palatine processes of the maxillae form the anterior portion of the hard palate (roof of the mouth and floor of the nasal cavity), part of the lateral walls of the nasal cavity, and the floors of the eye orbits.

A *cleft palate* results when the palatine processes of the maxillae and usually the palatine bones do not join before birth to form the hard palate. A *cleft lip,* a split upper lip, is often associated with a cleft palate. These conditions may be corrected surgically after birth.

Each maxilla possesses a downward projecting, curved ridge of bone that contains the teeth. This ridge is the *alveolar process,* and the sockets containing the teeth are called *alveoli.* The alveolar processes unite at the midline to form the U-shaped maxillary *alveolar,* or *dental, arch.* A large **maxillary sinus** is present in each maxilla just below the orbits.

The **palatine** (pal´-ah-tĭn) **bones** are fused at the midline to form the posterior portion of the hard palate. Each bone has a lateral portion that projects upward (superiorly) to form part of a lateral wall of the nasal cavity.

The **zygomatic bones** are the cheek bones. They form the prominences of the cheeks and the floors and lateral walls of the eye orbits. Each zygomatic bone has a posteriorly projecting process, the *temporal process,* that extends to unite with the zygomatic process of the adjacent temporal bone. Together, they form the *zygomatic arch.*

The **lacrimal** (lak´-ri-mal) **bones** are small, thin bones that form part of the medial surfaces of the eye orbits. Each lacrimal bone is located between the ethmoid and maxilla.

The **nasal** (nā´-zal) **bones** are thin bones fused at the midline to form the bridge of the nose.

The **vomer** is a thin, flat bone located on the midline of the nasal cavity. It joins posteriorly with the perpendicular plate of the ethmoid, and these two bones form the nasal septum.

The **inferior nasal conchae** are scroll-like bones attached to the lateral walls of the nasal cavity inferior to the medial nasal conchae of the ethmoid bone. They project medially into the nasal cavity and support the mucous membrane.

The **mandible** is the lower jawbone, and it is the only movable bone of the skull. It consists of a U-shaped *body* with a superiorly (upward) projecting portion, a *ramus,* extending from each end of the body. The superior portion of the body forms the mandibular *alveolar arch,* which contains the teeth of the lower jaw. The superior part of each ramus is Y-shaped and forms two projections: an anterior *coronoid process* and a posterior *mandibular condyle.* The coronoid process is a site of attachment for muscles used in chewing. The mandibular condyle articulates with the mandibular fossa of the temporal bone to form a *temporomandibular joint.* These joints are sometimes involved in a variety of dental problems associated with an improper bite.

Hyoid Bone

The **hyoid** (hĭ´-oyd) is a small, U-shaped bone located in the anterior portion of the neck, inferior to the mandible. It does not articulate with any bone. Instead, it is suspended from the styloid processes of the temporal bones by ligaments. Muscles of the tongue are attached to the hyoid.

The Infant Skull

The skull of a newborn infant is incompletely developed. The face is relatively small with large eye orbits, and the bones are thin and incompletely ossified. The bones of the cranium are separated by fibrous membranes, and there are six rather large, nonossified areas called **fontanels** (fon´-tah-nels), or soft spots (table 6.5). The frontal bone is formed of two separate parts that fuse later in development. Incomplete ossification of

Table 6.5   Fontanels in an Infant Skull

Fontanel	Number	Location
Anterior	1	On the midline at the junction of the frontal and parietal bones
Mastoid	2	Superior to the mastoid process at the junction of the occipital, parietal, and temporal bones
Posterior	1	On the midline at the junction of the occipital and parietal bones
Sphenoid	2	Superior to the temporomandibular joint at the junction of the frontal, parietal, sphenoid, and temporal bones

Chapter 6   **Skeletal System**

the skull bones and the abundance of fibrous membranes make the skull somewhat flexible and allow partial compression of the skull during birth. After birth, they allow growth of the skull without compressing the growing brain. Compare the infant skull in figure 6.11 with the adult skull in figure 6.8.

Check My Understanding

5. What bones form the cranium?
6. What bones form the face?

Vertebral Column

The vertebral column extends from the skull to the pelvis and forms a somewhat flexible but sturdy longitudinal support for the trunk. It is formed of 24 slightly movable vertebrae, the sacrum, and the coccyx. The vertebrae are separated from each other by **intervertebral disks** that serve as shock absorbers and allow bending of the spinal column. The upright posture of humans produces four distinct curvatures in the vertebral column. From top to bottom they are the *cervical, thoracic, lumbar,* and *pelvic curvatures.* Locate these curvatures and the basic components of the vertebral column in figure 6.12.

Structure of a Vertebra

Vertebrae are divided into three groups: cervical, thoracic, and lumbar vertebrae. Although each type has a distinctive anatomy, they have many features in common (figure 6.13).

The anterior, drum-shaped mass is the *body,* which serves as the major load-bearing portion of a vertebra. A bony *neural arch* surrounds the large *vertebral foramen* through which the spinal cord passes. A *spinous process* projects posteriorly and *transverse processes* project laterally from each vertebra.

A pair of *superior articulating facets* (fa´-sets) of one vertebra articulates with the *inferior articulating facets* of the adjacent vertebra above it. When joined by ligaments, the vertebrae form a flexible bony cylinder that protects the spinal cord.

Small *intervertebral foramina* occur between adjacent vertebrae. They serve as lateral passageways for spinal nerves that exit the spinal cord (see figure 6.12).

Cervical Vertebrae

The first seven vertebrae are the **cervical** (ser´-vi-kul) **vertebrae** that support the neck. They are unique in having a *transverse foramen* in each transverse process. It serves as a passageway for blood vessels and nerves.

The first two cervical vertebrae are distinctly different from the rest. The first vertebra is the **atlas,** whose superior facets articulate with the condyles of the occipital bone and support the head. The second vertebra is the **axis,** which has a prominent *odontoid* (ō-don´-toyd) *process* (*dens*) that projects upward from the vertebral body, providing a pivot point for the atlas. When the head is turned, the atlas rotates on the axis (figure 6.14).

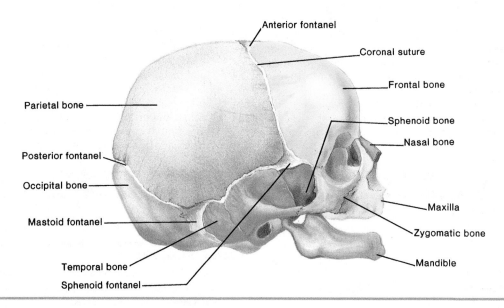

Figure 6.11   A lateral view of a newborn infant's skull. Note the fontanels and the membranes between the cranial bones.

Part 2   **Covering, Support, and Movement of the Body**

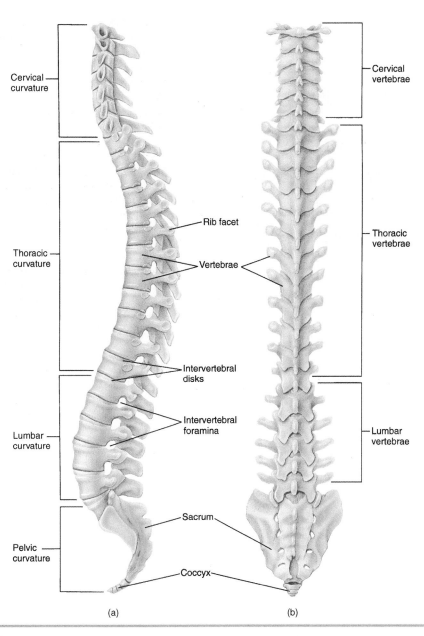

Figure 6.12   The vertebral column consists of 24 movable vertebrae, separated by intervertebral disks, sacrum, and coccyx. (*a*) Lateral view. (*b*) Posterior view.   AP|R

Thoracic Vertebrae

The 12 **thoracic vertebrae** are larger than the cervical vertebrae, and their spinous processes are longer and slope downward. The ribs articulate with **facets** on the transverse processes and bodies of thoracic vertebrae.

Lumbar Vertebrae

The five **lumbar vertebrae** have heavy, thick bodies to support the greater stress and weight that is placed on this region of the vertebral column. The spinous processes are blunt, and they provide a large surface area for the attachment of heavy back muscles.

Chapter 6   Skeletal System

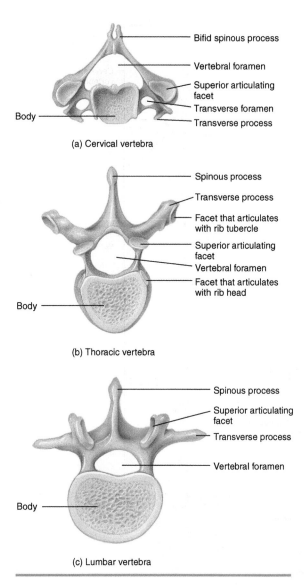

(a) Cervical vertebra

- Bifid spinous process
- Vertebral foramen
- Superior articulating facet
- Transverse foramen
- Transverse process
- Body

(b) Thoracic vertebra

- Spinous process
- Transverse process
- Facet that articulates with rib tubercle
- Superior articulating facet
- Vertebral foramen
- Facet that articulates with rib head
- Body

(c) Lumbar vertebra

- Spinous process
- Superior articulating facet
- Transverse process
- Vertebral foramen
- Body

Figure 6.13 Superior view of (*a*) a cervical vertebra, (*b*) a thoracic vertebra, and (*c*) a lumbar vertebra. AP R

Sacrum

The **sacrum** (sā-k´rum) is composed of five fused vertebrae (figure 6.15). It articulates with the fifth lumbar vertebra and forms the posterior wall of the pelvic girdle. The spinous processes of the fused vertebrae are reduced to a series of **tubercles** on the posterior midline. On either side of the tubercles are the *posterior sacral foramina,* passageways for blood vessels and nerves. Foramina on the anterior surface serve a similar function. The *sacral canal* is formed

by the fused neural arches, and it continues to an inferior opening, the *sacral hiatus,* proximal to the coccyx.

Coccyx

The most inferior part of the vertebral column is the **coccyx** (kok´-six), or tailbone, which is formed of three to five fused, rudimentary vertebrae.

Thoracic Cage

The thoracic vertebrae, ribs, costal cartilages, and sternum form the **thoracic,** or **rib, cage.** It provides protection for the internal organs of the thorax and supports the upper trunk, shoulder girdle, and upper extremities (figure 6.16).

Ribs

Twelve pairs of **ribs** are attached to the thoracic vertebrae. The *head* of each rib articulates with the body of its own vertebra, and a *tubercle* near the head articulates with the transverse process. The head also articulates with the body of the next higher vertebra. The *shaft* of each rib curves around the thorax and slopes slightly downward.

The upper seven pairs of ribs are attached directly to the sternum by the **costal** (kos´-tal) **cartilages,** which extend medially from the ends of the ribs. These ribs are the *true ribs.* The remaining five pairs are the *false ribs.* The first three pairs of false ribs are attached by cartilages to the costal cartilages of the ribs just superior to them. The last two pairs of false ribs are called *floating ribs* because they lack cartilages and are not attached anteriorly. The costal cartilages give some flexibility to the thoracic cage.

Check My Understanding

7. How do cervical, thoracic, and lumbar vertebrae differ in structure and location?
8. How does the axial skeleton protect vital organs?

Sternum

The **sternum,** or breastbone, is a flat, elongated bone located at the midline in the anterior portion of the thoracic cage. It consists of three bones that are fused together. The *manubrium* (mah-nū´-brē-um) is the T-shaped upper portion that articulates with the first two pairs of ribs; the *body* is the larger middle segment; and the *xiphoid* (zīf´-oyd) *process* is the small inferior portion.

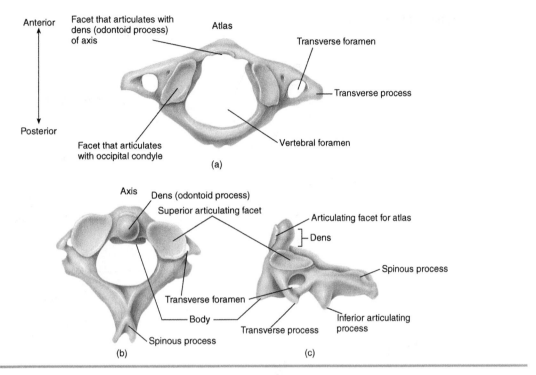

Anterior

Posterior

Facet that articulates with dens (odontoid process) of axis

Atlas

Transverse foramen

Transverse process

Vertebral foramen

Facet that articulates with occipital condyle

(a)

Axis

Dens (odontoid process)

Superior articulating facet

Articulating facet for atlas

Dens

Spinous process

Transverse foramen

Body

Transverse process

Inferior articulating process

Spinous process

(b)

(c)

Figure 6.14 The structures of the (a) atlas and (b) axis function together to allow movement of the head. (c) Lateral view of the axis. APR

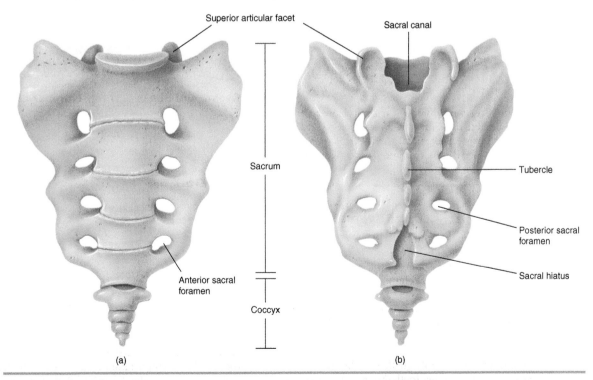

Superior articular facet

Sacral canal

Sacrum

Tubercle

Anterior sacral foramen

Posterior sacral foramen

Sacral hiatus

Coccyx

(a)

(b)

Figure 6.15 (a) Anterior view and (b) posterior view of the sacrum and coccyx. APR

Chapter 6   Skeletal System

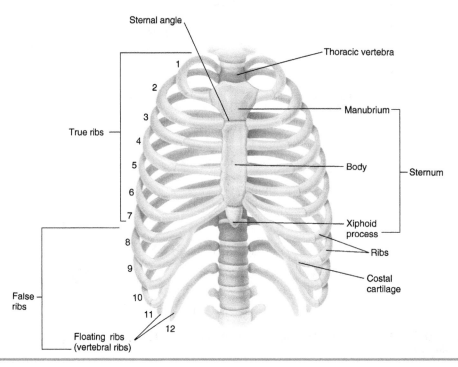

Figure 6.16   The thoracic cage is formed by thoracic vertebrae, ribs, costal cartilages, and the sternum. Note the difference between true and false ribs. AP|R

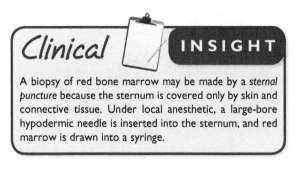

A biopsy of red bone marrow may be made by a *sternal puncture* because the sternum is covered only by skin and connective tissue. Under local anesthetic, a large-bore hypodermic needle is inserted into the sternum, and red marrow is drawn into a syringe.

6.6 Appendicular Skeleton

The appendicular skeleton consists of (1) the pectoral girdle and the bones of the upper extremities and (2) the pelvic girdle and the bones of the lower extremities.

The appendicular skeleton is composed of 126 bones. The bones of the pectoral girdle and upper extremities are listed in table 6.6. Bones of the pelvic girdle and lower extremities are listed in table 6.7.

Pectoral Girdle

The **pectoral** (pek´-to-ral) **girdle,** or shoulder girdle, consists of two clavicles (collarbones) and two scapulae (shoulder blades) (figure 6.17). Each S-shaped

Table 6.6   Bones of the Pectoral Girdle and Upper Extremities

Region and Bones	Number of Bones
Pectoral Girdle	
Clavicle	2
Scapula	2
	4
Upper Extremities	
Humerus	2
Ulna	2
Radius	2
Carpals	16
Metacarpals	10
Phalanges	28
	60
	Total = 64

clavicle (klav´-i-cul) articulates with the acromion process of a scapula laterally and with the sternum medially. The **scapulae** (skap´-ū-le) are flat, triangular-shaped bones located on each side of the vertebral

Part 2   Covering, Support, and Movement of the Body

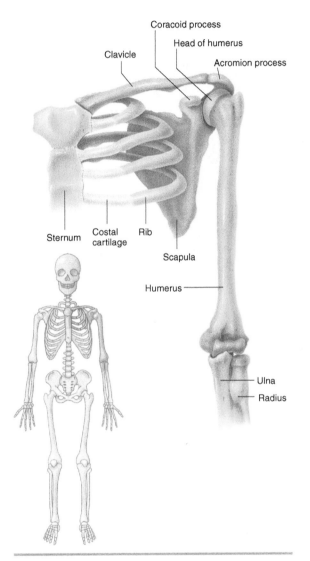

Figure 6.17 The pectoral girdle consists of a scapula and clavicle on each side of the body. Note how the head of the humerus fits into the glenoid fossa of the scapula. AP|R

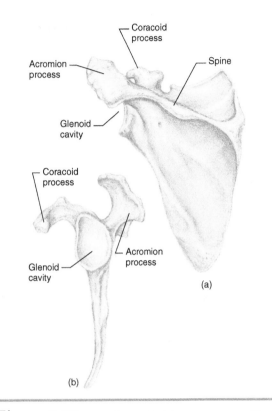

Figure 6.18 The left scapula: (*a*) posterior view; (*b*) lateral view. AP|R

column, but they do not articulate with the axial skeleton (figure 6.18). Instead, they are held in place by muscles, an arrangement that enables freedom of movement for the shoulders.

The anterior surface of each scapula is flat and smooth where it moves over the ribs. The scapular *spine* runs diagonally across the posterior surface from the *acromion* (ah-krōm´-ē-on) *process* to the medial margin. On its lateral margin is the shallow *glenoid cavity,* which articulates with the head of the humerus. The *coracoid* (kor´-ah-koyd) *process* proj-

ects anteriorly from the superior margin and extends under the clavicle.

Upper Extremity

The skeleton of each **upper extremity** is composed of a humerus, an ulna, a radius, carpals, metacarpals, and phalanges. See figures 6.17 to 6.21 as you study this section.

Humerus

The **humerus** (hū´-mer-us) articulates with the scapula at the shoulder, and the ulna and radius at the elbow (figure 6.19). The rounded *head* of the humerus fits into the glenoid cavity of the scapula. Just inferior to the head are two large tubercles where muscles attach. The *greater tubercle* (tū´-ber-cul) is on the lateral surface, and the *lesser tubercle* is on the anterior surface. An *intertubercular groove* lies between them. Just below these tubercles is the *surgical neck,* which gets its name from the frequent fractures that occur in this area. Near the midpoint on the lateral surface is the *deltoid tuberosity*

Chapter 6   **Skeletal System**

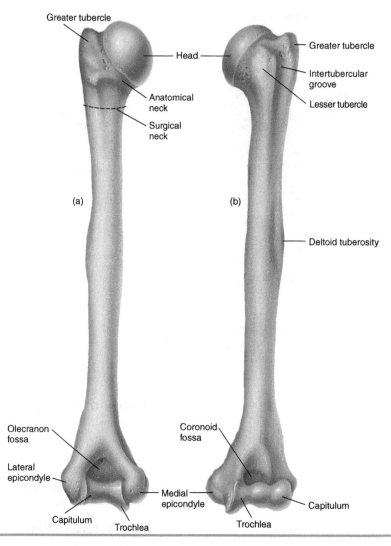

Figure 6.19   The left humerus: (*a*) posterior view; (*b*) anterior view. AP|R

(tū-be-ros´-i-tē), a rough, raised area where the deltoid muscle attaches.

The distal end of the humerus has two condyles. The *trochlea* (trok´-lē-ah) is the medial condyle, which articulates with the ulna. The *capitulum* (kah-pit´-ū-lum) is the lateral condyle, which articulates with the radius. Just above these condyles are two enlargements that project laterally and medially: the *lateral epicondyle* (ep-i-kon´-dĭl) and the *medial epicondyle*. On the anterior surface between the epicondyles is a depression, the *coronoid* (kor´-o-noyd) *fossa,* that receives the coronoid process of the ulna whenever the

forearm is flexed at the elbow. The *olecranon* (o-lek´-rah-non) *fossa* is in a similar location on the posterior surface of the humerus, and it receives the olecranon process of the ulna when the arm is straightened at the elbow.

Ulna

The **ulna** (ul´-na) is the medial bone (little finger side) of the forearm (figure 6.20). The proximal end of the ulna forms the *olecranon process,* the bony point of the elbow. The large, half-circle depression just distal to the olecranon process is the *trochlear notch,* which

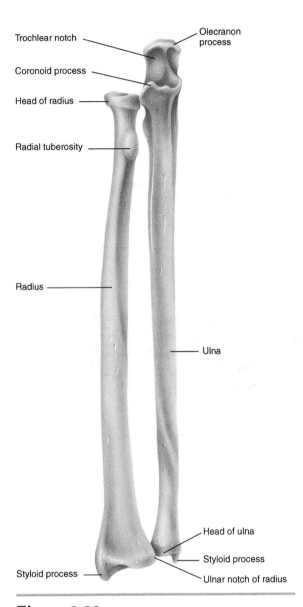

Trochlear notch

Coronoid process

Head of radius

Radial tuberosity

Radius

Ulna

Head of ulna

Styloid process

Styloid process

Ulnar notch of radius

Olecranon process

Figure 6.20   An anterior view of the right radius and ulna. AP|R

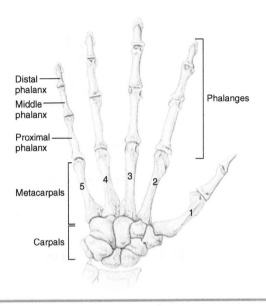

Distal phalanx

Middle phalanx

Proximal phalanx

Metacarpals

Carpals

Phalanges

5 4 3 2 1

Figure 6.21   A posterior view of the bones of the left hand. AP|R

Radius

The **radius** (rā´-dē-us) is the lateral bone (thumb side) of the forearm. The disklike *head* of the radius articulates with the capitulum of the humerus in a way that enables the head to rotate freely when the hand is rotated. A short distance distally from the head is the *radial tuberosity,* a raised, roughened area where the biceps muscle attaches. At its distal end, the radius articulates with the carpal bones. A small lateral *styloid process* serves as an attachment site for ligaments of the wrist.

Carpals, Metacarpals, and Phalanges

The skeleton of the hand consists of the carpals, metacarpals, and phalanges (figure 6.21). The **carpals** (kar´-pulz), or wrist bones, consist of eight small carpal bones that are arranged in two transverse rows of four bones each. They are joined by ligaments that allow limited gliding movement.

The **metacarpals,** bones of the palm of the hand, consist of five metacarpal bones that are numbered 1 to 5 starting with the thumb. The bones of the fingers are the **phalanges** (fah-lan´-jēz). Each finger consists of three phalanges—proximal, middle, and distal—except the thumb, which has proximal and distal phalanges only.

articulates with the trochlea of the humerus. This articulation is secured by the *coronoid process* on the distal lip of the notch.

At the distal end, the knoblike *head* of the ulna articulates with the medial surface of the radius and with a fibrocartilaginous disk that separates it from the wrist bones. The *styloid process* is a small medial projection to which ligaments of the wrist are attached.

Chapter 6   **Skeletal System**

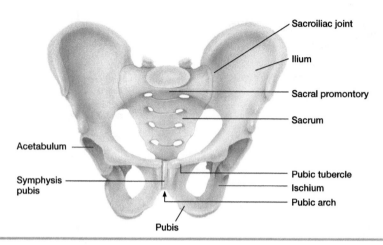

Figure 6.22 An anterior view of the bony pelvis. AP|R

Pelvic Girdle

The **pelvic** (pel´-vik) **girdle** consists of two **coxal** (kok´sal) **bones,** or hipbones, that support the attachment of the lower extremities. The coxal bones articulate with the sacrum posteriorly and with each other anteriorly to form an almost rigid, bony **pelvis,** as shown in figure 6.22. Recall that the coccyx is attached to the inferior end of the sacrum.

Coxal Bones

Each coxal bone is formed by three fused bones—ilium, ischium, and pubis—that join at the *acetabulum* (as-e-tab´-ū-lum), the cup-shaped socket on the lateral surface (figure 6.23). The **ilium** is the broad upper portion whose superior margin forms the *iliac crest,* the prominence of the hip. Interior to the posterior superior iliac spine is the *greater sciatic* (sī-at´-ik) *notch,* which allows the passage of blood vessels and nerves from the pelvis to the thigh. Each ilium joins with the sacrum to form a *sacroiliac joint.*

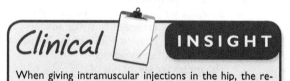

When giving intramuscular injections in the hip, the region near the greater sciatic notch must be avoided to prevent possible injury to the large blood vessels and nerves in this area.

The **ischium** forms the inferior, posterior portion of a coxal bone and supports the body when

Table 6.7 Bones of the Pelvic Girdle and Lower Extremities	
Region and Bones	**Number of Bones**
Pelvic Girdle	
Coxal bones	<u>2</u>
	2
Lower Extremities	
Femur	2
Patella	2
Tibia	2
Fibula	2
Tarsals	14
Metatarsals	10
Phalanges	<u>28</u>
	60
	Total = 62

sitting. The roughened projection at the posterior, inferior angle of the ischium is the *ischial tuberosity.* Just above this tuberosity is the *ischial spine,* which projects medially. The size of this spine in females is important during childbirth because it determines the diameter of the pelvic opening.

The **pubis** is the lower, anterior portion of a coxal bone. A portion of the pubis extends posteriorly to fuse with the anterior extension of the ischium. The large opening above this junction is the *obturator* (ob-tū-rā´-ter) *foramen,* through which blood vessels and nerves pass into the thigh. The pubic bones unite anteriorly to

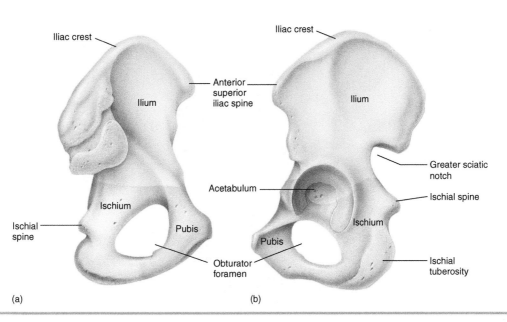

Figure 6.23 The left coxal bone. (*a*) Medial view. (*b*) Lateral view. APR

form the **symphysis pubis** where the bones are joined by a pad of fibrocartilage.

Table 6.8 lists the major differences between the male and the female pelvic girdles. Compare them with the male and female pelvic girdles in figure 6.24 and note the adaptations of the female pelvic girdle for childbirth.

Clinical **INSIGHT**

The fetus must pass through the pelvic opening during birth. Physicians carefully measure this opening before delivery to be sure that it is of adequate size. If not, the baby is delivered via a *cesarean section*. In a cesarean section, a transverse incision is made through the pelvic and uterine walls to remove the baby.

Lower Extremity

The bones of each **lower extremity** consist of a femur, a patella, a tibia, a fibula, tarsals, metatarsals, and phalanges. See figures 6.25 to 6.28 as you study this section.

Femur

The **femur** is the thighbone (figure 6.25). It is the largest and strongest bone of the body. Structures at the proximal end include the rounded *head,* a short *neck,* and two large processes that are sites of muscle attachment: a superior, lateral *greater trochanter* (trō-kan'-ter) and an inferior, medial *lesser trochanter.* The head of the femur fits into the acetabulum of the coxal bone. The neck is a common site of fractures in older people. At the enlarged distal end are the *lateral* and *medial condyles,* surfaces that articulate with the tibia.

Table 6.8	Sexual Differences of the Pelvic Girdle	
Characteristic	**Male**	**Female**
General structure	Heavier; processes prominent	Lighter; processes not so prominent
Pelvic opening	Narrower and heart-shaped	Wider and oval
Pubic arch angle	Less than 90°	More than 90°
Relative width	Narrower	Wider
Acetabulum	Faces laterally	Faces laterally but more anteriorly

Chapter 6   **Skeletal System**

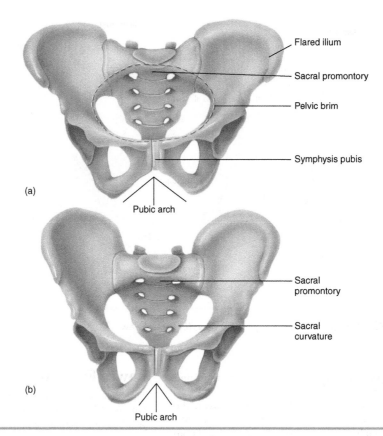

(a)

(b)

- Flared ilium
- Sacral promontory
- Pelvic brim
- Symphysis pubis
- Pubic arch
- Sacral promontory
- Sacral curvature
- Pubic arch

Figure 6.24   (*a*) Female and (*b*) male pelvic girdles. Note the obtuse angle of the pubic arch and greater pelvic width in the female pelvic girdle. APR

Patella

The **patella,** or kneecap, is located anterior to the knee joint. It is embedded in the tendon of the thigh muscle (quadriceps femoris), which extends over the anterior of the knee to insert on the tibia. Bones embedded in tendons are called **sesamoid bones.**

Tibia

The **tibia,** or shinbone, is the larger of the two bones of the lower leg (figure 6.26). It bears the weight of the body. Its enlarged proximal portion consists of the *lateral* and *medial condyles,* which articulate with the femur to form the knee joint. The *tibial tuberosity,* a roughened area on the anterior surface just below the condyles, is the attachment site for the patellar ligament. The distal end of the tibia articulates with the talus, a tarsus bone, and laterally with the

fibula. The *medial malleolus* (mah-lē-ō´-lus) forms the medial prominence of the ankle.

Fibula

The **fibula** is the slender, lateral bone in the lower leg. Both ends of the bone are enlarged. The proximal *head* articulates with the lateral surface of the tibia but is not involved in forming the knee joint. The distal end articulates with the tibia and tarsus. The *lateral malleolus* forms the lateral prominence of the ankle.

Tarsals, Metatarsals, and Phalanges

The skeleton of the foot consists of the tarsals (ankle), metatarsals (instep), and phalanges (toes) (figures 6.27 and 6.28). Seven bones compose the **tarsals.** The most prominent tarsal bones are the *talus,* which

Part 2   **Covering, Support, and Movement of the Body**

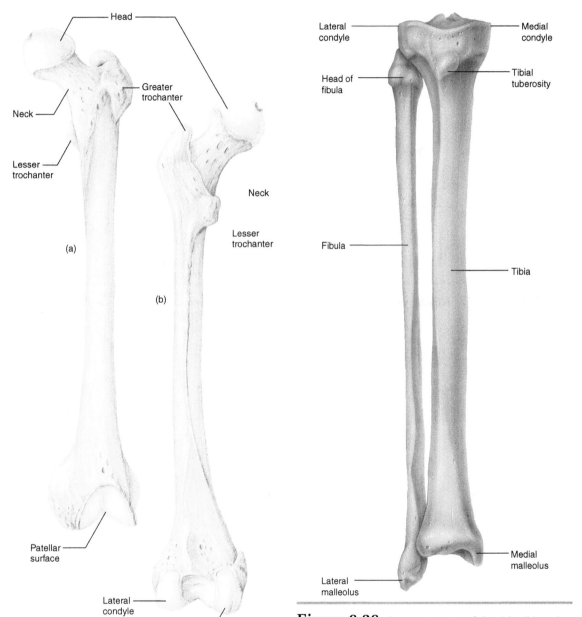

Figure 6.25 The left femur: (*a*) anterior view; (*b*) posterior view. AP|R

Figure 6.26 An anterior view of the right tibia and fibula. AP|R

articulates with the tibia and fibula, and the *calcaneus* (kal-kā′n-ē-us), or heel bone. Five **metatarsals** support the instep. They are numbered 1 to 5, starting with the great toe. The tarsals and metatarsals are bound together by ligaments to form strong, resilient arches of the foot. Each toe consists of three **phalanges**— proximal, middle, and distal—except for the great toe, which has only two.

Chapter 6 **Skeletal System**

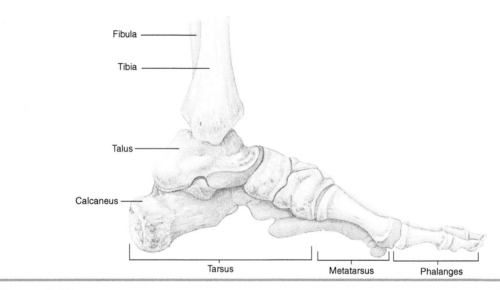

Fibula

Tibia

Talus

Calcaneus

Tarsus

Metatarsus

Phalanges

Figure 6.27 A medial view of the bones of the left foot showing articulation of the talus with the tibia. AP|R

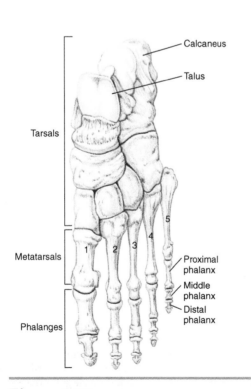

Calcaneus

Talus

Tarsals

Metatarsals

Proximal phalanx

Middle phalanx

Distal phalanx

Phalanges

Figure 6.28 A superior view of the bones of the left foot. AP|R

Clinical **INSIGHT**

Total hip replacement (THR) has become commonplace among older persons as a way to overcome the pain and immobility caused by osteoarthritis of the hip joint. This procedure utilizes two prostheses. A polyurethane cup replaces the damaged acetabular socket, and a metal shaft and ball replace the diseased femoral head. Surfaces of the prostheses in contact with bone are porous, allowing bone to grow into them to ensure a firm attachment. Patient recovery involves stabilization of the prostheses while bone tissue grows into them as well as normal healing from the surgery.

Check My Understanding

9. What bones form the pectoral girdle and upper extremities?
10. What bones form the pelvic girdle and lower extremities?

6.7 Articulations

The junction between two bones forms an **articulation**, or **joint**. Joints allow varying degrees of movement. Joints are categorized as immovable, slightly movable, or freely movable. As you read the following descriptions, locate the different types of articulations on the corresponding illustrations of skeletal parts in figures presented earlier in the chapter.

Immovable Joints

Bones forming immovable, or **synarthrosis** (sin-ar-thrō´-sis), **joints** are tightly joined and are separated by a thin layer of fibrous connective tissue. For example, skull bones, except the mandible, are joined by immovable joints called *sutures* because they resemble stitches (see figure 6.8).

Slightly Movable Joints

Bones forming slightly movable, or **amphiarthrosis** (am-fē-ar-th-rō´-sis), **joints** are separated by a layer of cartilage or fibrous connective tissue. For example, the joints formed by adjacent vertebrae contain intervertebral disks formed of fibrocartilage. The limited flexibility of the disks allows slight movement between adjacent vertebrae. Other examples include the symphysis pubis and sacroiliac joints.

Freely Movable Joints

Most articulations are freely movable. The structure of freely movable, or **diarthrosis** (di-ar-thro´-sis), **joints** is more complex. The ends of the bones form-ing the joint are bound together by an *articular, or joint, capsule* formed of **ligaments**. A *synovial* (si-nō´-vē-al) *membrane* lines the interior of the capsule and secretes *synovial fluid* that lubricates the joint. The ends of the bones are covered with *articular cartilage*, which protects bones and reduces friction (figure 6.29). Freely movable joints are categorized into several types based on their structure and types of movements.

Gliding Joints

Gliding joints occur between small bones that slide over one another. They occur between carpal bones, between tarsal bones, and between the clavicle and scapula.

Condyloid Joints

Condyloid joints allow movements in two planes: side to side or back and forth. The joints between the carpals and bones of the forearm (radius and ulna) and the metacarpals and first phalanges are examples.

Hinge Joints

Hinge joints allow movement in one plane only, like a door hinge. The elbow, knee, and joints between phalanges are all hinge joints. Examine the sagittal section of a knee joint in figure 6.30. Note the articular capsule

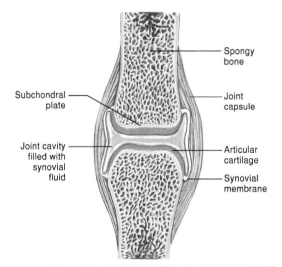

Figure 6.29 The basic structure of a freely movable joint. AP|R

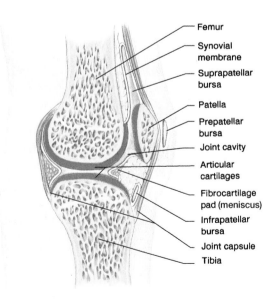

Figure 6.30 A sagittal section of a knee joint, a hinge joint. Note the articular cartilages, synovial membrane, fibrocartilage pads, bursae, and joint capsule. AP|R

Chapter 6   Skeletal System

(formed of ligaments), which binds the bones together; the bursae (sacs filled with synovial fluid); the articular cartilages, which reduce friction; and the cartilaginous pads, which cushion the ends of the bones.

Saddle Joints

Saddle joints occur where the ends of each bone are saddle-shaped: convex in one direction and concave in the other. Movement is side to side and back and forth. A joint of this type occurs between the trapezium (a carpal bone) and the metacarpal bone of the thumb.

Pivot Joints

Pivot joints allow rotational movement in a single plane. The rotation of the atlas on the axis is an example of a pivot joint.

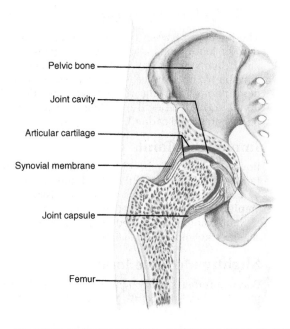

A "torn cartilage" is a damaged cartilaginous pad (meniscus) in a knee joint, a common athletic injury. Treatment usually requires removal of the damaged cartilage by *arthroscopic surgery*. An arthroscope is a pencil-sized instrument containing lenses and a light source. It may be inserted into a joint through a small incision to enable a physician to observe the interior of the joint. While viewing the interior of the joint, the surgeon may insert small instruments to remove damaged tissue, make repairs, and flush out the joint.

Figure 6.31 A coronal section of a hip joint, a ball-and-socket joint. Note the joint capsule formed of ligaments. AP|R

Check My Understanding

11. Where are immovable, slightly movable, and freely movable joints found in the skeleton?
12. What types of freely movable joints occur in the body, and where are they located?

Ball-and-Socket Joints

Ball-and-socket joints occur where a rounded head of one bone fits into a concavity of the other bone. These joints allow the greatest freedom of movement. Movement may be rotational or in any plane. The shoulder and hip joints are ball-and-socket joints. Examine the structure of a hip joint in figure 6.31.

Movements at Freely Movable Joints

Movement at a joint results from the contraction of skeletal muscles that span across the joint. The type of movement that occurs is determined by the type of joint and the location of the muscle or muscles involved. The more common types of movements are listed in table 6.9 and illustrated in figure 6.32.

Older persons are prone to "breaking a hip," which means that a weakened femur breaks at the neck. This usually is a consequence of osteoporosis, the excessive loss of calcium from bones. Osteoporosis is caused by a combination of factors: insufficient calcium in the diet, lack of minimal exercise, and a decline in sex hormones, especially in postmenopausal women. Older persons are not only more prone to fractures, but healing of fractures takes much longer than in younger persons.

Table 6.9	Movements at Freely Movable Joints
Movement	**Description**
Flexion	Decrease in the angle of bones forming joint
Extension	Increase in the angle of bones forming joint
Dorsiflexion	Flexion of the foot at the ankle
Plantar flexion	Extension of the foot at the ankle
Abduction	Movement of a bone away from the midline
Adduction	Movement of a bone toward the midline
Rotation	Movement of a bone around its longitudinal axis
Circumduction	Movement of the distal end of a bone in a circle while the proximal end forms the pivot joint
Eversion	Movement of the sole of the foot laterally
Inversion	Movement of the sole of the foot medially
Pronation	Rotation of the forearm when the palm is turned downward or posteriorly
Supination	Rotation of the forearm when the palm is turned upward or anteriorly
Protraction	Movement of the mandible anteriorly
Retraction	Movement of the mandible posteriorly
Elevation	Movement of a body part upward
Depression	Movement of a body part downward

6.8 Disorders of the Skeletal System

Common disorders of the skeletal system may be categorized as disorders of bones or disorders of joints. **Orthopedics** (or-thō-pē-diks) is the branch of medicine that specializes in treating diseases and abnormalities of the skeletal system.

Disorders of Bones

Fractures are broken bones. Fractures are the most common type of bone injury. Fractures are categorized as either complete or incomplete. There are also several specific subtypes, such as the examples noted here and in figure 6.33.

- **Complete:** The break is completely through the bone.
- **Compound:** A broken bone pierces the skin.
- **Simple:** A bone does not pierce the skin.
- **Comminuted:** The bone is broken into several pieces.
- **Segmental:** Only one piece is broken out of the bone.
- **Spiral:** The fracture line spirals around the bone.
- **Oblique:** The break angles across the bone.
- **Transverse:** The break is at right angles to the long axis of the bone.
- **Incomplete:** The bone is not broken completely through.

- **Green stick:** The break is only on one side of the bone, and the bone is bowed.
- **Fissured:** The break is a lengthwise split in the bone.

Osteomyelitis is an inflammation of bone and bone marrow caused by bacterial infection. It is treatable with antibiotics but not easily cured.

Osteoporosis (os-tē-ō-pō-rō´-sis) is a weakening of bones due to the removal of calcium salts, which increases the risk of fractures. This is a common problem in older persons due to inactivity and a decrease in hormone production. It is more common in postmenopausal women because of the lack of estrogen. Exercise and calcium supplements retard the decline in bone density. Therapy includes drugs that retard bone loss or those that promote bone formation. However, such drugs must be used with caution because they can have serious side effects.

Rickets is a disease of children that is characterized by a deficiency of calcium salts in the bones. Affected children have a bowlegged appearance due to the bending of weakened femurs, tibiae, and fibulae. Rickets results from a dietary deficiency of calcium and/or vitamin D. It is rare in industrialized nations.

Disorders of Joints

Arthritis (ar-thrĭ´-tis) is the general term for many different diseases of joints that are characterized by inflammation, swelling (edema), and pain.

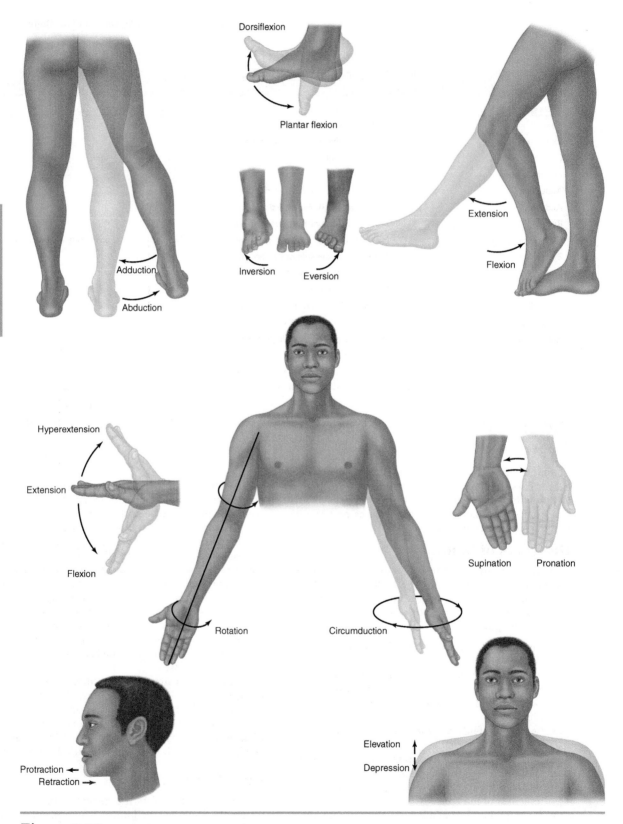

Figure 6.32 Common movements at freely movable joints.

Part 2   Covering, Support, and Movement of the Body

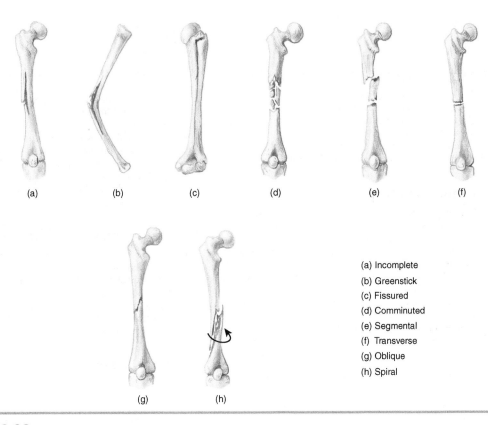

(a)   (b)   (c)   (d)   (e)   (f)

(g)   (h)

(a) Incomplete
(b) Greenstick
(c) Fissured
(d) Comminuted
(e) Segmental
(f) Transverse
(g) Oblique
(h) Spiral

Figure 6.33   Some types of bone fractures.

Rheumatoid arthritis and osteoarthritis are the most common types.

Rheumatoid (rū´-mah-toid) *arthritis* is the most painful and crippling type. The synovial membrane thickens, synovial fluid accumulates causing swelling, and articular cartilages are destroyed. The joint is invaded by fibrous connective tissue that ultimately ossifies, making the joint immovable.

Osteoarthritis, the most common type, is a degenerative disease that results from aging and wear. The articular cartilages gradually disintegrate, which causes pain and restricts movement.

Bursitis (bur-sī´-tis) is the inflammation of a bursa. It may be caused by excessive use or injury.

Dislocation is the displacement of bones forming a joint. Pain, swelling, and reduced movement are associated with a dislocation.

Herniated disk is a condition in which an intervertebral disk protrudes beyond the edge of a vertebra. A ruptured, or slipped, disk refers to the same problem. It is caused by excessive pressure on the vertebral column, which compresses a disk and causes it to bulge outward. The protruding disk may place pressure on a spinal nerve and cause considerable pain.

Spinal curvatures are usually congenital disorders. There are three major types:

1. *Kyphosis* (kī-fō-sis) is an excessive thoracic curvature of the vertebral column, which produces a humpback condition.
2. *Lordosis* is an excessive lumbar curvature of the vertebral column, which produces a swayback condition.
3. *Scoliosis* is an abnormal lateral curvature of the vertebral column. For some reason, it is more common in adolescent girls.

Sprains result from tearing or excessive stretching of the ligaments and tendons at a joint without a dislocation.

Check My Understanding

13. What are some common types of fractures?
14. How do osteoarthritis and rheumatoid arthritis differ?

Chapter 6 **Skeletal System**

CHAPTER SUMMARY

6.1 Functions of the Skeletal System

- The skeletal system provides support for the body and protection for internal organs.
- The bones of the skeleton serve as sites for the attachment of skeletal muscles.
- Blood cells are formed by red bone marrow.
- Bones serve as reservoirs for calcium salts.

6.2 Bone Structure

- The diaphysis is a long shaft of bone that lies between the epiphyses, the enlarged ends of the bone.
- Each epiphysis is joined to the diaphysis by an epiphyseal plate in immature bones, or by fusion at the epiphyseal line in mature bones.
- Articular cartilages protect and cushion the articular surfaces of the epiphyses.
- The periosteum covers the bone surface except for the articular cartilages.
- Compact bone forms the diaphysis and the surface layer of the epiphyses.
- Spongy bone forms the interior of the epiphyses.
- Red marrow fills the spaces in spongy bone.
- The diaphysis contains a medullary cavity filled with fatty yellow marrow.
- Compact bone is formed of numerous osteons fused together.
- Osteonic (central) canals contain blood vessels and nerves.
- Spongy bone lacks osteons; its cells are nourished by diffusion from blood vessels in the red marrow.

6.3 Bone Formation

- Intramembranous bones are first formed by connective tissue membranes, which are replaced by bone tissue.
- Connective tissue cells are transformed into osteoblasts, which deposit the spongy bone within the membrane.
- Osteoblasts from the periosteum form a layer of compact bone over the spongy bone.
- Endochondral bones are first formed of hyaline cartilage, which is later replaced by bone tissue.
- In long bones, a primary ossification center forms in the center of the diaphysis and extends toward the epiphyses.
- Secondary ossification centers form in the epiphyses.
- An epiphyseal plate of cartilage remains between the epiphyses and the diaphysis in immature bones.
- Growth in length occurs at the epiphyseal disk, which is gradually replaced by bone.
- Compact bone is deposited by osteoblasts from the periosteum, and they are responsible for growth in the diameter of a bone.

- Osteoclasts hollow out the medullary cavity and reshape the bone.
- Bones are dynamic, living organs that are reshaped throughout life by the actions of osteoclasts and osteoblasts.
- Calcium salts may be removed from bones for other body needs and redeposited in bones later on.
- The concentration of protein fibers decreases with age. The bones of older persons tend to be brittle and weak due to the loss of fibers and calcium salts, respectively.

6.4 Divisions of the Skeleton

- The skeleton is divided into the axial and appendicular divisions.
- The axial skeleton includes the bones that support the head, neck, and trunk.
- The appendicular skeleton includes the bones of the pectoral girdle and upper extremities and the bones of the pelvic girdle and the lower extremities.

6.5 Axial Skeleton

- The axial skeleton consists of the skull, vertebral column, and thoracic cage.
- The skull consists of cranial and facial bones; all are joined by immovable joints except the mandible.
- The cranial bones are the frontal bone (1), parietal bones (2), sphenoid bone (1), temporal bones (2), occipital bone (1), and ethmoid bone (1).
- The frontal, sphenoid, and ethmoid bones contain sinuses.
- The facial bones are the maxillae (2), palatine bones (2), zygomatic bones (2), lacrimal bones (2), nasal bones (2), inferior nasal conchae (2), vomer bone (1), and mandible (1).
- Each maxilla contains a large sinus.
- Cranial bones of an infant skull are separated by membranes and several fontanels, which allow some flexibility of the skull during birth.
- The vertebral column consists of 24 vertebrae, the sacrum, and the coccyx.
- Vertebrae are separated by intervertebral disks and are categorized as cervical (7), thoracic (12), and lumbar (5) vertebrae.
- The first two cervical vertebrae are unique. The atlas rotates on the axis when the head is turned.
- Thoracic vertebrae have facets on the body and transverse processes for articulation with the ribs.
- The bodies of lumbar vertebrae are heavy and strong.
- The sacrum is formed of five fused vertebrae and forms the posterior portion of the pelvic girdle.
- The coccyx is formed of three to five rudimentary vertebrae and forms the inferior end of the vertebral column.

- The thoracic cage consists of thoracic vertebrae, ribs, and sternum. It supports the upper trunk and protects internal thoracic organs.
- There are seven pairs of true ribs and five pairs of false ribs. The inferior two pairs of false ribs are floating ribs.
- The sternum is formed of three fused bones: manubrium, body, and xiphoid process.

6.6 Appendicular Skeleton

- The appendicular skeleton consists of the pectoral and pelvic girdles and of the bones of the extremities.
- The pectoral girdle consists of clavicles (2) and scapulae (2), and it supports the upper extremities.
- The bones of the upper extremity are the humerus, the ulna, the radius, carpals, metacarpals, and phalanges.
- The humerus articulates with the glenoid cavity of the scapula to form the shoulder joint and with the ulna and radius to form the elbow joint.
- The ulna is the medial bone of the forearm. It articulates with the humerus at the elbow and with the radius and a fibrocartilaginous disk at the wrist.
- The radius is the lateral (thumb side) bone of the forearm. It articulates with the humerus at the elbow and with the ulna and carpus at the wrist.
- The bones of the hand are the carpals (8), metacarpals (5), and phalanges (14).
- The carpal bones are joined by ligaments to form the bones of the wrist; metacarpal bones support the palm of the hand; and the phalanges are the bones of the fingers.
- The pelvic girdle consists of two coxal bones that are joined to the sacrum posteriorly and to each other anteriorly. It supports the lower extremities.
- Each coxal bone is formed by the fusion of three bones: the ilium, ischium, and pubis.
- The ilium forms the upper portion of a coxal bone and joins with the sacrum to form a sacroiliac joint.
- The ischium forms the inferior, posterior portion of a coxal bone and supports the body when sitting.
- The pubis forms the lower, anterior part of a coxal bone. The pubic bones unite anteriorly to form the symphysis pubis joint.
- Each lower extremity consists of a femur, a patella, a tibia, a fibula, tarsals, metatarsals, and phalanges.

- The head of the femur is inserted into the acetabulum of a coxal bone to form a hip joint. Distally, it articulates with the tibia at the knee joint.
- The patella is a sesamoid bone in the anterior portion of the knee joint.
- The tibia (shinbone) articulates with the femur at the knee joint and with the talus to form the ankle joint.
- The fibula lies lateral to the tibia. It articulates proximally with the tibia and distally with the talus.
- The skeleton of the foot consists of tarsals (7), metatarsals (5), and phalanges (14).
- Tarsal bones form the ankle, metatarsal bones support the instep, and phalanges are the bones of the toes.

6.7 Articulations

- There are three types of joints: immovable, slightly movable, and freely movable.
- Bones forming immovable joints are closely joined and are separated by a thin layer of fibrous connective tissue. Articulations of skull bones, except the mandible, are examples.
- Bones forming slightly movable joints are separated by fibrocartilage pads or fibrous connective tissue. Joints between vertebrae are examples.
- Bones forming freely movable joints are bound together by a ligamentous articular capsule that is lined by a synovial membrane. The articular surfaces of the bones are covered by articular cartilages. Synovial fluid lubricates the joint, and bursae may be present to reduce friction.
- There are several types of freely movable joints: gliding, condyloid, hinge, saddle, pivot, and ball-and-socket.
- Movements at freely movable joints include flexion, extension, dorsiflexion, plantar flexion, hyperextension, abduction, adduction, rotation, circumduction, inversion, eversion, protraction, retraction, elevation, and depression.

6.8 Disorders of the Skeletal System

- Disorders of bones include fractures, osteomyelitis, osteoporosis, and rickets.
- Disorders of joints include arthritis, bursitis, dislocation, herniated disk, spinal curvatures, and sprains.

BUILDING MY VOCABULARY

1. **Selected New Terms**
   abduction, p. 119
   adduction, p. 119
   amphiarthrosis, p. 117
   appendicular skeleton, p. 97
   axial skeleton, p. 97
   circumduction, p. 119

   condyle, p. 99
   diarthrosis, p. 117
   epicondyle, p. 99
   extension, p. 119
   facet, p. 99
   flexion, p. 119
   foramen, p. 94

Chapter 6   **Skeletal System**

head, p. 106
pronation, p. 119
red marrow, p. 94
supination, p. 119
suture, p. 97
synarthrosis, p. 117
trochanter, p. 113
tubercle, p. 106
tuberosity, p. 109
yellow marrow, p. 94

2. **Related Clinical Terms**
Ankylosis (ang-ki-lō´-sis) Abnormal stiffness of a joint.
Arthralgia (ar-thral´-jē-ah) Pain in a joint.
Osteomalacia (os-tē-ō-mah-lā´-she-ah) Softening of bone tissue due to abnormal calcium and phosphorus metabolism.
Osteomyelitis (os-tē-ō-mī-e-lī´-tis) Inflammation of a bone and bone marrow caused by a fungus or bacteria.

SELF-REVIEW

Answers are located in appendix B.

1. The skeletal system provides _____ for the body and _____ for many internal organs.
2. The enlarged ends of a long bone are the _____, which are composed of _____ bone that is coated with a thin layer of compact bone.
3. Blood vessels and nerves enter a bone through a _____.
4. Cranial bones are formed by _____ ossification.
5. Growth in diameter of a long bone occurs by deposition of bone tissue by osteoblasts from the _____.
6. The skull, vertebral column, and sacrum are part of the _____ skeleton.
7. The bone forming the lower jaw is the _____, and it articulates with the _____ bone.
8. The first vertebra, the _____, articulates with the _____ bone of the skull.
9. True ribs are attached directly to the sternum by the _____.
10. The clavicles and scapulae form the _____.
11. The upper arm bone, the _____, articulates with two forearm bones, the _____ and the _____.
12. Each coxal bone is formed of three fused bones: the _____, _____, and _____.
13. The thigh bone is the _____, and it articulates distally with the _____.
14. Among freely movable joints, the elbow is an example of a _____ joint, and the shoulder is an example of a _____ joint.
15. _____ is a weakening of bones due to removal of calcium salts.

CRITICAL THINKING

1. Complete the learning objectives on the first page of this chapter.
2. Explain why both osteoclasts and osteoblasts are required for proper bone development.
3. Bone repairs itself faster than cartilage. Explain why.
4. What damage might result from a hyperextended knee?
5. Why is osteomyelitis more likely to occur after a compound fracture than after a greenstick fracture?

Visit this book's website at www.mhhe.com/
gunstream5 **for practice quizzes, learning exercises,
case studies, and other study tools.**

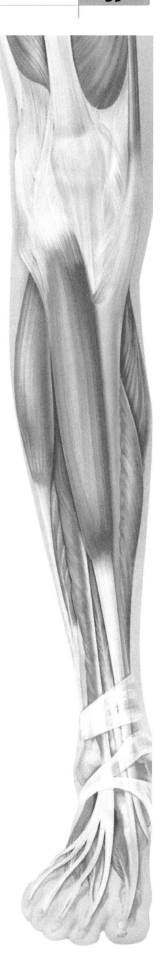

CHAPTER 7

Muscular System

Module 6
Muscular System

Chapter 7 **Muscular System**

SELECTED KEY TERMS

Antagonist (anti = against) A muscle whose contraction opposes an action of another muscle.

Aponeurosis (apo = from; neur = cord) A broad sheet of fibrous connective tissue that attaches a muscle to another muscle or connective tissue.

Creatine phosphate A molecule that stores a small amount of energy in a muscle fiber.

Insertion The attachment of a muscle that moves when the muscle contracts.

Motor unit A motor neuron and the muscle fibers that it controls.

Muscle fiber A single muscle cell.

Muscle tone The state of slight contraction in a skeletal muscle.

Myofibril (myo = muscle; fibril = little fiber) One of many contractile fibers within a muscle cell.

Myoglobin (myo = muscle) A molecule that stores a small amount of oxygen in a muscle fiber.

Neurotransmitter (neuro = nerve; transmit = to send across) A chemical released by axon tips of

neurons that activates a muscle fiber, gland, or another neuron.

Origin The attachment of a muscle that remains fixed when the muscle contracts.

Sarcomere (sarc = flesh) The smallest contractile unit of a myofibril.

Tendon A narrow band of fibrous connective tissue that attaches a muscle to a bone.

Tetanic contraction (tetan = rigid, stiff) A sustained muscle contraction.

uscle tissue is the only tissue in the body that is specialized for *contraction* (shortening). Contraction of muscle tissue produces the movements of the body and body parts. The body contains three types of muscle tissue: skeletal, smooth, and cardiac. Each type of muscle tissue exhibits unique structural and functional characteristics. Refresh your understanding of these tissues by referring to the discussion of muscle tissue in chapter 4. Table 7.1 summarizes the characteristics of muscle tissues.

7.1 Structure of Skeletal Muscle

Skeletal muscles are the organs of the muscular system. They are called skeletal muscles because most of them are attached to bones. A skeletal muscle is mainly composed of many skeletal **muscle fibers,** or cells, that are bound together by dense fibrous

connective tissue. Muscle fibers extend the full length of a muscle, and they are arranged in small bundles called *fascicles* (fah´-si-kuls). Dense fibrous connective tissue envelopes each fiber and each fascicle, binds fascicles together, and envelops the entire muscle. Connective tissue covering a muscle is sometimes called *deep fascia* (fash´-e-ah). It extends beyond the end of the muscle tissue to form a tough, cordlike **tendon,** which attaches the muscle to a bone (figure 7.1). Fibers of the tendon and periosteum intermesh to form a secure attachment. A few muscles attach to other muscles or connective tissues rather than to bones. In these muscles, the connective tissue forms a sheetlike attachment called an **aponeurosis** (ap˝-ō-nū-rō´-sis).

Skeletal Muscle Fibers

Each muscle fiber is a multinucleated skeletal muscle cell. It is a long, thin cylinder with rounded ends that usually extends the full length of the muscle.

Table 7.1	**Types of Muscle Tissue**		
Characteristic	**Skeletal**	**Smooth**	**Cardiac**
Striations	Present	Absent	Present
Nucleus	Many peripherally located nuclei	Single centrally located nucleus	Single centrally located nucleus
Fibers	Long and parallel	Short; tapered ends; parallel	Short and branching; intercalated disks join fibers end to end to form network
Neural control	Voluntary	Involuntary	Involuntary
Contractions	Fast or slow	Slow; resistant to fatigue	Rhythmic; resistant to fatigue
Location	Attached to bones	Walls of hollow visceral organs and blood vessels	Wall of the heart

Part 2 **Covering, Support, and Movement of the Body**

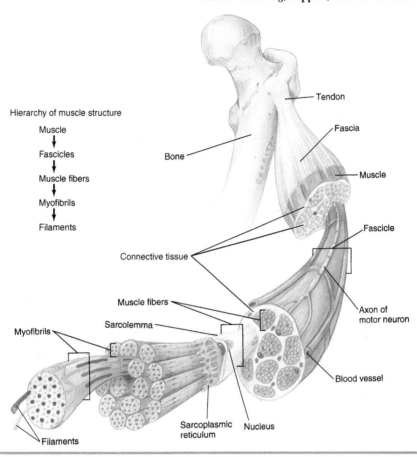

Hierarchy of muscle structure

Muscle
↓
Fascicles
↓
Muscle fibers
↓
Myofibrils
↓
Filaments

Tendon

Fascia

Bone

Muscle

Fascicle

Connective tissue

Muscle fibers

Sarcolemma

Axon of
motor neuron

Myofibrils

Blood vessel

Filaments

Sarcoplasmic
reticulum

Nucleus

Figure 7.1 A muscle is primarily composed of skeletal muscle fibers supported and bound together in fascicles by connective tissue. Myofibrils are the contractile elements of a muscle fiber.

The plasma membrane of a muscle fiber is called the **sarcolemma** (sar-kō-lem′-ah), and its cytoplasm is the **sarcoplasm**.

Each muscle fiber contains many threadlike **myofibrils,** which extend the length of the fiber, as shown in figure 7.1. Myofibrils are the contractile elements of a muscle fiber. They consist of two kinds of myofilaments that interact to produce muscle contractions: (1) *thin myofilaments* composed mostly of the protein **actin** and (2) *thick myofilaments* composed of the protein **myosin** (Table 7.2).

A thin myofilament consists of two twisted strands of actin molecules joined together like tiny strings of pearls. Two additional proteins, *troponin* and *tropomyosin,* are present on actin myofilaments and play a role in muscle contraction. Double strands of tropomyosin coil over each actin strand, and troponin occurs at regular intervals on the tropomyosin strands. A thick myofilament is composed of hundreds of myosin molecules, each shaped like a double-headed golf club. The heads are able to bind to actin myofilaments to form cross-bridges (figure 7.2). The organization of

Table 7.2 **Microscopic Anatomy of a Skeletal Muscle Fiber**	
Structure	**Description/Function**
Sarcolemma	Plasma membrane of a muscle fiber maintaining the integrity of the cell
Sarcoplasm	Cytoplasm of a skeletal muscle fiber that contains organelles
Nuclei	Contain DNA, which determines cell structure and function
Sarcoplasmic reticulum	Smooth ER in a muscle fiber that stores Ca^{++}
Transverse tubules	Extensions of the sarcolemma that penetrate into the fiber carrying nerve impulses, which trigger the release of ca^{++} from the sarcoplasmic reticulum
Myofibril	A bundle of myofilaments
Myofilaments	Thin actin myofilaments and thick myosin myofilaments that interact to produce contractions

Chapter 7 **Muscular System**

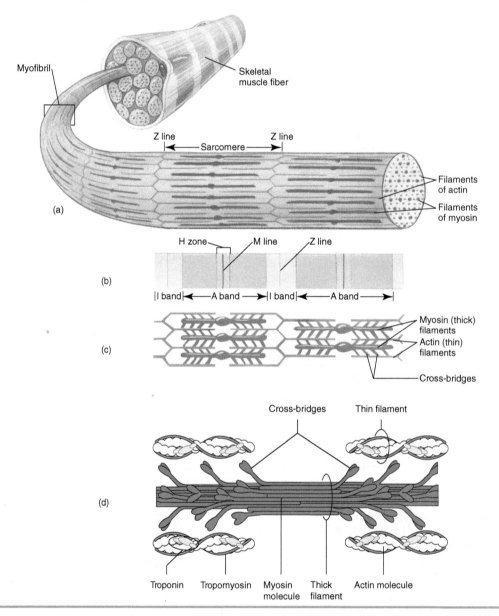

Figure 7.2 Structure of a myofibril. *(a)* A skeletal muscle fiber contains many myofibrils. Each myofibril consists of repeating contractile units called sarcomeres. *(b)* The characteristic bands of sarcomeres. *(c)* The arrangement of actin and myosin filaments within the sarcomeres. *(d)* Details of thin actin filaments and thick myosin filaments. AP|R

actin and myosin myofilaments within a muscle fiber produces *striations*—the light and dark cross bands that are characteristic of skeletal muscle fibers when viewed microscopically.

As shown in figure 7.2, the arrangement of thin actin and thick myosin myofilaments repeats itself throughout the length of a myofibril. These repeating units are called sarcomeres. A **sarcomere** is a contractile unit of skeletal muscle—that is, it is the smallest portion of a **myofibril** capable of contraction. A sarcomere extends from a Z line to the next Z line. Z lines are composed of proteins arranged transverse to the longitudinal axis of the myofilament. Thin actin myofilaments are attached to each side of the Z lines and extend toward the middle of the sarcomeres. Note that they do not meet. Thick myosin myofilaments occur only in the A band of the sarcomere.

Part 2   **Covering, Support, and Movement of the Body**

Check My Understanding

1. How are muscle tissue and connective tissue arranged in a skeletal muscle?
2. What composes a muscle fiber?

Figure 7.3 illustrates the arrangement of the sacroplasmic reticulum and transverse (T) tubule system to myofibrils in a skeletal muscle fiber. The **sacroplasmic reticulum** is the name given to the smooth endoplasmic reticulum in a muscle cell. It plays an important role in contraction by storing calcium (Ca^{++}) ions. The **transverse (T) tubule system** consists of invaginations of the sarcolemma that penetrate into the fiber so that they lie alongside and contact the sarcoplasmic reticulum.

Neuromuscular Interaction

A muscle fiber must be stimulated by nerve impulses in order to contract. Nerve impulses are carried from the brain or spinal cord to a muscle fiber by a long, thin process (an axon) of a motor neuron. A *motor neuron* is an action-causing neuron—its impulses produce an action in the target cells. In muscle fibers, this action is contraction. Each muscle fiber is innervated and controlled by a motor neuron.

Motor Units

A motor neuron and all of the muscle fibers to which it is attached form a **motor unit** (figure 7.4). Whereas a muscle fiber is attached to only one motor neuron, a

Clinical | **INSIGHT**

The number of skeletal muscle fibers cannot be increased after birth. However, heavy exercise, such as weight training, increases the number of myofibrils, which increases the diameter and strength of the muscle fibers and of the whole muscle itself.

Anabolic steroids, substances similar to the male sex hormone testosterone, have been used by some athletes to promote muscle development and strength. However, physicians have warned that such use can produce a number of harmful side effects, including damage to kidneys, increased risk of heart disease and liver cancer, and increased irritability. Other side effects include decreased testosterone and sperm production in males and increased facial hair and deepening of the voice in females.

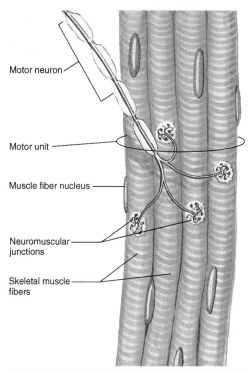

Figure 7.4 A motor unit consists of one motor neuron and all the muscle fibers that it innervates. Note the attachment of the axon terminals to the muscle fibers. AP|R

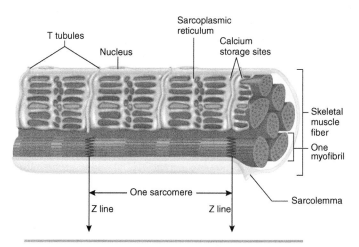

Figure 7.3 A portion of a skeletal muscle fiber showing the sarcoplasmic reticulum and the transverse (T) tubule system associated with the myofibrils.

single motor neuron may innervate from 3 to 2,000 muscle fibers. Where precise muscle control rather than strength is needed, such as in the fingers, a motor unit contains very few muscle fibers. Large numbers of motor units are involved in the manipulative movements of the fingers. In contrast, where strength rather than precise control is needed, such as in the postural muscles, a motor unit controls hundreds of muscle fibers. Whenever a motor neuron is activated, it stimulates contraction of all the muscle fibers that it controls.

Neuromuscular Junction

The part of a motor neuron that leads to a muscle fiber is called an *axon.* The connection between the terminal branches of an axon and the sarcolemma of a muscle fiber is known as a **neuromuscular junction** (figure 7.4). As shown in figure 7.5, the axon tips fit into depressions, the *motor end plates,* in the sarcolemma. The tiny space between the axon terminal and the sarcolemma is the *synaptic cleft.* Numerous secretory vesicles in the axon tip contain the **neurotransmitter** (nū-rō-trans′-mit-er) **acetylcholine** (as″-ē-til-kō′-lēn). When a motor neuron is activated and an impulse reaches the axon terminals, acetylcholine is released from secretory vesicles into the synaptic cleft. The attachment of acetylcholine to receptors on the sarcolemma triggers a series of reactions causing the muscle fiber to contract.

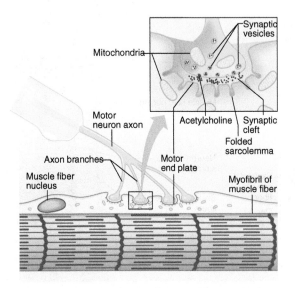

Figure 7.5 A neuromuscular junction is formed by the tip of a motor axon and the sarcolemma of a muscle fiber. The detailed insert shows the synaptic vesicles, the synaptic cleft, and the folded surface of the sarcolemma. APR

7.2 Physiology of Muscle Contraction

Contraction of a skeletal muscle fiber is a complex process that involves a number of rapid structural and chemical changes within the fiber. The molecular mechanism of contraction is explained by the *sliding-filament model* described in the next section.

Mechanism of Contraction APR

Contraction of a muscle fiber is initiated when the axon tip of an activated motor neuron releases acetylcholine into the synaptic cleft. Acetylcholine binds to receptors on the sarcolemma causing the formation of a muscle impulse (similar to a nerve impulse), which spreads over the sarcolemma and is carried into the muscle fiber by the transverse (T) tubule system. This triggers the release of Ca^{++} from the sarcoplasmic reticulum. When Ca^{++} binds to troponin, it causes the tropomyosin strands to change position, exposing the myosin-binding sites on actin molecules. The cross-bridges of myosin molecules bind to the binding sites on actin molecules. Then the cross-bridges exert a power stroke that pulls the thin actin filaments toward the center of the sarcomere. The cross-bridges detach from the actin molecules, become straightened ("cocked") and bind to the next myosin-binding sites, and produce another power stroke that pulls the thin actin filaments farther toward the center of the sarcomere. This cycle rapidly repeats itself to attain a maximum contraction as long as ATP and Ca^{++} are available.

Carefully study figure 7.6, which illustrates the sliding-filament model of muscle contraction. Note the configuration of thin actin filaments and thick myosin filaments in a relaxed muscle fiber, how they interact in the steps of the contraction mechanism, and how contraction is powered by ATP. Although the sliding filaments produce contraction (i.e., the shortening of the sarcomeres), the lengths of the thin actin filaments and thick myosin filaments remain unchanged (figure 7.7).

Once contraction occurs, the sarcolemma secretes the enzyme *acetylcholinesterase,* which decomposes acetylcholine in the synaptic cleft. This action of acetylcholinesterase is necessary to prevent continued stimulation of the muscle fiber and to prepare the fiber

Check My Understanding

3. What are the structure and function of a neuromuscular junction?
4. How do actin and myosin filaments interact during muscle contraction?

Part 2 **Covering, Support, and Movement of the Body**

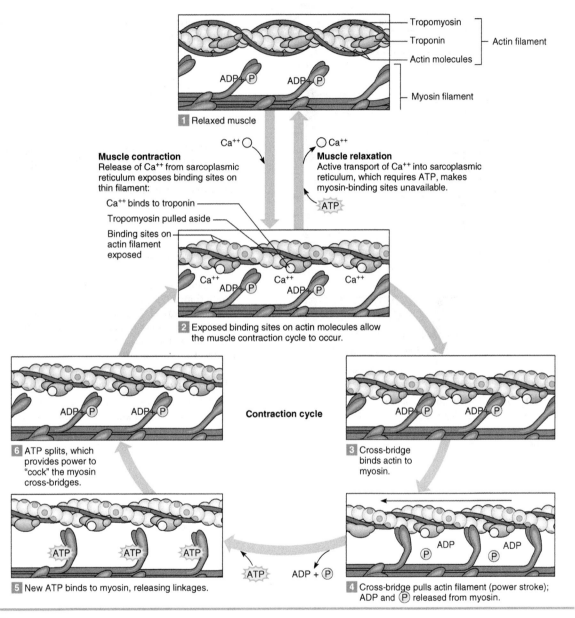

Figure 7.6 Sliding-filament model of muscle contraction. The release of Ca++ causes the exposure of myosin-binding sites on actin molecules, enabling the contraction cycle to begin. ATP powers the contraction mechanism. AP R

for the next stimulus. For each contraction, acetylcholine is released into the synaptic cleft, and then it is decomposed by acetylcholinesterase.

Energy for Contraction

The energy for muscle contraction comes from ATP molecules in the muscle cell. Recall that ATP is a product of cellular respiration. However, there is only a small amount of ATP in each muscle fiber. Once it is used up, more ATP must be formed in order for additional contractions to occur. Figure 7.8 summarizes the process of cellular respiration.

During cellular respiration, the energy released from nutrients is transferred to the high-energy phosphate bonds of ATP. Once there are sufficient amounts of ATP available in the cell, the high-energy phosphate

Chapter 7   **Muscular System**

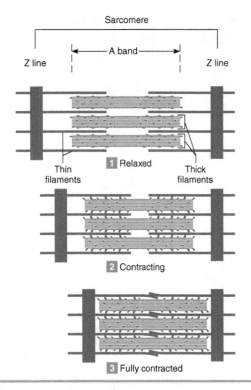

Figure 7.7 Contraction pulls the Z lines closer together, shortening the sarcomere. Note that the lengths of thin actin filaments and thick myosin filaments are unchanged. AP|R

is transferred to creatine to form **creatine phosphate,** which serves as a limited storage form of readily available energy.

When ATP supplies are decreased by muscle contractions, a high-energy phosphate group is transferred from creatine phosphate to ADP to form ATP, which can then be used to power additional contractions.

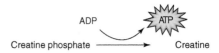

There is four to six times more creatine phosphate than ATP in a muscle cell, so it is an important source for rapid ATP formation without waiting for the slower process of cellular respiration. However, it can also be depleted rather quickly in a muscle that is contracting repeatedly.

Oxygen and Cellular Respiration

Recall from chapter 3 that cellular respiration takes place in two steps: (1) an anaerobic phase in the cytoplasm (sarcoplasm in muscle cells) and (2) an aerobic phase in mitochondria. The small amount of ATP produced by

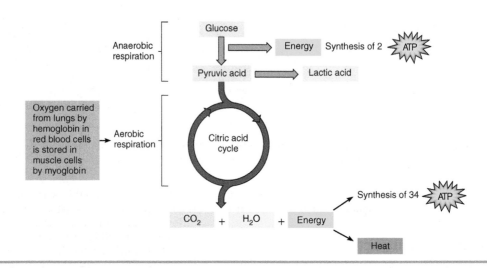

Figure 7.8 A summary of anaerobic and aerobic phases of cellular respiration. When the oxygen supply is inadequate, lactic acid accumulates in muscle cells, producing an oxygen debt.

anaerobic respiration cannot keep a person alive, except for very brief periods. Oxygen is life-sustaining because it enables the aerobic phase of cellular respiration to operate and produce adequate amounts of ATP.

Oxygen is transported from lungs to body cells in loose combination with **hemoglobin,** the red pigment in red blood cells. Muscle cells have another pigment, **myoglobin,** that can also combine loosely with oxygen. In times of muscle inactivity, some of the oxygen carried to muscle cells can be stored in combination with myoglobin and released later for aerobic cellular respiration during periods of muscle activity. This function of myoglobin reduces for a brief period the muscle cell's dependence on oxygen carried to it by the blood.

During inactivity or moderate physical activity, muscle cells receive sufficient oxygen via the blood to carry on the aerobic phase of cellular respiration. As shown in figure 7.8, this process involves the breakdown of *pyruvic acid* into carbon dioxide and water. However, during periods of strenuous exercise, the respiratory and circulatory systems cannot provide oxygen to muscle cells fast enough to maintain aerobic respiration. This causes some of the pyruvic acid to be converted to *lactic acid* as anaerobic respiration continues to break down glucose to form pyruvic acid and small amounts of ATP.

The accumulation of lactic acid causes discomfort and rapid, deep breathing in an attempt to provide adequate oxygen for aerobic respiration. About 80% of the lactic acid is carried by blood from the muscle cells to the liver, where it is later converted back into glucose and is reused. Lactic acid must be either broken down by aerobic respiration or converted back into glucose; because oxygen is required for both processes, an **oxygen debt** develops as lactic acid accumulates. The oxygen debt is the amount of oxygen required to metabolize the accumulated lactic acid and to resupply the normal amounts of ATP and creatine phosphate in the muscle cells. When the strenuous muscle activity ceases, rapid, deep breathing continues until the oxygen debt is fully paid. Endurance training enhances the efficiency of aerobic cellular respiration in muscle cells by increasing (1) the number of mitochondria, (2) the efficiency of obtaining oxygen from the blood, and (3) the concentration of myoglobin.

Fatigue

If a muscle is stimulated to contract for a long period, its contractions will gradually decrease until it no longer responds to stimulation. This condition is called **fatigue.** Fatigue seems to result primarily from an accumulation of lactic acid and carbon dioxide and the depletion of ATP, which cause chemical changes in the muscle fiber that prevent it from responding to stimulation.

Heat Production

Heat production by muscular activity is an important mechanism in maintaining a normal body temperature because muscles are active organs and form a large proportion of the body weight. Heat produced by muscles results from cellular respiration and other chemical reactions within the cells. Recall that 60% of the energy released by cellular respiration is heat energy, with only 40% of the released energy captured in ATP. The importance of muscle activity in maintaining body temperature is evident by the fact that a major response to a decrease in body temperature is shivering, which is caused by involuntary muscle contractions.

Check My Understanding

5. What are the roles of ATP and creatine phosphate in muscle contraction?
6. What is the relationship among cellular respiration, lactic acid, and oxygen debt?

Contraction Characteristics

When studying muscle contraction, physiologists consider both single-fiber contraction and whole-muscle contraction.

Contraction of a Single Fiber

It is possible to remove a single muscle fiber in order to study its contraction in the laboratory. By using electrical stimuli to initiate contraction and by gradually increasing the strength (voltage) of each stimulus, it has been shown that the fiber will not contract until the stimulus reaches a certain minimal strength. This minimal stimulus is called the **threshold stimulus.**

Whenever a muscle fiber is stimulated by a threshold stimulus or by a stimulus of greater strength, it always contracts *completely*. Thus, a muscle fiber either contracts completely or not at all—contraction is *not* proportional to the strength of the stimulus. This characteristic of individual muscle fibers is known as the **all-or-none response.**

Contraction of Whole Muscles

Much information has been gained by studying the contraction of a whole muscle of an experimental animal. In such studies, electrical stimulation is used to cause contraction, and the contraction is recorded to produce a tracing called a *myogram.*

If a single threshold stimulus is applied, some of the muscle fibers will contract to produce a single, weak contraction (a muscle twitch) and then relax, all within a fraction of a second. The myogram will look

Chapter 7 **Muscular System**

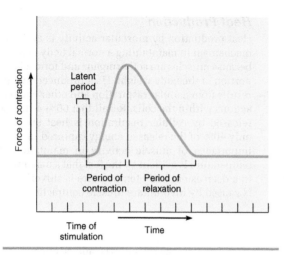

Figure 7.9   A myogram of a single muscle twitch. Note the brief latent period, rapid contraction period, and longer relaxation period.

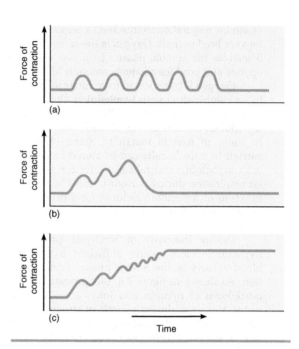

Figure 7.10   Myograms of (*a*) a series of simple twitches, (*b*) summation caused by incomplete relaxation between stimuli, and (*c*) tetanic contraction when there is no relaxation between stimuli.

like the one shown in figure 7.9. After the stimulus is applied, there is a brief interval before the muscle starts to contract. This interval is known as the *latent period*. Then, the muscle contracts (shortens) rapidly during the *period of contraction* and relaxes (returns to its former length) during the longer *period of relaxation*. If a muscle is stimulated again after it has relaxed completely, it will contract and produce a similar myogram. A series of single stimuli applied in this manner will yield a myogram like the one in figure 7.10*a*.

If the interval between stimuli is shortened so that the muscle fibers cannot completely relax, the force of individual twitches combines by *summation*, which increases the force of contraction (figure 7.10*b*). If stimuli are so frequent that relaxation is not possible, a **tetanic contraction** results (figure 7.10*c*).

Graded Responses   Unlike individual muscle fibers that exhibit all-or-none responses, whole muscles exhibit *graded responses*—that is, varying degrees of contraction. Graded responses enable the degree of muscle contraction to fit the task being performed. Obviously, more muscle fibers are required to lift a 14 kg (30 lb) weight than to lift a feather. Yet both activities can be performed by the same muscles.

Graded responses are possible because a muscle is composed of many different *motor units*, each responding to different thresholds of stimulation. In the laboratory, a weak stimulus that activates only low-threshold motor units produces a minimal contraction. As the strength of the stimulus is increased, the contractions get stronger as more motor units are activated until a **maximal stimulus** (one that activates all motor units) is applied, which produces a maximal

contraction. Further increases in the strength of the stimulus cannot produce a greater contraction. The same results occur in a normally functioning body, but it is the nervous system that provides the stimulation and controls the number of motor units activated in each muscle contraction. The activation of more and more motor units is known as *recruitment*.

Sustained Contractions   A sustained (tetanic) contraction lacks even partial relaxation and produces a myogram as shown in figure 7.10*c*. Sustained contractions for short time periods is the usual way in which muscles contract to produce body movements. Sustained contractions result from a rapid series of impulses carried by motor neurons to the muscle fibers.

Muscle Tone   Even when a muscle is relaxed, some of its fibers are contracting. At any given time, some of the fibers in a muscle are involved in a sustained contraction that produces a constant partial, but slight, contraction of the muscle. This state of constant partial contraction is called **muscle tone** and keeps a muscle ready to respond. Muscle tone results from the alternating activation of different motor units by the nervous system so that some muscle fibers are always in sustained contraction. Muscle tone of postural muscles plays an important role in maintaining erect posture.

If a nerve to a muscle is severed, the muscle is not only paralyzed but becomes soft and flabby due to the absence of muscle tone. Such a muscle will decrease in size due to lack of use, a process known as *atrophy*.

Check My Understanding

7. What is meant by the all-or-none response?
8. How are muscles able to make graded responses?

7.3 Actions of Skeletal Muscles

Skeletal muscles are usually arranged so that the ends of a muscle are attached to bones on each side of a joint. Thus, a muscle usually extends across a joint. The type of movement produced depends upon the type of joint and the locations of the muscle attachments. Common movements at joints were discussed in chapter 6.

Origin and Insertion

During contraction, a bone to which one end of the muscle is attached moves, but the bone to which the other end is attached does not. The movable attachment of a muscle is called the **insertion,** and the immovable attachment is called the **origin.** When a muscle contracts, the insertion is pulled toward the origin.

Consider the *biceps brachii* muscle in figure 7.11. It has two origins, and both are attached to the scapula.

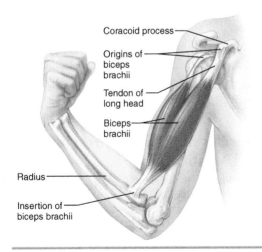

Coracoid process

Origins of biceps brachii

Tendon of long head

Biceps brachii

Radius

Insertion of biceps brachii

Figure 7.11 The biceps brachii muscle showing its two origins and single insertion. Note how the muscle extends across the elbow joint so that contraction flexes the forearm.

The insertion is on the radius, and the muscle lies along the anterior surface of the humerus. When the biceps contracts, the insertion is pulled toward the origin, which results in the flexion of the forearm at the elbow.

Most muscle contractions are *isotonic contractions,* which cause movement at a joint. Walking and breathing are examples. However, some contractions may not produce movement but only increase tension within a muscle. Pushing against an immovable object is an example. Such contractions are *isometric contractions,* and they are used by body builders to strengthen and enlarge muscles.

Exercise has a profound effect on skeletal muscles. Strength training, which involves isometric exercise and weight lifting, produces hypertrophy—an increase in muscle size and strength. Hypertrophy results from an increase in the number of myofibrils in muscle fibers, although the number of muscle fibers does not increase. Aerobic exercise, or endurance training, does not produce hypertrophy, but it increases the number of mitochondria in muscle fibers and blood vessels supplying the muscle. The enhanced supply of oxygen, nutrients, and ATP improves the efficiency of muscle action.

Muscle Interactions

Muscles function in groups rather than singly, and the groups are arranged to provide opposing movements. For example, if one group of muscles produces flexion, the opposing group produces extension. A group of muscles producing an action are called *agonists,* and the opposing group of muscles are called **antagonists.** When agonists contract, antagonists must relax, and vice versa, for movement to occur. If both groups contract simultaneously, the movable body part remains rigid.

Clinical **INSIGHT**

Several poisons, including *curare* (cu-rah´-re), prevent muscle contraction by blocking acetylcholine receptors at the neuromuscular junction. This causes flaccid paralysis, a condition in which the muscle is limp and cannot contract. Curare is well known as a plant extract used by South American Indians to make poisonous blowgun darts. It can cause death by asphyxiation if thoracic muscles are paralyzed. It has been used in surgery as a muscle relaxant, but it has now been replaced in most cases by other relaxants.

7.4 Naming of Muscles

Learning the complex names and functions of muscles can sometimes be confusing. However, the names of muscles are informative if their meaning is known. A few of the criteria used in naming muscles and examples of terms found in the names of muscles are listed following:

- **Function:** extensor, flexor, adductor, and pronator.
- **Shape:** trapezius (trapezoid), rhomboideus (rhomboid), deltoid (delta-shaped or triangular), biceps (two heads).
- **Relative position:** external, internal, abdominal, medial, lateral.
- **Location:** intercostal (between ribs), pectoralis (chest).
- **Site of attachment:** temporalis (temporal bone), zygomaticus (zygomatic bone).
- **Origin and insertion:** sternohyoid (sternum = origin; hyoid = insertion), sternocleidomastoid (sternum and clavicle = origins; mastoid process = insertion).
- **Size:** maximus (larger or largest), minimus (smaller or smallest), brevis (short), longus (long).
- **Orientation of fibers:** oblique (diagonal), rectus (straight), transverse (across).

7.5 Major Skeletal Muscles

This section is concerned with the name, location, attachment, and function of the major skeletal muscles. There are more than 600 muscles in the body, but only a few of the major muscles are considered here. Nearly all of them are superficial muscles. Most of this information is presented in tables and figures to aid your learning. The tables are organized according to the primary actions of the muscles. The pronunciation of each muscle is included, because being able to pronounce the names correctly will help you memorize the names of the muscles.

As you study this section, locate each muscle listed in the tables on the related figures 7.12 to 7.26. This will help you visualize the location and action of each muscle. Also, if you visualize the locations of the origin and insertion of a muscle, its action can be determined because contraction pulls the insertion toward the origin. It may help to refresh your understanding of the skeleton by referring to appropriate figures in chapter 6. Begin your study by examining figures 7.12 and 7.13 to learn the major superficial muscles that will be considered in more detail as you progress through the chapter.

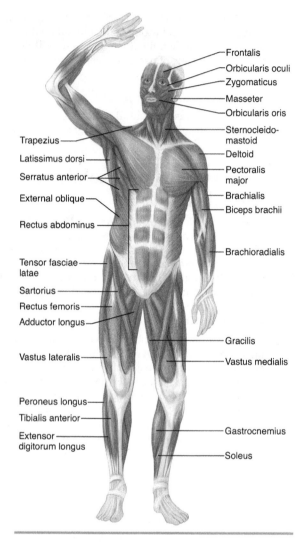

Figure 7.12 Anterior view of superficial skeletal muscles.

Muscles of Facial Expression and Mastication

Muscles of the face and scalp produce the facial expressions that help communicate feelings, such as anger, sadness, happiness, fear, disgust, pain, and surprise. Most have origins on skull bones and insertions on connective tissue of the skin (Table 7.3 and figure 7.14).

The *epicranius* is an unusual muscle. It has a large aponeurosis that covers the top of the skull and two contractile portions: the *frontalis* over the frontal bone and the *occipitalis* over the occipital bone.

Part 2   **Covering, Support, and Movement of the Body**

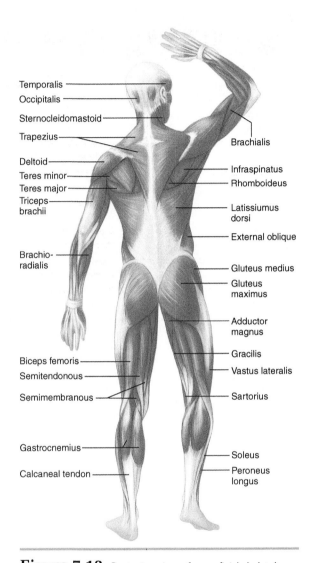

Temporalis
Occipitalis
Sternocleidomastoid
Trapezius
Deltoid
Teres minor
Teres major
Triceps brachii
Brachioradialis
Biceps femoris
Semitendonous
Semimembranous
Gastrocnemius
Calcaneal tendon

Brachialis
Infraspinatus
Rhomboideus
Latissiumus dorsi
External oblique
Gluteus medius
Gluteus maximus
Adductor magnus
Gracilis
Vastus lateralis
Sartorius
Soleus
Peroneus longus

Figure 7.13 Posterior view of superficial skeletal muscles.

Two major pairs of muscles raise the mandible in the process of mastication: the *masseter* and the *temporalis* (Table 7.4 and figure 7.14).

Muscles That Move the Head

Several pairs of neck muscles are responsible for flexing, extending, and turning the head. Table 7.5 lists two of the major muscles that perform this function: the *sternocleidomastoid* and the *splenius capitis.* As noted in Table 7.8, the *trapezius* can also extend the head, although this is not its major function (figures 7.14, 7.15, and 7.16).

Check My Understanding
9. What are the names and locations of the two parts of the epicranius muscle?
10. What muscles are involved in chewing your food?
11. What muscles turn your head to the side?

Muscles of the Abdominopelvic Wall

These paired muscles provide support for the anterior and lateral portions of the abdominal and pelvic regions, including support for the internal organs. The muscles are named for the direction of their muscle fibers: *rectus abdominis, external oblique, internal oblique,* and *transversus abdominis.* They are arranged in overlapping layers and are attached by larger aponeuroses that merge at the anterior midline to form the *linea alba,* or white line (Table 7.6 and figure 7.15).

Muscles of Breathing

Movement of the ribs occurs during breathing and is brought about by the contraction of two sets of muscles that are located between the ribs. The *external intercostals* lift the ribs upward and outward during inspiration, and the *internal intercostals* draw the ribs down and inward during expiration (Table 7.7 and figure 7.15). The primary breathing muscle is the *diaphragm,* a thin sheet of muscle that separates the thoracic and abdominal cavity. It is not shown in the figures.

Muscles That Move the Pectoral Girdle

These muscles originate on bones of the axial skeleton and insert on the scapula or clavicle. Because the scapula is supported mainly by muscles, it may be moved more freely than the clavicle. The *trapezius* is a superficial trapezoid-shaped muscle that covers much of the upper back. The *rhomboideus major* and the *levator scapulae* lie under the trapezius. The *serratus anterior* muscles are located on the lateral surfaces of the upper ribs near the axillary regions. The *pectoralis minor* lies under the pectoralis major. It pulls the scapula forward and downward (Table 7.8 and figures 7.15 to 7.18).

Chapter 7   **Muscular System**

Table 7.3   Muscles of Facial Expression

Muscle	Origin	Insertion	Action
Buccinator (buk´-si-nā-tor)	Lateral surfaces of maxilla and mandible	Orbicularis oris	Compresses cheeks inward
Epicranius (ep-i-krā´-nē-us)	This muscle consists of two parts: the frontalis and the occipitalis. They are joined by the epicranial aponeurosis, which covers the top of the skull.		
Frontalis (fron-ta´-lis)	Epicranial aponeurosis	Skin and muscles above the eyes	Raises eyebrows and wrinkles forehead horizontally
Occipitalis (ok-sip-i-tal´-is)	Base of occipital bone	Epicranial aponeurosis	Pulls scalp posteriorly
Orbicularis oculi (or-bik´-ū-lar-is ok´-ū-li)	Frontal bone and maxillae	Skin around eye	Closes eye
Orbicularis oris (or-bik´-ū-lar-is- o´-ris)	Muscles around mouth	Skin around lips	Closes and puckers lips; shapes lips during speech
Platysma (plah-tiz´-mah)	Fascia of upper chest	Mandible and muscles around mouth	Draws angle of mouth downward; opens mouth
Zygomaticus (zī-gō-mat´-ik-us)	Zygomatic bone	Orbicularis oris at corners of the mouth	Pulls angle of mouth upward

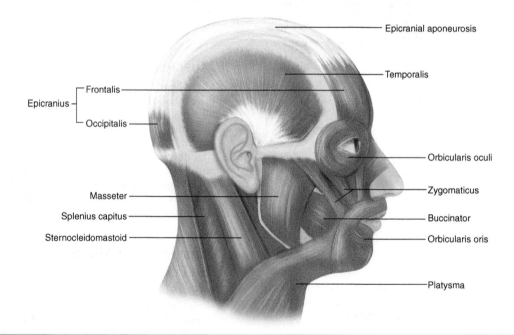

Figure 7.14 Muscles of facial expression and mastication. AP|R

Table 7.4   Muscles of Mastication

Muscle	Origin	Insertion	Action
Masseter (mas-se´-ter)	Zygomatic arch	Lateral surface of mandible	Raises mandible
Temporalis (tem-po-ra´-lis)	Temporal bone	Coronoid process of mandible	Raises mandible

Part 2   Covering, Support, and Movement of the Body

Table 7.5   Muscles That Move the Head

Muscle	Origin	Insertion	Action
Sternocleidomastoid (ster-nō-klī-dō-mas´-toid)	Clavicle and sternum	Mastoid process of temporal bone	Contraction of both muscles flexes head toward chest; contraction of one muscle turns head away from contracting muscle
Splenius capitus (splē´-nē-us kap´-i-tis)	Lower cervical and upper thoracic vertebrae	Mastoid process of temporal bone	Contraction of both muscles extends head; contraction of one muscle turns head toward same side as contracting muscle

Table 7.6   Muscles of the Abdominopelvic Wall

Muscle	Origin	Insertion	Action
Rectus abdominis (rek´-tus ab-dom´-i-nis)	Pubic symphysis and pubic crest	Xiphoid process of sternum and costal cartilages of ribs 5 to 7	Tightens abdominopelvic wall; compresses internal organs; flexes the vertebral column
External oblique (eks-ter´-nal o-blēk´)	Anterior surface of lower eight ribs	Iliac crest and linea alba	Tightens abdominopelvic wall and compresses internal organs
Internal oblique (in-ter´-nal o-blēk´)	Iliac crest and inguinal ligament	Cartilage of lower four ribs, pubic crest, and linea alba	Same as above
Transversus abdominis (trans-ver´-sus ab-dom´-i-nis)	Iliac crest, cartilages of lower six ribs, processes of lumbar vertebrae	Pubic crest and linea alba	Same as above

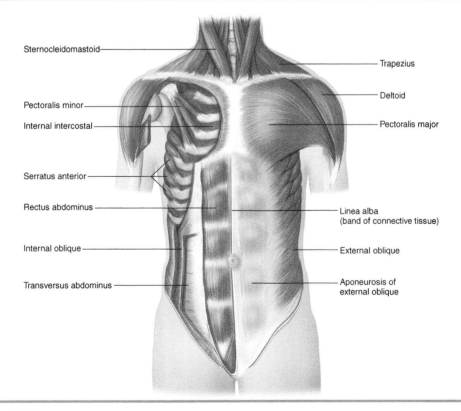

Figure 7.15 Muscles of the anterior chest and abdominal wall. The right pectoralis major is removed to show the pectoralis minor. AP|R

Chapter 7 **Muscular System**

Table 7.7 Muscles of Breathing

Muscle	Origin	Insertion	Action
Diaphragm (dĭ-a-fram)	Lumbar vertebrae, costal cartilages of lower ribs, xiphoid process	Central tendon located at midpoint of muscle	Forms floor of thoracic cavity; lowers during contraction, causing inspiration
External intercostals (eks-ter′-nal in-ter-kos′-tals)	Inferior border of rib above	Superior border of rib below	Raises ribs upward and outward during inspiration
Internal intercostals (in-ter′-nal in-ter-kos′-tals)	Superior border of rib below	Inferior border of rib above	Draws ribs downward and inward during expiration

Table 7.8 Muscles That Move the Pectoral Girdle

Muscle	Origin	Insertion	Action
Trapezius (trah-pē-zē′-us)	Occipital bone; cervical and thoracic vertebrae	Clavicle; spine and acromion process of scapula	Elevates clavicle; adducts and elevates scapula; extends head
Rhomboideus major (rom-boid′-ē-us)	Upper thoracic vertebrae	Medial border of scapula	Adducts and elevates scapula
Levator scapulae (le-va′-tor skap′-ū-lē)	Cervical vertebrae	Superior medial margin of scapula	Elevates scapula
Serratus anterior (ser-ra′-tus)	Upper eight to nine ribs	Medial border of scapula	Pulls scapula downward and anteriorly
Pectoralis minor (pek-to-rah′-lis)	Anterior surface of upper ribs	Coracoid process of scapula	Pulls scapula anteriorly and downward

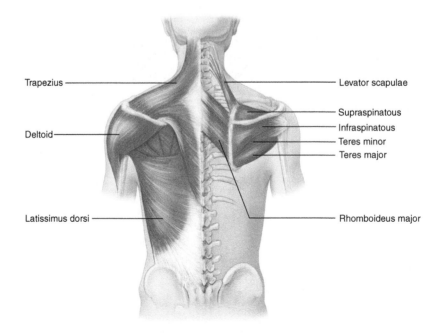

Figure 7.16 Muscles of the posterior shoulder. The right trapezius is removed to show underlying muscles. AP|R

Muscles That Move the Arm and Forearm

Movement of the humerus is enabled by the muscles that originate on the pectoral girdle, ribs, or vertebrae and insert on the humerus. The arrangement of these muscles and the ball-and-socket joint between the humerus and scapula enable great freedom of movement for the arm. The *pectoralis major* is the large superficial muscle of the chest. The *deltoid* is the thick muscle that caps the shoulder joint. The *coracobrachialis* is a relatively small muscle that lies under the pectoralis major and biceps brachii. It flexes and adducts the arm. The *supraspinatus, infraspinatus, teres major,* and *teres minor* cover the posterior surfaces of the scapulae (plural of *scapula*). The *latissimus dorsi* is a broad, sheetlike muscle that covers the lower back (Table 7.9 and figures 7.15 to 7.20).

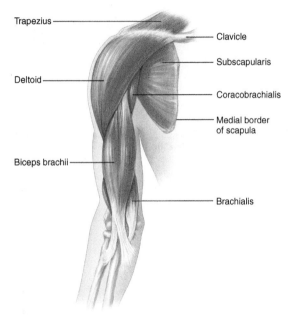

Figure 7.17 Muscles of the posterior surface of the scapula and arm. AP|R

Figure 7.18 Muscles of the anterior shoulder and arm, with the rib cage removed. AP|R

Table 7.9   Muscles That Move the Arm

Muscle	Origin	Insertion	Action
Pectoralis major (pek-tō-rah´-lis)	Clavicle; sternum, and cartilages of upper ribs	Greater tubercle of humerus	Adducts humerus; draws it forward across chest
Coracobrachialis (kōr˝-a-kō-brā-kē-ah´-lis)	Coracoid process of scapula	Shaft of humerus	Adducts and flexes humerus
Deltoid (del´-toid)	Clavicle and spine, and acromion of scapula	Deltoid tuberosity of humerus	Abducts, flexes, and extends humerus
Supraspinatus (su-prah-spi˝-na-tus)	Posterior surface of scapula above spine	Greater tubercle of humerus	Assists deltoid in abducting humerus
Infraspinatus (in-frah-spi˝-na-tus)	Posterior surface of scapula below spine	Greater tubercle of humerus	Rotates humerus laterally
Latissimus dorsi (lah-tis´-i-mus dor´si̅)	Lower thoracic, lumbar, and sacral vertebrae; lower ribs; iliac crest	Intertubercular groove of humerus	Adducts and extends humerus; rotates humerus medially
Teres major (te´r-ez)	Inferior angle of scapula	Distal to lesser tubercle of humerus	Extends, adducts, and rotates humerus medially
Teres minor	Lateral border of scapula	Greater tubercle of humerus	Rotates humerus laterally

Chapter 7 **Muscular System**

Check My Understanding

12. What muscle separates the abdominal and thoracic cavities?
13. Name the abdominal muscles from inside out.
14. What three muscles raise the scapula?

Muscles moving the forearm originate on either the humerus or scapula and insert on either the radius or ulna. Three flexors occur on the anterior surface of the upper arm: the *biceps brachii, brachialis,* and *brachioradialis.* One extensor, the *triceps brachii,* is located on the posterior surface of the upper arm (Table 7.10 and figures 7.15, 7.19, and 7.20).

Table 7.10   Muscles That Move the Forearm

Muscle	Origin	Insertion	Action
Biceps brachii (bī´-seps brā´-kē-ī)	Coracoid process and tubercle above glenoid cavity of scapula	Radial tuberosity of radius	Flexes and rotates forearm laterally (supination)
Brachialis (brā´-kē-al-is)	Distal, anterior surface of humerus	Coronoid process of ulna	Flexes forearm
Brachioradialis (brā-kē-ō-rā-dē-a´-lis)	Lateral surface of distal end of humerus	Lateral surface of radius just above styloid process	Flexes forearm
Triceps brachii (trī´-seps brā´-kē-ī)	Lateral and medial surfaces of humerus and tubercle below glenoid cavity of scapula	Olecranon process of ulna	Extends forearm

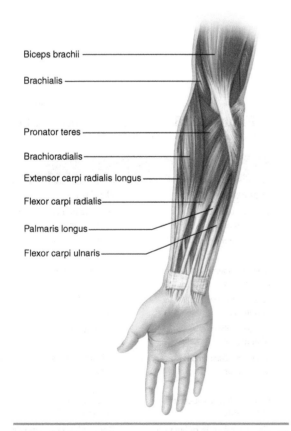

Biceps brachii
Brachialis
Pronator teres
Brachioradialis
Extensor carpi radialis longus
Flexor carpi radialis
Palmaris longus
Flexor carpi ulnaris

Figure 7.19 Muscles of the anterior forearm. AP|R

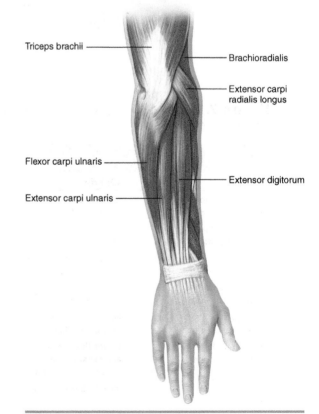

Triceps brachii
Brachioradialis
Extensor carpi radialis longus
Flexor carpi ulnaris
Extensor carpi ulnaris
Extensor digitorum

Figure 7.20 Muscles of the posterior forearm. AP|R

Muscles That Move the Wrist and Fingers

Many muscles that produce the various movements of the wrist and fingers are located in the forearm. Only a few of the larger superficial muscles are considered here. They originate from the distal end of the humerus and insert on carpals, metacarpals, or phalanges. Flexors on the anterior surface include the *flexor carpi radialis, flexor carpi ulnaris,* and *palmaris longus.* Extensors on the posterior surface include the *extensor carpi radialis longus, extensor carpi ulnaris,* and *extensor digitorum* (Table 7.11 and figure 7.20). Note that the tendons of these muscles are held in position by a circular ligament at the wrist.

Muscles That Move the Thigh and Leg

Muscles moving the thigh span the hip joint. They insert on the femur, and most originate on the pelvic girdle. The *iliacus* and *psoas major* are located anteriorly, the *gluteus maximus* is located posteriorly and forms the buttocks, the *gluteus medius* is located under the gluteus maximus posteriorly and extends laterally, and the *tensor fasciae latae* is

Check My Understanding

15. What muscle abducts and extends your arm?
16. What muscle extends your forearm?
17. What muscle extends your fingers?

located laterally. The *adductor longus* and *adductor magnus* are both located medially (Table 7.12 and figures 7.21, 7.22, and 7.23).

The leg is moved by muscles located in the thigh. They span the knee joint and originate on the pelvic girdle or thigh and insert on the tibia or fibula. The *quadriceps femoris* is composed of four muscles that have a common tendon that inserts on the patella. However, this tendon continues as the patellar ligament, which attaches to the tibial tuberosity—the functional insertion for these muscles. The *biceps femoris, semitendinosus,* and *semimembranosus* on the posterior surface of the thigh are often collectively called the "hamstrings." The medially located *gracilis* has two insertions that give it dual actions. The long, straplike *sartorius*

Clinical INSIGHT

Intramuscular injections are commonly used when quick absorption is desired. Such injections are given in three sites: (1) the lateral surface of the deltoid; (2) the gluteus medius in the upper, outer portion of the buttock; and (3) the vastus lateralis near the midpoint of the lateral surface of the thigh. These injection sites are chosen because there are no major nerves or blood vessels present that could be damaged, and the muscles have a good blood supply to aid absorption. The site chosen may vary with the age and condition of the patient.

Table 7.11   Muscles That Move the Wrist and Fingers

Muscle	Origin	Insertion	Action
Flexor carpi radialis (flek´-sor kar´-pī rā-dē-a´-lis)	Medial epicondyle of humerus	Second and third metacarpals	Flexes and abducts wrist
Flexor carpi ulnaris (flek´-sor kar´-pī ul-na´-ris)	Medial epicondyle of humerus and olecranon process of ulna	Carpal bones and fifth metacarpal	Flexes and adducts wrist
Palmaris longus (pal-ma´-ris long´-gus)	Medial epicondyle of humerus	Fascia of palm	Flexes wrist
Extensor carpi radialis longus (eks-ten´-sor kar´-pī rā-dē-a´-lis long´-gus)	Lateral epicondyle of humerus	Second metacarpal	Extends and abducts wrist
Extensor carpi ulnaris (eks-ten´-sor kar´-pī ul-na´-ris)	Lateral epicondyle of humerus	Fifth metacarpal	Extends and adducts wrist
Extensor digitorum (eks-ten´-sor dij-i-to´-rum)	Lateral epicondyle of humerus	Posterior surfaces of phalanges 2–5	Extends fingers

Chapter 7 **Muscular System**

Table 7.12 Muscles That Move the Thigh

Muscle	Origin	Insertion	Action
Iliacus (il'-ē-ak-us)	Fossa of ilium	Lesser trochanter of femur	Flexes thigh
Psoas major (so'-as)	Lumbar vertebrae	Lesser trochanter of femur	Flexes thigh
Gluteus maximus (glū'-tē-us mak'-si-mus)	Posterior surfaces of ilium; sacrum; and coccyx	Posterior surface of femur and lateral fascia of thigh	Extends and rotates thigh laterally
Gluteus medius (glū'-tē-us mē'-dē-us)	Lateral surface of ilium	Greater trochanter of femur	Abducts and rotates thigh medially
Tensor fasciae latae (ten'-sor fash'-ē-ē lah-tē')	Anterior iliac crest	Lateral fascia of thigh	Flexes and abducts thigh
Adductor longus (ad-duk'-tor long'-gus)	Pubic bone near symphysis pubis	Posterior surface of femur	Adducts, flexes, and rotates thigh laterally
Adductor magnus (ad-duk'-tor mag'-nus)	Inferior portion of ischium and pubis	Same as above	Same as above

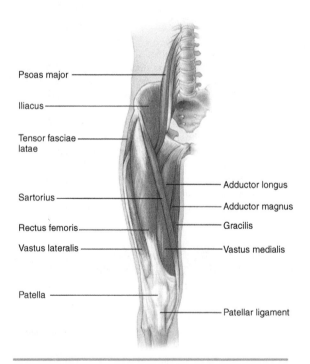

Figure 7.21 Muscles of the anterior right thigh. (Note that the vastus intermedius is a deep muscle not visible in this view.)

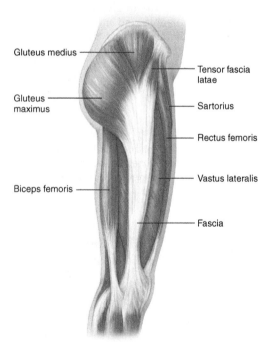

Figure 7.22 Muscles of the lateral right thigh.

Muscles That Move the Foot and Toes

extends diagonally across the anterior surface of the thigh and spans both the hip and knee joints. Its contraction enables the legs to cross (Table 7.13 and figures 7.21, 7.22, and 7.23).

Many muscles are involved in the movement of the foot and toes. They are located in the leg and originate on the femur, tibia, or fibula and insert on the

Table 7.13   Muscles That Move the Leg

Muscle	Origin	Insertion	Action
Quadriceps femoris (quad´-ri-seps fem´-or-is)	A composite thigh muscle formed of four parts that are usually described as separate muscles. Each muscle has a common tendon that attaches to the patella and continues as the patellar ligament to the tibial tuberosity.		
Rectus femoris (rek´-tus fem´-or-is)	Anterior inferior iliac spine and superior margin of acetabulum	Patella; tendon continues as patellar ligament, which attaches to tibial tuberosity	Extends leg and flexes thigh
Vastus lateralis (vas´-tus lat-er-a´lis)	Greater trochanter and posterior surface of femur	Same as above	Extends leg
Vastus medialis (vas´-tus me-de-a´lis)	Medial and posterior surfaces of femur	Same as above	Extends leg
Vastus intermedius (vas´-tus in-ter-mē´dē-us)	Anterior and lateral surfaces of femur	Same as above	Extends leg
Hamstrings	Three distinct muscles of the posterior thigh.		
Biceps femoris (bi´-seps fem´-or-is)	Ischial tuberosity and posterior surface of femur	Head of fibula and lateral condyle of tibia	Flexes and rotates leg laterally; extends thigh
Semitendinosus (sem-ē-ten-di-nō´-sus)	Ischial tuberosity	Medial surface of tibia	Flexes and rotates leg medially; extends thigh
Semimembranosus (sem-ē-mem-brah-nō´-sus)	Ischial tuberosity	Medial condyle of tibia	Flexes and rotates leg medially; extends thigh
Gracilis (gras´-il-is)	Pubis near symphysis	Medial surface of tibia	Flexes and rotates leg medially; adducts thigh
Sartorius (sar-to´r-ē-us)	Anterior superior iliac spine	Medial surface of tibia	Flexes thigh; rotates leg medially and thigh laterally as when crossing legs

Table 7.14   Muscles That Move the Foot and Toes

Muscle	Origin	Insertion	Action
Gastrocnemius (gas-trōk-nē´m-ē-us)	Medial and lateral condyles of femur	Calcaneus by the calcaneal tendon	Plantar flexes foot and flexes leg
Soleus (sō´l-ē-us)	Posterior surface of tibia and fibula	Calcaneus by the calcaneal tendon	Plantar flexes foot
Peroneus longus (per-ō-nē´-us long´-gus)	Lateral condyle of tibia and head and body of fibula	First metatarsal and tarsal bones	Plantar flexes and everts foot; supports arch
Tibialis anterior (tib-ē-a´l-is an-te´rē-or)	Lateral condyle and surface of tibia	First metatarsal and tarsal bones	Dorsiflexes and inverts foot
Extensor digitorum longus (eks-ten´-sor dig-i-tor´-um long´-gus)	Lateral condyle of tibia and anterior surface of fibula	Phalanges of toes 2–5	Dorsiflexes and everts foot; extends toes

tarsals, metatarsals, or phalanges. The posterior leg muscles include the *gastrocnemius* and *soleus,* which insert on a common tendon, the calcaneal tendon, which attaches to the calcaneus (heel bone). The *tibialis anterior* is anteriorly located, and the *extensor digitorum longus* lies lateral to it. Note that although the extensor digitorum extends the toes, as its name implies, it also dorsiflexes the foot. The *peroneus longus* is located on the lateral surface of the leg (Table 7.14 and figures 7.24 to 7.26).

Chapter 7   Muscular System

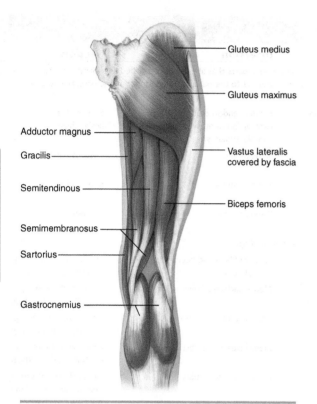

Gluteus medius

Gluteus maximus

Adductor magnus

Gracilis

Vastus lateralis covered by fascia

Semitendinous

Biceps femoris

Semimembranosus

Sartorius

Gastrocnemius

Figure 7.23 Muscles of the posterior right thigh. AP|R

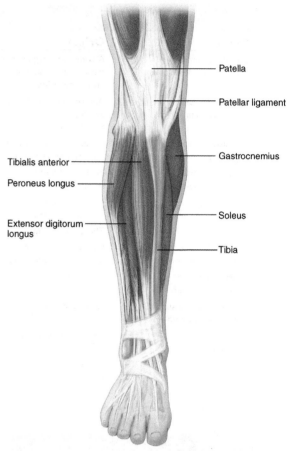

Patella

Patellar ligament

Tibialis anterior

Gastrocnemius

Peroneus longus

Extensor digitorum longus

Soleus

Tibia

Figure 7.24 Muscles of the anterior right leg. AP|R

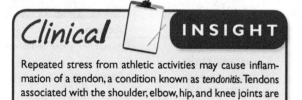

Clinical INSIGHT

Repeated stress from athletic activities may cause inflammation of a tendon, a condition known as *tendonitis*. Tendons associated with the shoulder, elbow, hip, and knee joints are most commonly affected.

Check My Understanding

18. Name the muscles that flex the thigh.
19. What are the four parts of the quadriceps femoris?
20. What is the action of muscles inserting on the calcaneus?

Foot movements include moving the foot upward (dorsiflexion), moving the foot downward (plantar flexion), turning the sole inward (inversion), and turning the sole outward (eversion). Note how the tendons are held in position by the bands of ligaments at the ankle.

7.6 Disorders of the Muscular System

Some disorders of the muscle system may result from factors associated only with muscles, while others are caused by disorders of the nervous system. Certain neurological disorders are included here because of their obvious effect on muscle action.

Muscle Disorders

Cramps are involuntary, painful, sustained tetanic contractions of a muscle. The precise cause is unknown, but a cramp may result from chemical changes in the muscle, such as lactic acid accumulation or calcium deficiencies. Sometimes a severe blow to a muscle can produce a cramp.

Fibrosis (fĭ-brō′-sis) is an abnormal increase of fibrous connective tissue in a muscle. Usually, it

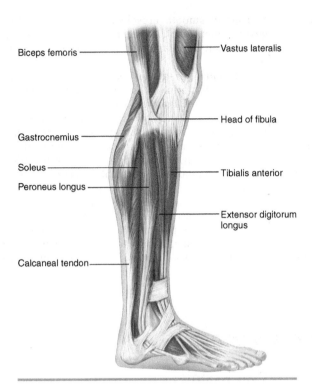

Biceps femoris

Vastus lateralis

Gastrocnemius

Head of fibula

Soleus

Peroneus longus

Tibialis anterior

Extensor digitorum longus

Calcaneal tendon

Figure 7.25 Lateral view of muscles of the right lower leg.

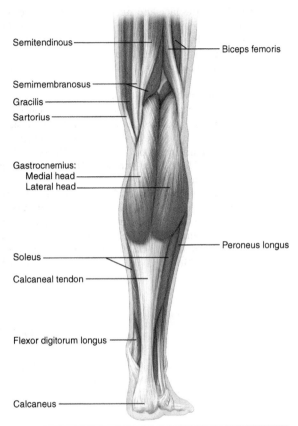

Semitendinous

Biceps femoris

Semimembranosus

Gracilis

Sartorius

Gastrocnemius:
  Medial head
  Lateral head

Soleus

Peroneus longus

Calcaneal tendon

Flexor digitorum longus

Calcaneus

Figure 7.26 Muscles of the posterior right leg. AP|R

results from connective tissue replacing dead muscle fibers following an injury.

Fibrositis (fĭ-brō-sī´-tis) is the inflammation of the connective tissue, especially muscle sheaths and fascia associated with muscles. It produces soreness and stiffness that is commonly called *muscular rheumatism.*

Muscular dystrophy (dis´-trō-fē) is a general term for a number of inherited muscular disorders that are characterized by the progressive degeneration of muscles. The affected muscles gradually weaken and atrophy (shrink), producing a progressive crippling of the patient. There is no specific drug cure, but patients are encouraged to keep active and are given muscle-strengthening exercises.

Myositis (mī-ō-sī´-tis) is the inflammation of muscle tissue. It produces soreness and stiffness similar to fibrositis of the muscles.

Strains, or "pulled muscles," result when a muscle is stretched excessively. This usually occurs when an antagonist has not relaxed quickly enough as an agonist contracts. The hamstrings are a common site of muscle strains. In mild strains, only a few muscle fibers are damaged. In severe strains, both connective and muscle tissues are torn, and muscle function may be severely impaired.

Neurological Disorders Affecting Muscles

Botulism (boch´-ū-lizm) poisoning is caused by a neurotoxin produced by the bacterium *Clostridium botulinum.* The toxin prevents release of acetylcholine from the tips of motor axons. Without prompt treatment with an antitoxin, death may result from paralysis of the muscles used in breathing. Poisoning results from eating improperly canned vegetables or meats that contain *C. botulinum* and the accumulated toxins.

Myasthenia gravis (mī-as-thē´-nē-ah grav´-is) is characterized by extreme muscular weakness caused by improper functioning of the neuromuscular junctions. It is an autoimmune disease in which antibodies are produced that attach to the acetylcholine receptors on the sarcolemma and reduce or block the stimulatory effect of acetylcholine. Myasthenia gravis occurs most frequently in women between 20 and 40 years of age. Usually, it first affects ocular muscles and other

Chapter 7   **Muscular System**

muscles of the face and neck, which may lead to difficulty in chewing, swallowing, and talking. Other muscles of the body may be involved later. Treatment typically involves the use of anticholinesterase drugs and immunosuppressive drugs, such as the steroid prednisone.

Poliomyelitis (pō-lē-ō-mĭ-e-lĭ´-tis) is a viral disease of motor neurons in the spinal cord. Destruction of the motor neurons leads to paralysis of skeletal muscles. It is now rare in industrialized countries due to the availability of a polio vaccine. Virtually all children in the United States receive this vaccine, which protects them from polio.

Spasms are sudden, involuntary contractions of a muscle or a group of muscles. They may vary from simple twitches to severe convulsions and may be accompanied by pain. Spasms may be caused by irritation of the motor neurons supplying the muscle, emotional stress, or neurological disorders.

Spasms of smooth muscle in the walls of the digestive tract, respiratory passages, or certain blood vessels can be hazardous. Hiccupping is one type of spasm.

Tetanus (tet´-ah-nus) is a disease caused by the anaerobic bacterium *Clostridium tetani,* which is common in soil. Infection usually results from puncture wounds. *C. tetani* produces a neurotoxin that affects motor neurons in the spinal cord, resulting in continuous stimulation and tetanic contractions of certain muscles. Because the first muscles affected are those that move the mandible, this disease is often called "lockjaw." Without prompt treatment, mortality is high. Young children usually receive injections of tetanus toxoid to stimulate production of antibodies against the neurotoxin. Booster injections are given at regular intervals to keep the concentration of antibodies at a high level in order to prevent the disease.

CHAPTER SUMMARY

- The three types of muscle tissue in the body are skeletal, smooth, and cardiac.
- Each type of muscle tissue has unique structural and functional characteristics.

7.1 Structure of Skeletal Muscle

- Each skeletal muscle is formed of many muscle fibers (cells) that are arranged in fasciculi.
- Connective tissue envelops each fiber, each fasiculus, and the entire muscle.
- Muscles are attached to bones or connective tissue by either tendons or aponeuroses.
- The sarcolemma is the plasma membrane of a muscle fiber, and the sarcoplasm (cytoplasm) surrounds the myofibrils, the contractile elements.
- Myofibrils consist of thick (myosin) and thin (actin) myofilaments. The arrangement of the myofilaments produces the striations that are characteristic of skeletal muscle fibers.
- Each myofibril consists of many sarcomeres joined end-to-end. A sarcomere is bounded by a Z line at each end.
- The axon tip of a motor neuron is attached to each muscle fiber at the neuromuscular junction. The axon tip fits into a synaptic cleft in the sarcolemma. The neurotransmitter acetylcholine is contained in tiny vesicles in the axon tip.
- Each muscle fiber is innervated and controlled by a motor neuron.
- A motor unit consists of a motor neuron and all muscle fibers to which it is attached.

7.2 Physiology of Muscle Contraction

- An activated motor axon releases acetylcholine into the synaptic cleft. Acetylcholine attaches to receptors of the sarcolemma and causes the release of Ca^{++} molecules. This, in turn, causes the crossbridges of myosin from the sarcoplastic reticulum to attach to binding sites on actin molecules. A series of ratchetlike movements pulls the thin filaments toward the center of the sarcomere, producing contraction.
- Acetylcholinesterase quickly breaks down acetylcholine to prevent continued stimulation and to prepare the muscle fiber for the next stimulus.
- Energy for contraction comes from high-energy phosphate bonds in ATP.
- After cellular respiration has formed a muscle cell's normal supply of ATP, excess energy is transferred to creatine to form creatine phosphate, which serves as a small reserve supply of energy.
- Small amounts of oxygen are stored in combination with myoglobin, which gives muscle cells a small reserve of oxygen for aerobic cellular respiration.
- Vigorous muscular activity quickly exhausts available oxygen, leading to the accumulation of lactic acid and producing an oxygen debt. Heavy breathing after exercise provides the oxygen required to metabolize lactic acid and pay the oxygen debt.
- Fatigue results primarily from the accumulation of lactic acid in a muscle fiber.

- Large amounts of heat are produced by the chemical and physical processes of muscle contraction.
- When stimulated by a threshold stimulus, individual muscle fibers exhibit an all-or-none contraction response.
- A simple contraction consists of a latent period, period of contraction, and period of relaxation.
- Whole muscles provide graded contraction responses, which are enabled by the number of motor units that are recruited.
- A sustained contraction of all motor units is a tetanic contraction.
- Muscle tone is a state of partial contraction that results from alternating contractions of a few motor units.

7.3 Actions of Skeletal Muscles

- The origin is the immovable attachment, and the insertion is the movable attachment.
- Muscles are arranged in groups with opposing actions: agonists and antagonists.

7.4 Naming of Muscles

- Several criteria are used in naming muscles.
- These criteria include function, shape, relative position, location, site of attachment, origin and insertion, size, and orientation of fibers.

7.5 Major Skeletal Muscles

- Muscles of facial expression originate on skull bones and insert on connective tissue of the skin. They include the epicranius, orbicularis oculi, orbicularis oris, buccinator, zygomaticus, and platysma.
- Muscles of mastication originate on fixed skull bones and insert on the mandible. They include the masseter and the temporalis.
- Muscles that move the head occur in the neck and upper back. They include the sternocleidomastoid and splenius capitis.
- Muscles of the abdominopelvic wall connect the pelvic girdle, rib cage, and vertebral column. They include the rectus abdominis, external oblique, internal oblique, and transversus abdominis.

- Muscles that move the ribs occur between the ribs. They are the external intercostals and internal intercostals.
- Muscles that move the pectoral girdle originate on the rib cage or vertebrae and insert on the pectoral girdle. They include the trapezius, rhomboideus major, levator scapulae, pectoralis minor, and serratus anterior.
- Muscles that move the arm originate on the rib cage, vertebrae, or pectoral girdle and insert on the humerus. They include the pectoralis major, coracobrachialis deltoid, supraspinatus, infraspinatus, latissimus dorsi, teres major, and teres minor.
- Muscles that move the forearm originate on the scapula or humerus and insert on the radius or ulna. They include the biceps brachii, brachialis, brachioradialis, and triceps brachii.
- Muscles that move the wrist and fingers are the muscles of the forearm. They include the flexor carpi radialis, flexor carpi ulnaris, palmaris longus, extensor carpi radialis longus, extensor carpi ulnaris, and extensor digitorum.
- Muscles that move the thigh originate on the pelvic girdle and insert on the femur. They include the iliacus, psoas major, gluteus maximus, gluteus medius, tensor fasciae latae, adductor longus, and adductor magnus.
- Muscles that move the leg originate on the pelvic girdle or femur and insert on the tibia or fibula. They include the quadriceps femoris, biceps femoris, semitendinosus, semimembranosus, gracilis, and sartorius.
- Muscles that move the foot and toes are the muscles of the lower leg. They include the gastrocnemius, soleus, peroneus longus, tibialis anterior, and extensor digitorum longus.

7.6 Disorders of the Muscular System

- Disorders of muscles include cramps, fibrosis, fibrositis, muscular dystrophy, myositis, and strains.
- Neurological disorders that directly affect muscle action include botulism, myasthenia gravis, poliomyelitis, spasms, and tetanus.

BUILDING MY VOCABULARY

1. **Selected New Terms**
   acetylcholine, p. 130
   actin myofilament, p. 127
   deep fascia, p. 126
   graded response, p. 134
   latent period, p. 134
   myosin myofilament, p. 127
   neuromuscular junction, p. 130
   recruitment, p. 134
   sarcolemma, p. 127
   sarcoplasm, p. 127

2. **Related Clinical Terms**
   Fibromyositis (fī-brō-mī-ō-sī´-tis) A general term for inflammation of a muscle and its associated connective tissue.
   Myalgia (mī-al´-jē-ah) Muscle pain from any cause.
   Myopathy (mī-op´-ah-thē) Any disease of muscles.
   Orthopedics (or-thō-pē´-diks) Branch of surgery dealing with repair of the skeletal and muscular systems.
   Spasm (Spaz´-um) An involuntary muscle contraction.

Chapter 7   **Muscular System**

SELF-REVIEW

Answers are located in appendix B.

1. A skeletal muscle consists of many _____, which are arranged in fasciculi.
2. Muscles are attached to bones by _____.
3. A contractile unit of a myofibril is a _____.
4. A muscle contraction is triggered by _____ binding to receptors on the sarcolemma.
5. Contraction occurs when thick myosin filaments pull _____ filaments toward the center of a sarcomere.
6. Accumulation of _____ during vigorous exercise results in an oxygen debt.
7. The movable end of a muscle is its _____.
8. The lower jaw is closed by the contraction of the temporalis and the _____.
9. The abdominal muscle extending from the sternum to the pubis is the _____.
10. The broad muscle of the lower back is the _____.
11. The shoulder muscle that raises the arm is the _____.
12. The arm muscle that extends the forearm is the _____.
13. The large muscle that extends and rotates the thigh laterally is the _____.
14. The four-part thigh muscle that extends the lower leg is the _____.
15. The large calf muscle that plantar flexes the foot is the _____.

CRITICAL THINKING

1. Complete the learning objectives on the first page of the chapter.
2. Describe the interaction of thin actin and thick myosin myofilaments enabling contraction.
3. Can the origin and insertion of some muscles be interchanged? Explain.
4. Explain the roles of agonists and antagonists in body movements.
5. As a cosmetic procedure, Botox is injected in very small doses into specific facial muscles to reduce wrinkles. It is derived from a neurotoxin that competes with acetylcholine at the neuromuscular junction. Explain how Botox works.

Visit this book's website at www.mhhe.com/ **gunstream5 for practice quizzes, learning exercises, case studies, and other study tools.**

18

Body Composition and Nutrition for Health

Objectives

By studying this chapter, you should be able to do the following:

1. Describe the recommended range for the dietary intake of carbohydrates, fats, and proteins.

2. Describe what is meant by the terms *Recommended Dietary Allowance* (RDA) and *Dietary Reference Intakes* (DRIs), and how they relate to the Daily Value (DV) used in food labeling.

3. List the classes of nutrients.

4. Identify the fat- and water-soluble vitamins, describe what toxicity is, and identify which class of vitamins is more likely to cause this problem.

5. Contrast major minerals with trace minerals, and describe the role of calcium, iron, and sodium in health and disease.

6. Identify the primary role of carbohydrates, the two major classes, and the recommended changes in the American diet to improve health status.

7. Identify the primary role of fat and the recommended changes in the American diet to improve health status.

8. Describe the common dietary recommendations from the major health-related organizations.

9. Describe the Dietary Approaches to Stop Hypertension (DASH) eating plan.

10. Describe the limitation of height/weight tables and the Body Mass Index in determining overweight and obesity.

11. Provide a brief description of the following methods of measuring body composition: isotope dilution, photon absorptiometry, potassium-40, hydrostatic (underwater weighing), dual energy X-ray absorptiometry,

near infrared interactance, radiography, ultrasound, nuclear magnetic resonance, total body electrical conductivity, bioelectrical impedance analysis, air displacement plethysmography, and skinfold thickness.

12. Describe the two-component model of body composition and the assumptions made about the density values for the fat-free mass and the fat mass; contrast this with the multicomponent model.

13. Explain the principle underlying the measurement of whole-body density with underwater weighing, and why one must correct for residual volume.

14. Explain why there is an error of 2.0% in the calculation of the percentage of body fat with the underwater weighing technique.

15. Explain how a sum of skinfolds can be used to estimate a percentage of body fatness value.

16. List the recommended percentage of body fatness values for health and fitness for males and females, and explain the concern for both high and low values.

17. Explain how deaths from cardiovascular disease have decreased while the prevalence of obesity has increased.

18. Distinguish between obesity due to hyperplasia of fat cells and obesity due to hypertrophy of fat cells.

19. Describe the roles of genetics and environment in the development of obesity.

20. Explain the set point theory of obesity, and give an example of a physiological and behavioral control system.

21. Describe the pattern of change in body weight and caloric intake over the adult years.

22. Discuss the changes in body composition when weight is lost by diet alone versus diet plus exercise.

23. Describe the relationship of the fat-free mass and caloric intake to the BMR.

24. Define thermogenesis and explain how it is affected by both short- and long-term overfeeding.

25. Describe the effect of exercise on appetite and body composition.

26. Explain quantitatively why small differences in energy expenditure and dietary intake are important in weight gain over the years.

27. Describe physical activity recommendations for preventing overweight and obesity, and for the prevention of weight regain in those who were previously obese.

■ Outline

■ Key Terms

Adequate Intake (AI)
anorexia nervosa
basal metabolic rate (BMR)
bulimia nervosa
cholesterol
Daily Value (DV)
deficiency
Dietary Guidelines for Americans
Dietary Reference Intake (DRI)
elements
energy wasteful systems
Estimated Average Requirement (EAR)
Estimated Energy Requirement (EER)
ferritin
food records
HDL cholesterol
high-density lipoproteins (HDLs)

LDL cholesterol
lipoprotein
low-density lipoproteins (LDLs)
major minerals
nutrient density
osteoporosis
provitamin
Recommended Dietary Allowances (RDAs)
resting metabolic rate (RMR)
thermogenesis
tolerable upper intake level (UL)
toxicity
trace elements
transferrin
twenty-four-hour recall
underwater weighing
whole-body density

Chapter 14 described factors that limit health and fitness. These included hypertension, obesity, and elevated serum cholesterol. These three risk factors are linked to an excessive consumption of salt, total calories, and dietary fat, respectively. Clearly, knowledge of nutrition is essential to our understanding of health-related fitness. Whereas chapters 3 and 4 described the metabolism of carbohydrates, fats, and proteins, this chapter focuses on the type of diet that should provide them. The first part of the chapter presents the nutritional guidelines for our nation, the nutrition standards and what they mean, a summary of the six classes of nutrients, and a way to evaluate our present diets and meet our nutritional goals. The second part of the chapter discusses the role of exercise and diet in altering body composition. Nutrition related to athletic performance is covered in chapter 23.

NUTRITIONAL GUIDELINES

We are all familiar with the work of the American Heart Association (AHA), the American Cancer Society (ACS), and the American Diabetes Association (ADA) to bring special attention on the importance of diet in the prevention and treatment of cardiovascular diseases, cancers, and diabetes, respectively. As mentioned in chapter 14, an underlying component associated with these diseases is a chronic low-grade systemic inflammation, which can be altered with diet and physical activity. What are the dietary recommendations associated with good health?

The current recommendations for the distribution of calories in our diet comes from the Institute of Medicine (IOM) (99):

■ Adults should get 45% to 65% of their calories from carbohydrates, 20% to 35% from fat, and 10% to 35% from protein. Acceptable ranges for children are similar to those for adults, except that infants and younger children need a slightly higher proportion of fat (25–40%).

How to best meet those standards, and those associated with vitamins and minerals (see later), is addressed in the **Dietary Guidelines for Americans,** which has been published every 5 years since 1980. The 2005 update of the *Dietary Guidelines for Americans* reflects the work of the Institute of Medicine and provides guidance on how to meet those nutritional standards (219). Excerpts of recommendations from this document follow:

■ Consume a variety of nutrient-dense foods and beverages within and among the basic food groups while choosing foods that limit the intake of saturated and trans fats, cholesterol, added sugars, salt, and alcohol.
  ● Choose a variety of fruits and vegetables each day. In particular, select from all five vegetable subgroups (dark green, orange, legumes, starchy vegetables, and other vegetables) several times a week.
  ● Consume 3 or more ounce-equivalents of whole-grain products per day, with the rest of the recommended grains coming from enriched or whole-grain products.
  ● Consume 3 cups per day of fat-free or lowfat milk or equivalent milk products.
  ● Keep total fat intake between 20% and 35% of calories, with most fats coming from sources of polyunsaturated and monounsaturated fatty acids, such as fish, nuts, and vegetable oils.
  ● Choose fiber-rich fruits, vegetables, and whole grains often, and prepare foods and beverages with little added sugars or caloric sweeteners.
  ● Choose and prepare foods with little salt. At the same time, consume potassium-rich foods, such as fruits and vegetables.
  ● Those who choose to drink alcoholic beverages should do so sensibly and in moderation.
■ To maintain body weight in a healthy range, balance calories from foods and beverages with calories expended, engage in regular physical activity, and reduce sedentary activities.

The 2010 *Dietary Guidelines for Americans* (see Suggested Readings) provided direct support for those recommendations by emphasizing the following themes:

■ Balancing calories to manage weight
■ Foods and food components to reduce
■ Foods and nutrients to increase, and
■ Building healthy eating patterns

We will incorporate these new guidelines as we move through the various sections of this chapter.

IN SUMMARY

■ Current recommendations for the distribution of calories in foods include a broad range, rather than a single goal: carbohydrates: 45% to 65%, fats: 20% to 35%, and proteins: 10% to 35%.
■ The *Dietary Guidelines for Americans* has been revised over time to reflect new science and to deal with nutrition (and physical activity) and health-related issues. The 2005 edition provided recommendations to meet the 2002 IOM nutritional standards with special focus on achieving energy balance. The 2010 *Dietary Guidelines for Americans* emphasized what to reduce and add to our diet to improve health.

STANDARDS OF NUTRITION

Food provides the carbohydrates, fats, protein, minerals, vitamins, and water needed for life. The quantity of each nutrient needed for proper function and health is defined in one of the **Dietary Reference Intakes (DRIs),** an umbrella term encompassing specific standards for dietary intake (99).

If you had a nutrition class, or even a few lectures dealing with nutrition, you would have been introduced to the Recommended Dietary Allowance (RDA) standards for nutrients such as protein, vitamins, and minerals. With the expansion of knowledge about the role of specific nutrients in preventing deficiency diseases and reducing the risk of chronic diseases, there was a need for a new approach to setting nutrient standards. In collaboration with Health Canada, the Food and Nutrition Board of the National Academy of Sciences has developed new nutrient standards. The term *Dietary Reference Intakes (DRIs)* is the umbrella term given to these new standards. The following descriptions will help us make the transitions from where we are to where we will be when the full implementation of the standards takes place (233).

■ **Recommended Dietary Allowance (RDA).**
  The average daily dietary nutrient intake level

sufficient to meet the nutrient requirement of nearly all (97–98%) healthy individuals in a particular group.

■ **Adequate Intakes (AI).** Formerly the Estimated Safe and Adequate Daily Dietary Intake, the AI describes the recommended average daily intake level based on observed or experimentally determined approximations or estimates of nutrient intake by a group (or groups) of apparently healthy people. Levels are assumed to be adequate and are used when an RDA cannot be determined. (See appendix E.)

■ **Tolerable Upper Intake Level (UL).** The highest average daily nutrient intake level that is likely to pose no risk of adverse health effects to almost all individuals in the general population. As intake increases above the UL, the potential risk of adverse effects may increase.

■ **Estimated Average Requirement (EAR).** The average daily nutrient intake level estimated to meet the requirement of half the healthy individuals in a particular group. This value is needed to set the RDA values.

The values for each nutrient vary due to gender, body size, whether long-bone growth is taking place, pregnancy, and lactation (149). Given that individuals differ in their need for each nutrient, some requiring more than the average and others less, the standards were set high enough to meet the needs of almost everyone (97.5% of the population) and also account for inefficient utilization by the body (149). Previous RDA tables did not provide recommendations for carbohydrate and fat intake, but that has changed. We will provide recommendations from the Institute of Medicine report (99) when we discuss each.

In the past, RDA tables did not have standards for energy intake set at the same level as for the nutrients like vitamins and minerals (sufficient to meet 97% to 98% of the population). Instead, average values of energy intake were provided, which assumed an average level of physical activity. In the current recommendations, a new standard, the **Estimated Energy Requirement (EER),** is identified: the average dietary energy intake that is predicted to maintain energy balance in a healthy adult of a defined age, gender, weight, height, and level of physical activity, consistent with good health (99). The report provides energy intake recommendations for four levels of physical activity, with the stated purpose of achieving a healthy body weight (see appendix F). When it comes to the RDA for specific nutrients like vitamins and minerals, how do we know how much is contained in the food we eat?

The **Daily Value (DV)** is a standard used in nutritional labeling. For the essential nutrients (protein, vitamins, and minerals), the DVs are based on the nutrition standards (e.g., RDA). In addition, the food label contains important information about the calorie and fat content of the food. For example, if one serving of a product provides 50% of the DV for fat, it contains 50% of the total amount of fat recommended for one day (based on a 2,000-calorie diet). Figure 18.1 provides an example of a food label; the following points are highlighted (233):

■ serving size information,

■ total calories and fat calories,

■ total fat grams, saturated fat grams, trans fat grams, cholesterol, and the percent of DV for each (based on a 2,000-calorie diet),

■ total carbohydrate and its sources, and

■ the percentage of the DV for certain vitamins (e.g., A and C) and minerals (e.g., calcium and iron); sodium is given special attention.

IN SUMMARY

■ The Recommended Dietary Allowance (RDA) is the quantity of a nutrient that will meet the needs of almost all healthy persons.

■ The Daily Value (DV) is a standard used in nutritional labeling.

CLASSES OF NUTRIENTS

There are six classes of nutrients: water, vitamins, minerals, carbohydrates, fats, and proteins. In the following sections each nutrient is described briefly, and the primary food sources of each are identified.

Water

Water is absolutely essential for life. Although we can go without food for weeks, we would not survive long without water. The body is 50% to 75% water, depending on age and body fatness, and a loss of more than 2% of body water adversely affects aerobic performance. Larger losses can lead to death (238). Under normal conditions without exercise, water loss equals about 2,500 ml/day, with most lost in urine. However, as higher environmental temperatures and heavy exercise are added, water loss can increase dramatically to 6 to 7 liters per day (84, 238).

Under normal conditions the 2,500 ml of water per day is replaced with beverages (1,500 ml), solid food (750 ml), and the water derived from metabolic processes (250 ml) (233). Most people are surprised

Serving size

Serving size is listed in household units (and grams). Pay careful attention to serving size to know how many servings you are eating: e.g., if you eat double the serving size, you must double the % Daily Values and calories.

Servings per container

The number of servings of the size given in the serving size above that are in one package of the food.

% Daily Value

This shows how a single serving compares to the DV. Recall that the DVs for fat, saturated fat, cholesterol, protein, and fiber are based on a 2000-calorie diet.

Sugars DV

There is no % Daily Value for sugar. Limiting intake is the best advice.

Protein DV

% Daily Value for protein is generally not included due to expensive testing required to determine protein quality.

Daily Value Footnote

This footnote appears on many labels. It is omitted when there is too little space on the label to print it. The footnote reports the DVs used to compute the % Daily Value for a 2000- and 2500-calorie diet.

Nutrient claims, such as "Good source," and health claims, such as "Reduce the risk of osteoporosis," must follow legal definitions.

Nutrients

These nutrients must appear on most labels. Labels of foods that contain few nutrients, such as candy and soft drinks, may omit some nutrients. Some manufacturers list more nutrients. Other nutrients must be listed if manufacturers make a claim about them or if the food is fortified with them.

A Quick Guide to Nutrient Sources

% Daily Value
20% or more = *Rich source*
10%–19% = *Good source*

Name and address of the food manufacturer.

Ingredients are listed in descending order by weight.

Nutrition Facts

Serving Size 1 Pouch (61g)

Serving Per Container 6

Amount Per Serving

Calories 250	Calories from Fat 70

	% Daily value*
Total Fat 7g	11%
Saturated Fat 2.5g	13%
Trans Fat 1g	**
Cholesterol 5mg	2%
Sodium 400mg	16%
Total Carbohydrate 38g	13%
Dietary Fiber <1g	3%
Sugars 6g	
Protein 7g	

Vitamin A 0% • Vitamin C 0%

Calcium 12% • Iron 8%

*Percent Daily Values are based on a 2,000 calorie diet. Your daily values may be higher or lower depending on your calorie needs:

	Calories:	2,000	2,500
Total Fat	Less than	65g	80g
Sat Fat	Less than	20g	25g
Cholest	Less than	300mg	300mg
Sodium	Less than	2,400mg	2,400mg
Total Carb		300g	375g
Fiber		25g	30g

Calories per gram:

Fat 9 • Carbohydrate 4 • Protein 4

**Intake should be as low as possible.

INGREDIENTS: ENRICHED MACARONI PRODUCT (DURUM WHEAT FLOUR, GLYCERYL MONO-STEARATE, SALT, NIACIN, FERROUS SULFATE, THIAMIN MONONITRATE [VITAMIN B1], RIBOFLAVIN [VITAMIN B2], FOLIC ACID], CHEESE SAUCE MIX (WHEY, PARTIALLY, HYDROGENATED SOYBEAN OIL, MALTODEXTRIN, WHEY PROTEIN CONCENTRATE, CORN SYRUP SOLIDS, SALT, MILKFAT, SUGAR, SODIUM, NATURAL FLAVOR, CITRIC ACID, MONOSODIUM GLUTAMATE, MODIFIED FOOD STARCH, LACTIC ACID, YELLOW 5.

Figure 18.1 Food packages must list product name, name and address of the manufacturer, amount of product in the package, and ingredients. The Nutrition Facts panel is required on virtually all packaged food products. The % Daily Value listed on the label is the percent of the amount of a nutrient needed daily that is provided by a single serving of the product.

by the large volume of water contributed by "solid" food until they consider the following percentages of water in solid food: baked potato—75%, apple—75%, lettuce—96% (233). A general recommendation under ordinary circumstances is to consume 1 to 1.5 ml of water per kcal of energy expenditure (149). The AI for total water intake (food + beverages) for women and men 19 to 70 years of age is set at 2.7 L/day and 3.7 L/day, respectively (98). However, to avoid

potential problems associated with dehydration, one should drink water before and during exercise; thirst is not an adequate stimulus to achieve water balance (see chapter 23).

Water weight can fluctuate depending on the body stores of carbohydrate and protein. Water is involved in the linkage between glucose molecules in glycogen and amino acid molecules in protein. The ratio is about 2.7 of water per gram of carbohydrate, and if an individual stores 454 g (1 lb) of carbohydrate, body weight would increase by 3.7 lbs. Of course, when one diets and depletes this carbohydrate store, the reverse occurs. This results in an apparent weight loss of 3.7 lbs when only 1,816 kcal (454 g of carbohydrate times 4 kcal/g) have been lost. More on this later.

Vitamins

Vitamins were introduced in chapter 3 as organic catalysts involved in metabolic reactions. They are needed in small amounts and are not "used up" in the metabolic reactions. However, they are degraded (metabolized) like any biological molecule and must be replaced on a regular basis to maintain body stores. Several vitamins are in a precursor, or **provitamin,** form in foods and are converted to the active form in the body. Beta-carotene, the most important of the provitamin A compounds, is a good example. A chronic lack of certain vitamins can lead to **deficiency** diseases, and an excess of others can lead to a **toxicity** condition (233). In our presentation, vitamins will be divided into the fat-soluble and water-soluble groups.

Fat-Soluble Vitamins The fat-soluble vitamins include A, D, E, and K. These vitamins can be stored in large quantities in the body; thus a deficiency state takes longer to develop than for water-soluble vitamins. However, because of their solubility, so much can be stored that a toxicity condition can occur. The Tolerable Upper Intake Level (UL) for vitamin A (3,000 μg), D (4,000 IU), and E (1,000 mg) have been established (97, 149). Toxicity, of course, is far from a health-related goal. Table 18.1 summarizes the information on these vitamins, including the RDA/AI standards, dietary sources, function, and signs associated with deficiency or excess.

Water-Soluble Vitamins The water-soluble vitamins include vitamin C and the B vitamins: thiamin (B_1), riboflavin (B_2), niacin, pyridoxine (B_6), folic acid, B_{12}, pantothenic acid, and biotin. Most are involved in energy metabolism. You have already seen the role of niacin, as NAD, and riboflavin, as FAD, in the transfer of energy in the Krebs cycle and electron transport chain. Thiamin (as thiamine pyrophosphate) is involved in the removal of CO_2 as pyruvate enters the Krebs cycle. Vitamin B_6, folic acid, B_{12}, pantothenic acid, and biotin are also involved as coenzymes in metabolic reactions. Vitamin C is involved in the maintenance of bone, cartilage, and connective tissue. Table 18.1 summarizes the information on these vitamins, including the RDA/AI standards, functions, dietary sources, and signs associated with deficiency or excess.

IN SUMMARY

- The fat-soluble vitamins include A, D, E, and K. These can be stored in the body in large quantities and toxicity can develop.
- The water-soluble vitamins include thiamin, riboflavin, niacin, B_6, folic acid, B_{12}, pantothenic acid, biotin, and C. Most of these are involved in energy metabolism. Vitamin C is involved in the maintenance of bone, cartilage, and connective tissue.

Minerals

Minerals are the chemical **elements,** other than carbon, hydrogen, oxygen, and nitrogen, associated with the structure and function of the body. We have already seen the importance of calcium in bone structure and in the initiation of muscle contraction, iron in O_2 transport by hemoglobin, and phosphorus in ATP. Minerals are important inorganic nutrients and are divided into two classes: (1) **major minerals** and (2) **trace elements.** The major minerals include calcium, phosphorus, magnesium, sulfur, sodium, potassium, and chloride, with whole-body quantities ranging from 35 g for magnesium to 1,200 g for calcium in a 70-kg man (233). The trace elements include iron, iodine, fluoride, zinc, selenium, copper, cobalt, chromium, manganese, molybdenum, arsenic, nickel, and vanadium. There are only 4 g of iron and 0.0009 g of vanadium in a 70-kg man. Like vitamins, some minerals taken in excess (e.g., iron and zinc) can be toxic. The following sections focus attention on calcium, iron, and sodium.

Calcium Calcium (Ca^{++}) and phosphorus combine with organic molecules to form the teeth and bones. The bones are a "store" of calcium that helps to maintain the plasma Ca^{++} concentration when dietary intake is inadequate (see parathyroid hormone in chapter 5). Bone is constantly turning over its calcium and phosphorus, so diet must replace what is lost. If the diet is deficient in calcium for a long period of time, loss of bone, or **osteoporosis,** can occur. This weakening of the bone due to the loss of calcium and phosphorus from its structure is more common in women than in men, is accelerated at menopause, and is directly related to the higher rate of hip fractures in women. Three major factors are implicated: dietary calcium intake, inadequate estrogen, and lack of physical activity (6).

There is concern that the increase in osteoporosis in our society is related to an inadequate calcium intake. The adult RDA for calcium is 1,000 mg/day, and although many men come close to meeting the standard, few women do (233). Given that the RDA is

TABLE 18.1   Summary of the Vitamins, Their Functions, Deficiency Conditions, and Food Sources

FAT-SOLUBLE

Vitamin	Major Functions	Deficiency Symptoms	People Most at Risk
Vitamin A (retinoids) and provitamin A (carotenoids)	Promote vision: light and color Promote growth Prevent drying of skin and eyes Promote resistance to bacterial infection	Night blindness Xerophthalmia Poor growth Dry skin	People in poverty, especially preschool children (still very rare in the United States) People with alcoholism People with AIDS
D (chole- and ergocalciferol)	Facilitate absorption of calcium and phosphorus Maintain optimal calcification of bone	Rickets Osteomalacia	Breastfed infants not exposed to sunlight, elderly
E (tocopherols)	Act as an antioxidant: prevent breakdown of vitamin A and unsaturated fatty acids	Hemolysis of red blood cells Nerve destruction	People with poor fat absorption, smokers (still rare as far as we know)
K (phyilo- and menaquinone)	Help form prothrombin and other factors for blood clotting and contribute to bone metabolism	Hemorrhage	People taking antibiotics for months at a time (still quite rare)

WATER-SOLUBLE

Vitamin	Major Functions	Deficiency Symptoms	People Most at Risk
Thiamin	Coenzyme involved in carbohydrate metabolism; nerve function	Beriberi: nervous tingling, poor coordination, edema, heart changes, weakness	People with alcoholism or in poverty
Riboflavin	Coenzyme involved in energy metabolism	Inflammation of mouth and tongue, cracks at corners of the mouth, eye disorders	Possibly people on certain medications if no dairy products consumed
Niacin	Coenzyme involved in energy metabolism, fat synthesis, fat breakdown	Pellagra: diarrhea, dermatitis, dementia	Severe poverty where corn is the dominant food; people with alcoholism
Pantothenic acid	Coenzyme involved in energy metabolism, fat synthesis, fat breakdown	Tingling in hands, fatigue, headache, nausea	People with alcoholism
Biotin	Coenzyme involved in glucose production, fat synthesis	Dermatitis, tongue soreness, anemia, depression	People with alcoholism
Vitamin B_6 pyridoxine, and other forms	Coenzyme involved in protein metabolism, neurotransmitter synthesis, hemoglobin synthesis, many other functions	Headache, anemia, convulsions, nausea, vomiting, flaky skin, sore tongue	Adolescent and adult women; people on certain medications; people with alcoholism
Folate (folic acid)	Coenzyme involved in DNA synthesis, other functions	Megaloblastic anemia, inflammation of tongue, diarrhea, poor growth, depression	People with alcoholism, pregnancy, people on certain medications
Vitamin B_{12} (cobalamins)	Coenzyme involved in folate metabolism, nerve function, other functions	Macrocytic anemia, poor nerve function	Elderly people because of poor absorption, vegans, people with AIDS
Vitamin C (ascorbic acid)	Connective tissue synthesis, hormone synthesis, neurotransmitter synthesis	Scurvy: poor wound healing, pinpoint hemorrhages, bleeding gums	People with alcoholism, elderly who eat poorly

Note: Values are the Recommended Dietary Allowances (RDAs) for adults 19 to 50 years, unless marked by an asterisk (*), in which case they represent the Adequate Intakes (AIs). The Tolerable Upper Intake Levels (ULs) are listed under toxicity; intakes above these values can lead to negative health consequences.

Dietary Sources*	RDA or AI*	Toxicity Symptoms or UL

Vitamin A
  Liver
  Fortified milk
  Fortified breakfast cereals
Provitamin A
  Sweet potatoes, spinach, greens, carrots,
  cantaloupe, apricots, broccoli
	Men: 900 micrograms
	Women: 700 micrograms
		Fetal malformations, hair loss, skin changes, pain in bones (UL = 3,000 micrograms)

Vitamin D-fortified milk Fortified breakfast cereals Fish oils Sardines Salmon	600 IU	Growth retardation, kidney damage, calcium deposits in soft tissue (UL = 4000 IU)
Vegetable oils Some greens Some fruits Fortified breakfast cereals	15 milligrams	Muscle weakness, headaches, fatigue, nausea, inhibition of vitamin K metabolism (UL = 1,000 mg)
Green vegetables Liver	Men: 120 micrograms* Women: 90 micrograms*	Anemia and jaundice (medicinal forms only)

Dietary Sources*	RDA or AI*	Toxicity Symptoms
Sunflower seeds, pork, whole and enriched grains, dried beans, peas, brewers yeast	Men: 1.2 milligrams Women: 1.1 milligrams	None possible from food
Milk, mushrooms, spinach, liver, enriched grains	Men: 1.3 milligrams Women: 1.1 milligrams	None reported
Mushrooms, bran, tuna, salmon, chicken, beef, liver, peanuts, enriched grains	Men: 16 milligrams Women: 14 milligrams	Toxicity can begin at over 35 milligrams (UL) (flushing of skin especially seen at over 100 milligrams per day)
Mushrooms, liver, broccoli, eggs; most foods have some	5 milligrams*	None
Cheese, egg yolks, cauliflower, peanut butter, liver	30 micrograms	Unknown
Animal protein foods, spinach, broccoli, bananas, salmon, sunflower seeds	1.3 milligrams	UL = 100 mg; nerve destruction at doses over 200 milligrams
Green leafy vegetables, orange juice, organ meats, sprouts, sunflower seeds	400 micrograms	UL = 1,000 micrograms
Animal foods, especially organ meats, oysters, clams (not natural in plants)	2.4 micrograms	None
Citrus fruits, strawberries, broccoli, greens	Men: 90 milligrams Women: 75 milligrams	UL = 2,000 mg

higher for 9–18 year olds (1,300 mg/day) and for females 51–70 years of age (1,200 mg/day), the concern is greater for those age groups. Part of the reason for the low intake of calcium is the relatively low caloric intake of women compared to men. One way of dealing with this is to increase energy expenditure through exercise and, in turn, caloric intake; another is to take calcium supplements. The latter has been shown (when combined with dietary intake) to increase the number of individuals meeting the RDA (11). Although menopause is the usual cause of a reduced secretion of estrogen, young, extremely active female athletes are experiencing this problem associated with amenorrhea (7). The decrease in estrogen secretion is associated with the acceleration of osteoporosis. Estrogen therapy, with or without calcium supplementation, has been used successfully in menopausal women to reduce the rate of bone loss, but not without the risk of increasing cardiovascular problems in some women. Because exercise has been shown to slow the rate of bone loss, we now have physical activity recommendations to build bone mass in early childhood and to hold on to it as we age (5, 6, 221) (see Ask the Expert 17.1 in chapter 17).

Iron   The majority of iron is found in hemoglobin in the red blood cells, which is involved with oxygen transport to cells (see chapter 10). Other iron-containing molecules include myoglobin in muscle and the cytochromes in mitochondria, accounting for about 25% of the body's iron. A large portion of the remaining iron is bound to **ferritin** in the liver, with the serum ferritin concentration being a sensitive measure of iron status (233, 238).

Iron is an important part of hemoglobin and myoglobin, as well as the cytochromes of the electron transport chain. To remain in iron balance, the RDA is set at 8 mg/day for an adult male and 18 mg/day for an adult female; the higher amount is needed to replace that which is lost in the menses.

In spite of the higher need for iron, American women take in only 13.7 mg/day, whereas men take in 17.7 mg/day (240). This is due to higher caloric intakes in males than females. Because there are only 6 mg of iron per 1,000 kcal of energy in the American diet, a woman consuming 2,000 kcal/day would take in only 12 mg of iron. The male, consuming about 3,000 kcal/ day, takes in 18 mg. The diet provides iron in two forms, heme (ferrous) and nonheme (ferric). Heme iron, found primarily in meats, fish, and organ meats, is absorbed better than nonheme iron, which is found in vegetables. However, the absorption of nonheme iron can be increased by the presence of meat, fish, and vitamin C (87, 233, 238).

Anemia is a condition in which the hemoglobin concentration is low: less than 13 g/dl in men and less than 12 g/dl in women. This can be the result of blood loss (e.g., blood donation or bleeding) or a lack of vitamins or minerals in the diet. The most common cause of anemia in North America is a lack of dietary iron (233, 238). In fact, iron deficiency is the most common nutrient deficiency. In iron deficiency anemia, more than hemoglobin is affected. The iron bound to **transferrin** in the plasma is reduced, and serum ferritin (an indicator of iron stores) is low (87). Although children aged 1 to 5 years, adolescents, young adult women, and the elderly are more apt to develop anemia, it also occurs in competitive athletes. This latter point is discussed in detail in chapter 23. The 2010 *Dietary Guidelines for Americans* call for an increase in iron intake, especially for women capable of becoming pregnant or who are pregnant or breast feeding (220).

Sodium   Sodium is directly involved in the maintenance of the resting membrane potential and the generation of action potential in nerves (see chapter 7) and muscles (see chapter 8). In addition, sodium is the primary electrolyte determining the extracellular fluid volume. If sodium stores fall, the extracellular volume, including plasma, decreases. This could cause major problems with the maintenance of the mean arterial blood pressure (see chapter 9) and body temperature (see chapter 12).

The problem in our society is not with sodium stores that are too small, but just the opposite. The estimated average intake of sodium for Americans ages 2 years and older is about 3,400 mg/day. This is considerably more than the AI for adults (1,500 mg/ day) and exceeds the UL for adults (2,300 mg/day) (220). There is no question about the link between sodium intake and blood pressure, with evidence showing that reducing salt intake is feasible and will result in a reduction in cardiovascular morbidity and mortality (109, 234). The *Dietary Guidelines for Americans* have consistently supported the need to reduce sodium intake, and they recommend the Dietary Approaches to Stop Hypertension (DASH) eating plan (see later) to accomplish that goal:

- Use reduced sodium or no-salt-added products. For example, choose low or reduced sodium, or no-salt-added versions of foods and condiments when available.

- Buy fresh, plain frozen, or canned with "no-salt-added" vegetables.

- Use fresh poultry, fish, and lean meat, rather than canned, smoked, or processed types.

- Choose ready-to-eat breakfast cereals that are lower in sodium.

- Limit cured foods (such as bacon and ham), foods packed in brine (such as pickles, pickled vegetables, olives, and sauerkraut), and condiments (such as MSG, mustard, horseradish, catsup, and barbecue sauce). Limit even lower-sodium versions of soy sauce and teriyaki sauce—treat these condiments as you do table salt.

■ Use spices instead of salt. In cooking and at the table, flavor foods with herbs, spices, lemon, lime, vinegar, or salt-free seasoning blends. Start by cutting salt in half.

■ Cook rice, pasta, and hot cereals without salt. Cut back on instant or flavored rice, pasta, and cereal mixes, which usually have added salt.

■ Choose "convenience" foods that are lower in sodium. Cut back on frozen dinners, mixed dishes such as pizza, packaged mixes, canned soups or broths, and salad dressing—these often have a lot of sodium.

■ Rinse canned foods, such as tuna, to remove some sodium.

Those involved in athletic competition or strenuous exercise or who work in the heat must be concerned about adequate sodium replacement. Generally, because these individuals consume more kcal of food (containing more sodium), this is usually not a problem. More on this in chapter 23.

The previous sections have focused attention on three minerals—calcium, iron, and sodium—because of their relationship to current medical and health-related problems. A summary of each of the minerals, their functions, and food sources is presented in table 18.2.

IN SUMMARY

■ The major minerals include calcium, phosphorus, magnesium, sulfur, sodium, potassium, and chloride. The trace elements include iron, iodine, fluoride, zinc, selenium, copper, cobalt, chromium, manganese, molybdenum, arsenic, nickel, and vanadium.

■ Inadequate calcium and iron intake has been linked with osteoporosis and anemia, respectively. The 2010 *Dietary Guidelines for Americans* recommends an increase in calcium and iron intake to address these problems, and a reduction in sodium intake, especially for those at risk of hypertension.

Carbohydrates

Carbohydrates and fats are the primary sources of energy in the average American diet (149) (for recommendations on carbohydrates, fats, and proteins from the Institute of Medicine, see Clinical Applications 18.1). Carbohydrates suffer a bad reputation from those on diets, especially when you consider that you would have to eat more than twice as much carbohydrate as fat to consume the same number of calories (4 kcal/g versus 9 kcal/g). Carbohydrates can be divided into two classes: those that can be digested and metabolized for energy (sugars and starches), and those that are undigestible (fiber). The sugars are found in jellies, jams, fruits, soft drinks, honey, syrups, and milk, whereas the starches are found in cereals, flour, potatoes, and other vegetables (233).

Sugars and Starches Carbohydrate is a major energy source for all tissues and a crucial source for two: red blood cells and neurons. The red blood cells depend exclusively on anaerobic glycolysis for energy, and the nervous system functions well only on carbohydrate. These two tissues can consume 180 grams of glucose per day (50). Given this need, it is no surprise that the plasma glucose concentration is maintained within narrow limits by hormonal control mechanisms (see chapter 5). During strenuous exercise the muscle can use 180 grams of glucose in less than 1 hour. As a result of these needs, one might expect that carbohydrate would make up a large fraction of our energy intake. Currently about 50% of energy intake is derived from carbohydrate (240), within the range of recommended carbohydrate intakes (99). There is great interest not only in the amount of carbohydrate in the diet, but also in the type of carbohydrate as it relates to the prevention and management of diabetes (see Clinical Applications 18.2). While the goal is to increase carbohydrate intake, one of the *Dietary Guidelines for Americans* is to avoid too much sugar (220). The following are helpful suggestions on how to limit intake of added sugars while meeting the overall carbohydrate goal (219, 220):

■ Choose and prepare foods and beverages with little added sugars or caloric sweeteners, such as amounts suggested in the DASH eating plan.

■ Replace sweetened beverages with water and unsweetened beverages.

Dietary Fiber Dietary fiber is an important part of the diet. Over the past few years, in an attempt to clarify what is and is not "fiber," fiber has been divided into the following classes (99):

■ *Dietary fiber* consists of nondigestible carbohydrates and lignin that are *intrinsic and intact* in plants. Examples of dietary fiber include plant nonstarch polysaccharides such as cellulose, pectin, gums, hemicellulose, β-glucans, and fibers in oat and wheat bran.

■ *Functional fiber* consists of *isolated, nondigestible carbohydrates* that have beneficial physiological effects in humans. Examples of functional

TABLE 18.2 A Summary of Minerals

Mineral	Major Functions	MAJOR MINERALS Deficiency Symptoms	People Most at Risk
Sodium	Functions as a major ion of the extracellular fluid; aids nerve impulse transmission	Muscle cramps	People who severely restrict sodium to lower blood pressure (250–500 milligrams)
Potassium	Functions as a major ion of intracellular fluid; aids nerve impulse transmission	Irregular heartbeat, loss of appetite, muscle cramps	People who use potassium-wasting diuretics or have poor diets, as seen in poverty and alcoholism
Chloride	Functions as a major ion of the extracellular fluid; participates in acid production in stomach; aids nerve transmission	Convulsions in infants	No one, probably
Calcium	Provides bone and tooth strength; helps blood clotting; aids nerve impulse transmission; required for muscle contractions	Inadequate intake increases the risk for osteoporosis	Women, especially those who consume few dairy products
Phosphorus	Required for bone and tooth strength; serves as part of various metabolic compounds; functions as major ion of intracellular fluid	Poor bone maintenance is a possibility	Older people consuming very nutrient-poor diets; people with alcoholism
Magnesium	Provides bone strength; aids enzyme function; aids nerve and heart function	Weakness, muscle pain, poor heart function	Women, and people on certain diuretics

Mineral	Major Functions	KEY TRACE MINERALS Deficiency Symptoms	People Most at Risk
Iron	Used for hemoglobin and other key compounds used in respiration; used for immune function	Low blood iron; small, pale red blood cells; low blood hemoglobin values	Infants, preschool children, adolescents, women in childbearing years
Zinc	Required for enzymes, involved in growth, immunity, alcohol metabolism, sexual development, and reproduction	Skin rash, diarrhea, decreased appetite and sense of taste, hair loss, poor growth and development, poor wound healing	Vegetarians, elderly people, people with alcoholism
Selenium	Aids antioxidant system	Muscle pain, muscle weakness, form of heart disease	Unknown in healthy Americans
Iodide	Aids thyroid hormone	Goiter; poor growth in infancy when mother is iodide deficient during pregnancy	None in America because salt is usually fortified
Copper	Aids in iron metabolism; works with many enzymes, such as those involved in protein metabolism and hormone synthesis	Anemia, low white blood cell count, poor growth	Infants recovering from semistarvation, people who use overzealous supplementation of zinc
Fluoride	Increases resistance of tooth enamel to dental caries	Increased risk of dental caries	Areas where water is not fluoridated and dental treatments do not make up for a lack of fluoride
Chromium	Enhances blood glucose control	High blood glucose after eating	People on intravenous nutrition, and perhaps elderly people with type 2 diabetes
Manganese	Aids action of some enzymes, such as those involved in carbohydrate metabolism	None in humans	Unknown
Molybdenum	Aids action of some enzymes	None in healthy humans	Unsupplemented intravenous nutrition

Note: Values are the Recommended Dietary Allowances (RDAs) for adults 19 to 50 years, unless marked by an asterisk (*), in which case they represent the Adequate Intakes (AIs). The Tolerable Upper Intake Levels (ULs) are listed under toxicity; intakes above these values can lead to negative health consequences.

RDA or AI*	Rich Dietary Sources	Results of Toxicity or UL
1,500 milligrams*	Table salt, processed foods, condiments, sauces, soups, chips	UL = 2,300 mg; contributes to high blood pressure in susceptible individuals; leads to increased calcium loss in urine
4,700 milligrams*	Spinach, squash, bananas, orange juice, other vegetables and fruits, milk, meat, legumes, whole grains	Results in slowing of the heartbeat; seen in kidney failure
2,300 milligrams*	Table salt, some vegetables, processed foods	UL = 3,600 mg; linked to high blood pressure in susceptible people when combined with sodium
1,000 milligrams	Dairy products, canned fish, leafy vegetables, tofu, fortified orange juice (and other fortified foods)	UL = 2,500 mg; higher intakes may cause kidney stones and other problems in susceptible people; poor mineral absorption in general
700 milligrams	Dairy products, processed foods, fish, soft drinks, bakery products, meats	UL = 4,000 milligrams; impairs bone health in people with kidney failure; results in poor bone mineralization if calcium intakes are low
Men: 420 milligrams Women: 320 milligrams	Wheat bran, green vegetables, nuts, chocolate, legumes	UL = 350 mg, but refers only to pharmacologic agents

RDA or AI*	Rich Dietary Sources	Results of Toxicity
Men: 8 milligrams Women: 18 milligrams	Meats, spinach, seafood, broccoli, peas, bran, enriched breads	UL = 45 mg; toxicity seen when children consume 60 milligrams or more in iron pills; also in people with hemochromatosis
Men: 11 milligrams Women: 8 milligrams	Seafoods, meats, greens, whole grains	UL = 40 milligrams; reduces copper absorption; can cause diarrhea, cramps, and depressed immune function
55 micrograms	Meats, eggs, fish, seafoods, whole grains	UL = 400 micrograms; nausea, vomiting, hair loss, weakness, liver disease
150 micrograms	Iodized salt, white bread, saltwater fish, dairy products	UL = 1,100 micrograms; inhibition of function of the thyroid gland
900 micrograms	Liver, cocoa, beans, nuts, whole grains, dried fruits	UL = 10 milligrams; vomiting; nervous system disorders
Men: 4 milligrams* Women: 3 milligrams*	Fluoridated water, toothpaste, dental treatments, tea, seaweed	UL = 10 mg; stomach upset; mottling (staining) of teeth during development; bone pain
Men: 30–35 micrograms* Women: 20–25 micrograms*	Egg yolks, whole grains, pork, nuts, mushrooms, beer	Liver damage and lung cancer (caused by industrial contamination, not dietary excess)
Men: 2.3 milligrams* Women: 1.8 milligrams*	Nuts, oats, beans, tea	UL = 11 milligrams
45 micrograms	Beans, grains, nuts	UL = 2,000 micrograms

CLINICAL APPLICATIONS 18.1

Institute of Medicine Report

At the beginning of the chapter, we indicated that a report from the Institute of Medicine (99) made a series of recommendations that has impacted a variety of existing nutritional recommendations from both federal agencies (e.g., U.S. Department of Agriculture) and professional organizations (e.g., American Heart Association). What follows is a brief summary of information and recommendations related to the intakes of carbohydrate, fat, and protein.

- An RDA for carbohydrate was established for the first time: 130 g/day to meet the glucose needs of the brain.
- An AI for fiber was set at 38 and 25 g/day for men and women, respectively.
- No RDA, AI, or EAR standards were set for saturated fat, mono-

saturated fat, and cholesterol because they have no known beneficial role in preventing chronic disease. In addition, because they are synthesized in the body, they are not required in the diet.

- AI values were set for the omega-6 fatty acid, linoleic acid (17 and 12 g/day for young men and women, respectively), and the omega-3 fatty acid, α-linoleic acid (1.6 and 1.1 g/day for men and women, respectively).
- The long-held adult protein requirement of 0.8 g/day per kilogram of body weight was maintained.
- The AI for water was set at 3.7 L/day and 2.7 L/day for men and women, respectively.

The Institute of Medicine's report recommends a new dietary standard, called the Acceptable Macronutrient Distribution Ranges (AMDRs). These are defined as ranges of intakes for a particular energy source that is associated with a reduced risk of chronic disease, while providing adequate intake of essential nutrients. The Institute recommends ranges of 20% to 35% fat, 45% to 65% carbohydrate, and the balance (10–35%), protein. There is evidence that at the *extreme* end of the range, diets low in fat and high in carbohydrate reduce HDL cholesterol and increase the total cholesterol:HDL cholesterol ratio and plasma triglycerides. At the opposite end, when fat intake is high, weight gain occurs and the metabolic consequences of obesity increase, as does the plasma LDL cholesterol. (99)

---

fiber include isolated, nondigestible plants (e.g., resistant starches, pectin, and gums) and animal (e.g., chitin and chitosan) or commercially produced (e.g., resistant starch, inulin, and indigestible dextrins) carbohydrates.

- *Total fiber* is the sum of dietary fiber and functional fiber.

Dietary fiber cannot be digested and metabolized, and consequently it provides a sense of fullness (satiation) during a meal without adding calories (59). This fact has been used by bakeries that lower the number of calories per slice of bread by adding cellulose from wood! Pectin and gum are used in food processing to thicken, stabilize, or emulsify the constituents of various food products (233).

Dietary fiber has long been linked to optimal health. Fiber acts as a hydrated sponge as it moves along the large intestine, making constipation less likely by reducing transit time (8, 59, 233). Vegetarian diets high in soluble fiber have been linked to lower serum cholesterol due to the loss of more bile (cholesterol-containing) acids in the feces. However, the fact that vegetarian diets are also lower in the percentage of calories from fat, which can also lower serum cholesterol, makes the interpretation of the

data more complicated (59). Although a high-fiber diet reduces the incidence of diverticulosis, a condition in which outpouchings (diverticula) occur in the colon wall, the role of fiber in preventing colon cancer is mixed (8, 59). A review by the American Dietetic Association (ADA) indicated strong epidemiological evidence that a diet rich in fiber reduces the risk of colon cancer. In contrast, intervention studies (in which individuals received added fiber) did not confirm the epidemiological evidence. However, on balance, the ADA believes that the abundance of evidence supports the promotion of a diet high in fiber to protect against colon cancer (8).

Given the broad role of dietary fiber in normal health, it is no surprise that the *Dietary Guidelines for Americans* recommends that Americans increase their intake of fiber (219). A new AI for total fiber, based on an intake level observed to protect against coronary heart disease, has been set at 38 and 25 g/day for men and women, 19 to 50 years of age, respectively. According to *Dietary Guidelines for Americans*, to increase the intake of fiber and complex carbohydrates, we should choose fiber-rich fruits, vegetables, and whole grains often. This can be accomplished by consuming whole fruit rather than fruit juices, eating dry beans and peas several times per week, and making sure at least half of the grain servings come from whole grains.

CLINICAL APPLICATIONS 18.2

Glycemic Index—What Is It and Is It Important?

We all know that when we eat, insulin secretion increases to promote the uptake, use, and storage of carbohydrates. The degree to which the blood glucose concentration increases and remains elevated depends on the kinds and amounts of carbohydrate ingested, as well as the person's insulin response and tissue sensitivity to the insulin (193).

It is well known that certain carbohydrates elicit a more rapid blood glucose response than others. The glycemic index (GI) has been used to describe the magnitude of those differences and help those who have difficulty processing glucose make better decisions in planning meals. The GI quantifies the blood glucose response (above fasting) to an individual carbohydrate food over a 2-hour period following ingestion. This response is compared to a reference food (glucose or white bread) of the same weight. Those foods with a low GI would provide less of a challenge to someone with a reduced capacity to take up and use glucose (e.g., type 2 diabetic). However, because these carbohydrates are compared on a

"per gram" basis, the GI does not consider the impact that the actual amount of carbohydrate in the meal has on the response. The "glycemic load (GL)" attempts to do that by multiplying the GI by the amount of carbohydrate in the serving (193).

The simplicity of the GI and GL is complicated by the fact that most meals do not contain a single carbohydrate. Factors such as the amount of protein and fat in the diet will impact the blood glucose response to the carbohydrate ingested. In spite of that, studies support the use of the GI as a tool to help shape the selection of carbohydrate-containing foods to reduce cholesterol and improve the metabolic control of diabetics (154). In addition, there is evidence that diets with a high GI and/or GL contribute to vascular inflammation that is tied to the development of atherosclerosis (115, 167). However, focus on the GI and GL should not ignore the importance of achieving a healthy body weight in the prevention and management of diabetes (193). This is supported in two studies of overweight subjects who were placed on either a low GL or high GL

weight-loss diet. Both groups lost similar amounts of weight and experienced similar improvements in insulin dynamics (60, 161). However, there is a new twist to this tale of the GI and GL.

Fructose makes up a substantial part of total carbohydrate intake in the average American's diet. Concern was raised several years ago when it was found that there was a parallel increase in the intake of high-fructose corn syrup and obesity prevalence in this country. The reason for the concern is that, in contrast to glucose, fructose does not increase the insulin and leptin responses as much, and consequently, provides less input to the brain centers associated with feeding and body weight (29). In concert with this, when fructose is administered directly into the brain, food intake actually increases, opposite of the effect of glucose (45, 120). It should be no surprise that some investigators suggest that we examine the role of the "fructose index" (FI) and "fructose load" (FL) on the development of cardiovascular disease and diabetes, rather than limit it to GI and GL alone (189). We are sure to hear more about this in the future.

Fats

Dietary lipids include triglycerides, phospholipids, and **cholesterol.** If solid at room temperature, lipids are fats; if liquid, oils. Lipids contain 9 kcal/g and represent about 33% of the American diet, slightly higher than the dietary goal of 30%, but lower than the 42% recorded in 1977 (47, 83, 149, 222, 233). However, part of the decrease in this percentage was due to an increase in total calorie consumption, primarily from carbohydrate (44).

Fat not only provides fuel for energy, it is important in the absorption of fat-soluble vitamins, and for cell membrane structure, hormone synthesis (steroids), insulation, and the protection of vital organs. Most fat is stored in adipose tissue, for subsequent release into the bloodstream as free fatty acids (see chapter 4). Because of fat's caloric density (9 kcal/g), we are able to carry a large energy reserve, with little weight. In fact, the energy content of one pound of adipose tissue, 3,500 kcal, is sufficient to cover the cost of running a

marathon. The other side of this coin is that because of this very high caloric density, it takes a long time to decrease the mass of adipose tissue when on a diet.

The focus of attention in the medical community has been on the role of dietary fat in the development of atherosclerosis, a process in which the arterial wall becomes thickened, leading to a narrowing of the lumen of the artery. This is the underlying problem associated with coronary artery disease and stroke (see chapter 14). In the section on dietary guidelines, two of the recommendations dealt with this problem of atherosclerosis: a reduction in salt intake (see minerals), and a reduction in fat, saturated fat, and cholesterol. A reduction in each of the last three has been shown to reduce serum cholesterol, and with it, the risk of atherosclerosis (3). See Clinical Applications 18.3 for more on the role of diet composition on risk factor development.

Usually the cholesterol concentration in the serum is divided into two classes on the basis of what type of **lipoprotein** is carrying the cholesterol.

CLINICAL APPLICATIONS 18.3

Diet Composition and Syndrome X

In chapter 14 we introduced you to "syndrome X" ("the deadly quartet" or the "metabolic syndrome") as an example of how scientists have tried to establish links among various cardiovascular risk factors to better understand how one affects the other. The risk factors included elevated levels of plasma insulin (hyperinsulinemia) and lipids (hyperlipidemia), high blood pressure (hypertension), and obesity. Some suggest that obesity, especially abdominal obesity, is the underlying cause of elevated cardiovascular disease risk, whereas others point to insulin resistance (and the resulting elevated insulin) as the cause. In one of a series of provocative studies, Barnard et al. (12) make a case for diet composition as the underlying cause of the problem. This is an important consideration given the potential to break up the deadly quartet.

These investigators put rats on either a high-fat, refined-sugar (HFS)

diet or a low-fat, complex carbohydrate (LFCC) diet for 2 years. Animals were taken from each group beginning at 2 weeks and ending at 2 years to evaluate changes in body fatness and fat cell size, insulin resistance (ability of a tissue to take up glucose), plasma insulin and lipid levels, and blood pressure. They found that:

- Insulin resistance and elevated levels of plasma insulin were present at 2 weeks in the HFS group and, therefore, preceded all other aspects of the syndrome.
- Plasma triglycerides were significantly elevated by the second month in the HFS group.
- Body fatness was not different until 6 months, but fat cell size was already increased in those on the HFS diet by 2 months.
- Blood pressure was not different until 12 months, but by 18 months

all the rats on the HFS diet had high blood pressure.

This study showed that the composition of the diet was the cause of the insulin resistance, and that the insulin resistance preceded the other aspects of the syndrome. However, the authors acknowledged that the obesity probably contributed to the gradual worsening of the insulin resistance (demanding higher levels of insulin) over time. Blood pressure was the slowest-responding component of the syndrome and may be linked to the insulin resistance as described in chapter 14. This study confirmed the importance of diet on risk factor development and supports the recommendation of a low-fat, high-complex carbohydrate diet.

Low-density lipoproteins (LDLs) carry more cholesterol than do the **high-density lipoproteins (HDLs)**. High levels of **LDL cholesterol** are directly related to cardiovascular risk, whereas high levels of **HDL cholesterol** offer protection from heart disease (3). The concentration of HDL cholesterol is influenced by heredity, gender, exercise, and diet. Diets high in saturated fats increase LDL cholesterol. A reduction in the sources of saturated fats, including meats, animal fat, palm oil, coconut oil, hydrogenated shortenings, whole milk, cream, butter, ice cream, and cheese would reduce LDL cholesterol. Just substituting unsaturated fats for these saturated fats will lower serum cholesterol. The most recent recommendation for fat intake from the Institute of Medicine provides a range of values (20–35%), with the emphasis on unsaturated fats.

Dietary restriction of cholesterol has been shown to be effective in lowering serum cholesterol (3); however, this effect is influenced by the percentage of saturated fat in the diet and the initial level of serum cholesterol (i.e., those with high serum cholesterol levels benefit the most) (62). Based on currently available evidence, it is reasonable and prudent to recommend a decrease in cholesterol in the diet to 300 mg/day or less (3, 148). In addition, there is a special emphasis on

eliminating trans fats from the diet. These fats rival saturated fats as a contributor to heart disease, and substituting polyunsaturated fats should reduce cholesterol levels (118). The following suggestions, provided as part of the 2005 *Dietary Guidelines for Americans*, were emphasized in the 2010 report (219, 220):

- Consume less than 10% of calories from saturated fatty acids and less than 300 mg/day of cholesterol, and keep trans fatty acid consumption as low as possible.

- Keep total fat intake between 20% and 35% of calories, with most fats coming from sources of polyunsaturated and monounsaturated fatty acids, such as fish, nuts, and vegetable oils.

- When selecting and preparing meat, poultry, dry beans, and milk or milk products, make choices that are lean, low fat, or fat free.

- Increase seafood intake in place of some meats and poultry.

- Limit intake of fats and oils high in saturated and/or trans fatty acids, and choose products low in such fats and oils.

- Replace solid fats with oils.

Protein

Even though protein has the same energy density as carbohydrate (4 kcal/g), it is not viewed as a primary energy source, as are fats and carbohydrates. Rather, it is important because it contains the nine essential (indispensable) amino acids, without which the body cannot synthesize all the proteins needed for tissues, enzymes, and hormones. The *quality* of protein in a diet is based on how well these essential amino acids are represented. In terms of quality, the best sources for protein are eggs, milk, and fish, with *good* sources being meat, poultry, cheese, and soybeans. *Fair* sources of protein include grains, vegetables, seeds and nuts, and other legumes. Given that a meal contains a variety of foods, one food of higher-quality protein tends to complement another of lower-quality protein to result in an adequate intake of essential amino acids (233).

The adult RDA protein requirement of 0.8 g/kg is easily met with diets that include a variety of the aforementioned foods. Although the vast majority of Americans meet this recommendation, an athlete's protein requirement is higher than this level. The protein requirement for athletes is discussed in chapter 23.

IN SUMMARY

- Carbohydrate is a primary source of energy in the American diet and is divided into two classes: that which can be metabolized (sugars and starches) and dietary fiber.
- Two recommendations to improve health status in the American population are to consume complex carbohydrates to represent about 45% to 65% of the calories, and to add more dietary fiber.
- Americans consume too much saturated fat, and the recommended change is to reduce this to no more than 10% of the total calories. Trans fat intake should be reduced as much as possible, and most fat intake should come from sources containing polyunsaturated and mono-unsaturated fatty acids.
- The protein requirement of 0.8 g/kg can be met with low-fat selections to minimize fat intake.

MEETING THE DIETARY GUIDELINES

A good diet would allow an individual to achieve the RDA/AI for protein, minerals, and vitamins, while emphasizing carbohydrates and minimizing fats. The 2005 *Dietary Guidelines for Americans* describes a healthy diet as one that:

- emphasizes fruits, vegetables, whole grains, and fat-free or low-fat milk and milk products;

- includes lean meats, poultry, fish, beans, eggs, and nuts; and
- is low in saturated fats, trans fats, cholesterol, salt (sodium), and added sugars.

A variety of food group plans have been developed to help plan a diet consistent with these guidelines.

Food Group Plans

The 2010 *Dietary Guidelines for Americans* provides some background on the research that helped them recommend specific eating patterns (plans). They considered a variety of eating patterns that have a solid research basis. These included the Dietary Approaches to Stop Hypertension (DASH) eating plan, traditional Mediterranean style diets, and vegetarian diets, including both lacto-ovo and vegan. Some elements common to all included the following:

- Abundant vegetables and fruits
- Whole gains
- Moderate amounts of foods high in protein (seafood, beans and peas, nuts, seeds, soy products, meat, poultry and eggs)
- Limited amounts of foods high in added sugars
- More oils than solid fats
- Most are low in full-fat milk and milk products, with some having substantial amounts of low-fat milk and milk products

These diets have a high unsaturated-to-saturated fat ratio, more fiber, and a high potassium content. At the beginning of this section we indicated that various organizations (e.g., AHA) emphasize the importance of diet in the prevention and treatment of various chronic diseases. Table 18.3 shows the consistency in dietary and physical activity recommendations across these organizations (212). These recommendations are clearly in tune with the *Dietary Guidelines for Americans*. The *Guidelines* recommended two major eating plans.

USDA Food Pattern This food plan identifies daily amounts of foods with a focus on **nutrient density** from the five major food groups (and *subgroups*):

Vegetables—includes *dark green* (broccoli and spinach) and *red and orange* (carrots and sweet potatoes) vegetables; *beans and peas, starchy vegetables* (corn, potatoes), and *others* (onions, iceberg lettuce)

Fruits—fresh, frozen, canned or dried

Grains—including *whole grain* products (whole-wheat bread) and *enriched grains* (white bread and pasta)

TABLE 18.3 Consistency of Dietary and Physical Activity Recommendations Among Chronic Disease Organizations

Lifestyle Factor	American Diabetes Association	American Heart Association	American Cancer Society/ American Institute for Cancer Research
Weight control	+++	+++	+++
Increase fiber	+	++	++
Increase plant food	+	++	+++
Decrease total fat	NA	+++	+++
Decrease saturated fat	++	++	+
Avoid trans-fatty acids	++	+++	+
Increase omega-3 fatty acids	++	++	++
Alcohol	moderation	moderation	moderation
Daily physical activity	++	+++	++

NA—not addressed
Note: from Thompson and Thompson (212).

Dairy products—with the emphasis on low-fat choices

Protein foods—All meat, poultry, seafood, eggs, nuts, seeds, and processed soy products, with an emphasis on low-fat choices.

The food plan has both a lacto-ovo and vegan adaptations. Details can be found at **http://www.health.gov/ dietaryguidelines/.**

Dietary Approaches to Stop Hypertension (DASH) The DASH eating plan (191) was also identified in the *Dietary Guidelines for Americans* as a means to meet DRI/RDA standards and the various recommendations set forth in the document. The DASH plan was developed (as indicated in the title) to deal with hypertension, both to prevent it and to lower blood pressure in those with the problem (see **http://www.nhlbi.nih.gov/health/public/ heart/hbp/dash/new_dash.pdf**). The DASH eating plan has been recognized for some time as an excellent approach to healthy eating consistent with reducing cardiovascular risk factors and achieving and maintaining a normal body weight. Those who follow the *Dietary Guidelines for Americans* have a lower risk of the metabolic syndrome (69). In addition, use of the DASH eating plan in a weight-loss program conveys more benefits to patients with the metabolic syndrome than a regular weight-loss diet (10).

The USDA developed a new online resource, *MyPlate,* to promote healthy eating and physical activity to achieve one's body weight goal. We encourage you to log on to this website **(http://www.choosemyplate .gov)** to get a feel for its user-friendly nature.

Evaluating the Diet

Independent of your dietary plan, the question arises as to how well you are achieving the guidelines. How do you analyze your diet? The first thing to do is to determine what you are eating, without fooling yourself. The use of the **twenty-four-hour recall** method relies on your ability to remember, from a specific time in one day, what you ate during the previous 24 hours. You have to judge the size of the portion you have eaten and make a judgment of whether that day was representative of what you normally eat. Other people use **food records,** in which a person records what is eaten throughout the day. It is recommended that a person obtain food records for 3 or 4 days per week to have a better estimate of usual dietary intake. Because the simple act of recording food intake may change our eating habits, one has to try to eat as normally as possible when recording food intake. It is important to remember that the RDA standards are to be met over the long run, and variations from those standards will exist from day to day (233).

IN SUMMARY

■ The *Dietary Guidelines for Americans* identified two major approaches to use to meet dietary standards and achieve a healthy body weight: the USDA Food Patterns, with adaptations for vegetarians, and the Dietary Approaches to Stop Hypertension (DASH) food plan.

■ The U.S. Department of Agriculture's MyPlate promotes a personalized approach to healthy eating and physical activity.

BODY COMPOSITION

Obesity is a major problem in our society, being related to hypertension, elevated serum cholesterol, and adult onset diabetes (147). In addition, there is growing concern that as the incidence of childhood obesity increases, so will the pool of obese adults. To deal with this problem, we must be able to assess the prevalence of overweight and obesity, as well as describe in more specific terms changes in body composition. This section presents a brief overview on how to do that. For those interested in a thorough discussion of body composition assessment issues, we refer you to Heyward and Wagner's *Applied Body Composition Assessment* and Roche, Heymsfield, and Lohman's *Human Body Composition* in the Suggested Readings, and Ratamess's chapter in the ACSM's *Resource Manual for Guidelines for Exercise Testing and Prescription* (170).

Methods of Assessing Overweight and Obesity

In the latter part of the twentieth century, one of the most common ways of making a judgment about whether a person was overweight was to use the Metropolitan Life Insurance height and weight tables (142). This has been replaced with a measure that has now been universally adopted—the Body Mass Index (BMI)—the ratio of body weight (in kilograms) to height (in meters) squared: BMI = wt [kg] ÷ ht [m²]. The BMI is easily calculated, and guidelines for classifying someone as overweight or obese have used percentile rankings or fixed BMI values (127). As these BMI guidelines were developed, some allowances were made for age (higher values), but some scientists felt that the higher values were too generous given their association with higher rates of morbidity and mortality (28, 236, 237). Current BMI standards that have been adopted worldwide include (147):

Underweight	<18.5
Normal	18.5–24.9
Overweight	25.0–29.9
Obesity—Class I	30.0–34.9
Obesity—Class II	35.0–39.9
Extreme Obesity—Class III	≥40

The BMI standards listed previously are for adults. Investigators and clinicians have relied on percentile cutoffs (e.g., 85th and 95th percentile) to classify the fatness of children, without labeling them as overweight or obese. However, there is now agreement to use a BMI >30.0 or the ≥95th percentile (for age and gender) for classifying obesity and a BMI of 30.0 or ≥85th percentile but <95th percentile for classifying overweight in children (116) .

One of the major problems associated with height/weight tables and the BMI is that there is no way to know if the person is heavily muscled or simply overfat. One of the earliest uses of body composition analysis showed that with height/weight tables, "All-American" football players weighing 200 lbs would have been found unfit for military service and would not have received life insurance (14), even though they were lean. Clearly there is a need to distinguish overweight from overfat, and that will be the purpose of the next section of this chapter.

Methods of Measuring Body Composition

The most direct way to measure body composition is to do a chemical analysis of the whole body to determine the amount of water, fat, protein, and minerals. This is a common method used in nutritional studies on rats, but it is useless in providing information for the average person. The following is a brief summary of techniques providing information about (a) the composition of the whole body and (b) the development or change in specific tissues of the body. The error involved in the estimates of percent body fat is given as the standard error of estimates (SEE), which is addressed at the end of this section.

Isotope Dilution Total body water (TBW) is determined by the isotope dilution method. In this method a subject drinks an isotope of water (tritiated water—^3H_2O), deuterated water (^2H_2O), or ^{18}O-labeled water ($H_2^{18}O$) that is distributed throughout the body water. After 3 to 4 hours to allow for distribution of the isotope, a sample of body fluid (serum or saliva) is obtained, and the concentration of the isotope is determined. The volume of TBW is obtained by calculating how much body water would be needed to achieve that concentration. A person with a large amount of body water will dilute the isotope to a greater extent. People with large TBW volumes possess more lean tissue and less fat tissue, so TBW can be used to determine body fatness (63, 182).

Photon Absorptiometry This method is used to determine the mineral content and density of bones. A beam of photons from iodine-125 is passed over a bone or bones, and the transmission of the photon beam through bone and soft tissue is obtained. There is a very strong positive relationship between the absorption of the photons and the mineral density of the bones (42, 127).

Potassium-40 Potassium is located primarily within the cells, along with a naturally occurring radioactive isotope of potassium: ^{40}K. The ^{40}K can be measured in a whole-body "counter" and is proportional to the mass of lean tissue (32).

Hydrostatic (Underwater) Weighing Water has a density of about 1 g/ml, and body fat, with a density of about 0.900 g/ml, will float in water. Lean tissue has a density of about 1.100 in adults and will sink in water. Whole-body density provides information about the portion of the body that is lean and fat. Underwater weighing methods are commonly used to determine body density and will be discussed in more detail (127). The SEE is ±2.5% (170).

Dual Energy X-Ray Absorptiometry (DEXA) In this new technology, a single X-ray source is used to determine whole-body and regional estimates of lean tissue, bone, mineral, and fat with a high degree of accuracy. The software required for this process continues to be refined, and DEXA continues to play a major role in the future of body composition analysis (61, 127, 138, 226). The SEE is approximately ±1.8%, but more research is needed (170).

Near Infrared Interactance (NIR) This method is based on the absorption of light, reflectance, and near infrared spectroscopy (33). A fiber-optic probe is placed over the biceps and an infrared light beam is emitted. The light passes through subcutaneous fat and muscle and is reflected by bone back to the probe. Generally, there has been little interaction between scientists and the manufacturers in the development and validation of this type of device (127), and as a result there is limited research on this technique. The SEE is about ±5% (170).

Radiography An X-ray of a limb allows one to measure the widths of fat, muscle, and bone, and has been used extensively in tracing the growth of these tissues over time (108). Fat-width measurements can also be used to estimate total body fat (74, 111).

Ultrasound Sound waves are transmitted through tissues and the echoes are received and analyzed. This technique has been used to measure the thickness of subcutaneous fat. Present technology allows for whole-body scans and the determination of the volumes of various organs (33).

Nuclear Magnetic Resonance (NMR) In this method, electromagnetic waves are transmitted through tissues. Select nuclei absorb and then release energy at a particular frequency (resonance). The resonant-frequency characteristics are related to the type of tissue. Computer analysis of the signal can provide detailed images, and the volumes of specific tissues can be calculated (33).

Total Body Electrical Conductivity (TOBEC) Body composition is analyzed by TOBEC on the basis that lean tissue and water conduct electricity better than does fat. In this method, the subject lies in a large cylindrical coil while an electric current is injected into the coil. The electromagnetic field developed in the space enclosed by the cylindrical coil is affected by the subject's body composition (166, 188, 224).

Bioelectrical Impedance Analysis (BIA) The basis for BIA is similar to that of TOBEC, but it uses a small portable instrument. An electrical current (50 μA usually set at a frequency of 50 kHz) is applied to an extremity and resistance to that current (due to the specific resistivity and volume of the conductor—the fat-free mass) is measured (127, 188, 224). Total body water is calculated, and the value can be used to estimate the percentage of body fatness, as was mentioned for the isotope dilution procedure. BIA devices using multiple frequencies (7, 54, and 100 kHz) show promise of improved accuracy (127, 186, 227). This technique may be an appropriate field method to use in place of or in addition to skinfolds in testing the elderly (78). However, one has to be careful to standardize hydration status to obtain valid and reliable measurements. The SEE is about ±3.5%–5% (170).

Air Displacement Plethysmography Body density can also be calculated from body volume measurements obtained via air displacement plethysmography (in contrast to water displacement that is used in hydrostatic weighing). Small changes in pressure, due to the change in volume of air in the chamber, are used to calculate the volume of the individual sitting in the chamber. The Bod Pod uses this technology to simplify the measurement of body volume and therefore the calculation of whole-body density (see figure 18.2). The information obtained is used in the same way as that collected in hydrostatic weighing (54). Although body fat percentage values derived from this method may not be the same as those from hydrostatic weighing, the differences are small (143). The SEE is approximately ±2.2–3.7% (170).

Skinfold Thickness An estimate of total body fatness is made from a measure of subcutaneous fat. A number of skinfold measurements are obtained and the values used in equations to calculate body density (127, 131). Details on this technique are presented in a later section. The SEE is approximately ±3.5% (170).

Some of these procedures are expensive in terms of personnel and equipment (e.g., potassium-40, TOBEC, radiography, ultrasound, NMR, DEXA, TBW) and are not used on a routine basis for body composition analysis. BIA has gained greater acceptance in the past few years, due in part to a collaborative

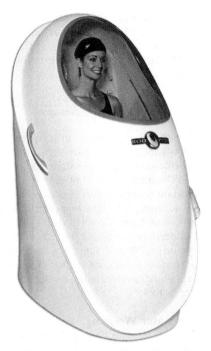

Figure 18.2 The Bod Pod system for measuring body volume using air displacement plethysmography.

multi-university research project that showed it to be comparable to skinfold estimates of body fatness in men and women (127, 231). The data from these techniques can be used alone or in combination to provide an assessment of body composition. A variety of models have been proposed for this purpose (94, 127, 133, 159):

- Four-component model—this model uses information on mineral, water, protein, and fat to assess body composition. The careful measurement of each of these components allows one to account for variations in bone density (mineral) and total body water that might vary dramatically in certain populations (e.g., growing children, the elderly). These procedures would give the best estimates of the percentage of fat.

- Three-component model—in this model the body is divided into three components:
  (a) body water, protein + mineral, and fat, or
  (b) body water + protein, mineral, and fat.
  The three-component model also allows one to account for variations in either bone density or body water and improve estimates of body fatness.

- Two-component model—this, the oldest model, divides the body into two components: the fat mass and the fat-free mass. Although it

is still the most commonly used approach to estimate the percentage of fat, the assumptions underlying this model have been questioned. The limitations of the two-component model have been addressed using information collected with the three- and four-component models. The details are provided in the following sections.

When using any of the body composition techniques, it is important to keep in mind that there is an inherent error involved in the estimations of percent body fat. The error is usually given as the standard error of estimate (SEE). If a technique estimates percent body fat as 20% and the SEE is ±2.5% (as it is for hydrostatic weighing), that means the actual percent body fat lies between 22.5% and 17.5% for 68% of subjects being measured as having 20% fat. Given that we don't know where in that range an individual is, caution is needed when interpreting percent body fat values. It is best to compare these estimates of percent body fat over time on the same subject, where the change in percent fat is indicative of changes in the fat mass or fat-free mass (170).

IN SUMMARY

- The BMI uses a simple ratio of weight-to-height squared (kg/m^2) to classify individuals as being normal weight, overweight, or obese. However, just like the old height-weight tables, the BMI does not consider the composition of the body weight (i. e., proportion of muscle tissue vs. fat tissue).

- Body composition can be measured in terms of total body water (isotope dilution, bioelectric impedance analysis), bone density (photon absorptiometry), lean tissue mass (potassium-40), density (underwater weighing, air displacement plethysmography), and thickness of various tissues (ultrasound, radiography, skinfolds).

- Body composition assessment can be based on four-component (mineral, water, protein, and fat), three-component (body water, protein + mineral, and fat, or body water + protein, mineral, and fat), or two-component (fat-free mass and fat mass) models. The four-component model is the most accurate.

Two-Component System of Body Composition

Two approaches that are used extensively to estimate percent fat include the **underwater weighing** and skinfold methods. In both of these methods, the investigator obtains an estimate of **whole-body density,** and from this calculates the percentage of the body that is fat and the percentage that is fat-free. This is the two-component body composition system described by Behnke that is commonly used to describe changes in body composition (14). The conversion of whole-body density values to fat and fat-free tissue components relies on "constants" used for each of those tissue components. Human fat tissue is believed to have a density of 0.900 g/ml, and fat-free tissue a density of 1.100 g/ml. Using these density values, Siri (197) derived an equation to calculate the percentage of body fat from whole-body density:

$$\% \text{ body fat} = \frac{495}{\text{Density}} - 450$$

This equation is correct only if the density values for fat tissue and fat-free tissue are 0.900 and 1.100 g/ml, respectively. Investigators sensed that certain populations might have fat-free tissue densities different from that of 1.100 g/ml when they observed high values for body fatness for children and the elderly, and extremely low values (<0% body fat) in professional football players (78, 134, 239). Children have lower bone mineral contents, less potassium, and more water per unit fat-free mass, yielding a lower density for fat-free mass (134). Lohman (128) reports density values (g/ml) of 1.080 at age 6, 1.084 at age 10, and 1.097 for boys aged 15½. The lower values in the prepubescent child would overestimate percent body fat by 5%. Based on data from the multicomponent models of body composition, Lohman (129) recommends the values found in table 18.4 for Siri's equation when applied to children, youth, and young adults (see table 18.4).

TABLE 18.4	Equations for Estimating % Fat from Body Density Based on Age and Gender			
	MALE		FEMALE	
Age, yrs.	C_1	C_2	C_1	C_2
1	572	536	569	533
1–2	564	526	565	526
3–4	553	514	558	520
5–6	543	503	553	514
7–8	538	497	543	503
9–10	530	489	535	495
11–12	523	481	525	484
13–14	507	464	512	469
15–16	503	459	507	464
Young adult	495	450	505	462

Note: C_1 and C_2 are the terms in percent fat equation to substitute for the Siri equation of percent fat $= \left[\dfrac{C_1}{D_b} - C_2 \right]$.

Reprinted, by permission, from T. G. Lohman, 1989, "Assessment of Body Composition in Children," in *Pediatric Exercise Science*, Vol. 1(1):22.

In contrast to children, who have density values below 1.100 for the fat-free mass, African Americans were shown to have a density of 1.113 g/ml (185). The Siri equation would have to be modified as follows:

$$\% \text{ body fat} = \frac{437}{\text{Density}} - 393$$

Although this may appear to be quite complicated, there is good reason to have the correct equation for a specific population. If judgments are to be made about the distribution of obesity in our society, it is important that estimates of body fatness be reasonably accurate. The following sections will discuss how whole-body density values are determined by underwater weighing and skinfold procedures. Heyward and Wagner's text (see the Suggested Readings) provides guidance in choosing the most appropriate equation depending on age, race, gender, or other factors.

Underwater Weighing Density is equal to mass divided by volume (D = M/V). Because we already know body mass (body weight), we only have to determine body volume to calculate whole-body density (80). The underwater weighing method applies Archimedes' principle, which states that when an object is placed in water it is buoyed up by a counterforce equal to the water it displaces. The volume of water displaced (spilled over) would equal the *loss of weight* while the object is completely submerged. Some investigators determine body volume by measuring the actual volume of water displaced; others measure weight while the subject is underwater, and obtain body volume by subtracting the weight measured in water (MW) from that measured in air (MA), or $(M_A - M_W)$. Both methods of determining volume are reproducible, but body fat percentage values are slightly but significantly (0.7%) lower with the volume displacement method (232). The weight of water displaced is converted to a volume by dividing by the density of the water (D_W) at the time of measurement:

$$D = \frac{M}{V} = \frac{M_A}{\dfrac{(M_A - M_W)}{D_W}}$$

This denominator must now be corrected for two other volumes: the volume of air in the lungs at the time of measurement [usually residual volume (V_R)], and the volume of gas in the gastrointestinal tract (V_{GI}). It is recommended that $\dot{V}_R$ be measured at the time that underwater weight is measured, but measurement on land with the subject in the same position is a suitable alternative (128). Residual volume can also be estimated with gender-specific regression equations, or by taking 24% (males) or 28% (females) of vital capacity. However, the latter two procedures introduce measurement errors of 2% to 3% fat for a given individual (146). V_{GI} can be quite variable, and although some investigators ignore this measure, others assume a 100 ml volume for all subjects (38, 127).

The density equation can now be rewritten:

$$D = \frac{M}{V} = \frac{M_A}{\dfrac{(M_A - M_W)}{D_W} - V_R - V_{GI}}$$

Figure 18.3 shows the equipment used to measure underwater weight. Water temperature is measured to obtain the correct water density. The subject is weighed on land on a scale accurate to within 100 grams. The subject puts on a diver's belt with sufficient weight to prevent floating during the weighing procedure, and sits on the chair suspended from the precision scale. The scale can be read to 10 grams and it has major divisions of 50 grams. The subject sits on the chair with the water at chin level and as a maximal exhalation is just about completed, the subject bends over and pulls the head under. When a maximal expiration is achieved, the subject holds that position for about 5 to 10 seconds while the investigator reads the scale. This procedure is repeated six to ten times until the values stabilize. The weight of the diver's belt and chair (measured under water) are subtracted from this weight to obtain the true value for M_W. If V_R were to be measured at the time underwater weight is measured, the subject would have to be breathing through a mouthpiece and valve assembly that could be activated at the correct time (165).

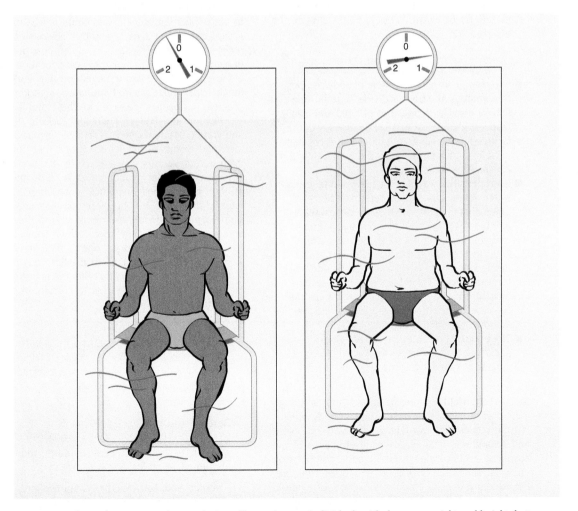

Figure 18.3 The underwater weighing technique illustrating two individuals with the same weight and height, but different body composition.

The following data were obtained on a white male, aged 36: $M_A = 75.20$ kg, $M_W = 3.52$ kg, $V_R = 1.43$ liters, $D_W = 0.9944$ at 34°C, $V_{GI} = 0.1$ liter.

$$D = \frac{M}{V} = \frac{75.20}{\dfrac{(75.20 - 3.52)}{0.9944} - 1.43 - 0.1} = \frac{75.20}{70.55} = 1.066$$

This density value is now used in Siri's equation to calculate the percentage of body fat:

$$\% \text{ body fat} = \frac{495}{\text{Density}} - 450$$

$$14.3 = \frac{495}{1.066} - 450$$

The underwater weighing procedure in which V_R is measured (and not estimated) has been used as the "standard" against which other methods are compared. However, remember that due to the normal biological variability in the fat-free mass in a given population, the body fat percentage value is estimated to be within about ±2.0–2.5% of the "true" value (127, 170).

IN SUMMARY

- In the two-component system of body composition analysis, the body is divided into fat-free and fat mass, with densities of 1.100 and 0.900, respectively. The estimate of the density of the fat-free mass must account for differences that exist in various populations (i.e., children and African Americans).
- Body density is equal to mass ÷ volume. Underwater weighing is used to determine body volume using the principle of Archimedes: When an object is placed in water it is buoyed up by a counterforce equal to the water it displaces. One can measure the actual volume of water displaced, or the loss of weight while underwater. The weight of water is divided by the density of water to yield body volume, which must then be corrected for the residual volume and the volume of gas in the GI tract.
- The body fat percentage value has an error of about ±2.0–2.5% due to the normal biological variation of the fat-free mass.

Sum of Skinfolds Underwater weighing, although a good way to obtain a measurement of body density, is time consuming and requires special equipment and personnel. Paralleling the development of the advanced technologies used in body composition analysis, scientists developed equations that predicted body density from a collection of skinfold measurements. The skinfold method relies on the observation that within any population a certain fraction of the total body fat lies just under the skin

(subcutaneous fat), and if one could obtain a representative sample of that fat, overall body fatness (density) could be predicted. Generally, these prediction equations were developed with the underwater weighing method used as the standard. For example, a group of college males and females would have body density measured by underwater weighing, and a variety of skinfold measures would also be obtained. The investigator would then determine what collection of skinfolds would most accurately predict the body density determined by underwater weighing.

Investigators found that subcutaneous fat represents a variable fraction of total fat (20–70%), depending on age, sex, overall fatness, and the measurement technique used. At a specific body fatness, women have less subcutaneous fat than men, and older subjects of the same sex have less than younger subjects (131). Given that these variables could influence an estimate of body density, it is no surprise that of the more than 100 equations developed, most were found to be "population specific" and could not be used for groups of different ages or sex. This obviously creates problems for exercise leaders in adult fitness programs or elementary or high school physical education teachers when they try to find the equation that works best for their particular group. Fortunately, a good deal of progress has been made to reduce these problems.

Jackson and Pollock (102) and Jackson, Pollock, and Ward (104) developed "generalized equations" for men and women—that is, equations that could be used across various age groups. In addition, these equations have been validated for athletic and non-athletic populations, including postpubescent athletes (128, 195, 196). In these equations, specific skinfold measurements are obtained and the values are used along with age to calculate body density. Here are two such equations, one for men and one for women, which can be used to predict body density (103). The body density value obtained is used in the Siri equation presented earlier to calculate body fat percentage.

Men

$$\text{Density} = 1.1125025 - 0.0013125\,(X_1) + 0.0000055\,(X_1)^2 - 0.0002440\,(X_2)$$

where X_1 = sum of chest, triceps, subscapular skinfolds, and X_2 = age in years.

Women

$$\text{Density} = 1.089733 - 0.0009245\,(X_1) + 0.0000025\,(X_1)^2 - 0.0000979\,(X_2)$$

where X_1 = sum of triceps, suprailium, and abdominal skinfolds, and X_2 = age in years.

Jackson and Pollock (103) simplified this procedure by providing tabulated body fatness percentage values for different skinfold thicknesses across age. All that is needed is the sum of skinfolds to obtain a body fatness percentage value. Appendixes G and H show the percent body fat tables for men and women, respectively, using the sum of three skinfolds. For example, a woman, aged 25, with a sum of skinfolds equal to 50 mm has a body fat percentage equal to 22.9% (look to the right of the sum of skinfold column where 48–52 is shown, over to the second column—ages 23–27). Body fatness percentage derived from skinfold measures is estimated to have an error of about ±3.5% relative to the "true" value (130, 170). Recently, concern has been expressed about the need to cross-validate the skinfold equations against the multicomponent models and to clarify the effects that age, gender, ethnicity, and fitness have on the various components of body composition—for example, the density of the fat-free mass (78, 127).

The use of skinfold measurements was extended to children in the schools for early identification of obesity. The American Alliance for Health, Physical Education, Recreation, and Dance (9, 132) developed a health-related fitness test to evaluate cardiorespiratory function, muscular strength, low back function, and body fatness. The body fatness assessment relies on a triceps and subscapular or calf skinfold(s), and percentile norms are provided. When this test was developed, the skinfold values could not be converted to body fatness percentage values because the assumption that the fat-free mass had a density of 1.100 g/cc was known to be false. However, based on recent research with young populations using the four-component model (202), appropriate equations are available to convert skinfolds to body fat for young African American and white girls and boys (127) (see table 18.5).

Body Fatness for Health and Fitness

The previous sections showed how to determine body density by underwater weighing and skinfold procedures. This information on body density is converted to percentage of body fat and can be used to make judgments about one's status relative to health and fitness. Lohman, Houtkooper, and Going (126) recommend the following range of percent fat values for health and fitness for men and women:

Health Standards

	Men	Women
Young adults	8–22	20–35
Middle age	10–25	25–38
Elderly	10–23	25–35

Fitness Standards for Active Individuals

	Men	Women
Young adults	5–15	16–28
Middle age	7–18	20–33
Elderly	9–18	20–33

TABLE 18.5	Prediction Equations of Percent Fat from Triceps and Calf and from Triceps and Subscapular Skinfolds in Children and Youth for Males and Females

Triceps and calf skinfolds
Males, all ages: % Fat $= 0.735\ \Sigma SF + 1.0$
Females, all ages: % Fat $= 0.610\ \Sigma SF + 5.0$

Triceps and subscapular skinfolds (>35 mm)
Males: % Fat $= 0.783\ \Sigma SF + 1$
Females: % Fat $= 0.546\ \Sigma SF + 9.7$

Triceps and subscapular skinfolds (<35 mm)[a]
Males: % Fat $= 1.21\ (\Sigma SF) - 0.008\ (\Sigma SF)^2 + 1$
Females: % Fat $= 1.33\ (\Sigma SF) - 0.013\ (\Sigma SF)^2 + 2.5$ (2.0 African Americans, 3.0 whites)

1 = Intercept varies with maturation level and racial group for males as follows:

Age	African Americans	Whites
Prepubescent	−3.5	−1.7
Pubescent	−5.2	−3.4
Postpubescent	−6.8	−5.5
Adult	−6.8	−5.5

[a]Thus for a white pubescent male with a triceps of 15 and a subscapular of 12, the % fat would be: % Fat $= 1.21\ (27) - 0.008\ (27)^2 - 3.4 = 23.4\%$

Note. Calculations were derived using the Slaughter et al. (1988) equation. Reprinted, by permission, from T. G. Lohman, 1992, *Advances in Body Composition Assessment* (Champaign, IL: Human Kinetics Publishers), 74.

Now that we know how to obtain a percent body fatness measure, and what the healthy and fitness percent body fat standards are, how can we determine the body weight associated with those values? In the following example, a female college student has 30% body fat and weighs 142 lbs. She wants to be at the low end of the healthy range, so her goal is 20% fat.

Step 1. Calculate fat-free weight:

100% − 30% fat = 70% fat free
70% × 142 lb = 99.4 lb fat-free weight

Step 2. Goal weight $= \dfrac{\text{fat-free weight}}{(1 - \text{goal \% fat})}$, with goal % fat expressed as a fraction:

For 20% $= \dfrac{99.4\ \text{lb}}{(1 - .20)} = 124$ lb;

Her weight at her 20% goal is 124 lb.

Lohman (130) also provides values for body fat percentages that are below the optimal range: for boys, 6% to 10% is classified as low and <6% as very low. Comparable values for girls are 12% to 15% and

<12%, respectively. There is a great pressure in our society to be thin, and this can be carried to an extreme. A far-too-common problem in our high schools and colleges is an eating disorder known as **anorexia nervosa,** in which young females have an exaggerated fear of getting fat. This fear leads to food restriction and increased exercise in an attempt to stay thin, when they are, in fact, already thin (73). **Bulimia nervosa** is an eating disorder in which large quantities of food are taken in (binging), only to be followed by self-induced vomiting or the use of laxatives to rid the body of the food that was eaten (purging). While anorexia nervosa is characterized by the cessation of the menstrual cycle and the development of an emaciated state, the majority of the bingers/purgers are in the normal weight range (233).

It is clear that to stay in the optimal body fat percentage range, one must balance the dietary consumption of calories with energy expenditure. We will now consider that topic.

IN SUMMARY

- Subcutaneous fat can be "sampled" as skinfold thicknesses, and a sum of skinfolds can be converted to a body fat percentage with formulas derived from the relationship of the sum of skinfolds to a body composition standard based on a two-, three-, or four-component model.
- The recommended range of body fatness for health for young men is 8% to 22%, and for young women is 20% to 35%; values for fitness are 5% to 15% and 16% to 28%, respectively.

OBESITY AND WEIGHT CONTROL

In chapter 14 we discussed the major risk factors associated with degenerative diseases. Although high blood pressure, cigarette smoking, elevated serum cholesterol, and inactivity have been accepted as major risk factors, more and more evidence points to obesity as being a separate and independent risk factor for CHD, and one directly tied to two of the major risk factors. A variety of diseases are linked to obesity: hypertension, type 2 diabetes, coronary heart disease (CHD), stroke, gallbladder disease, osteoarthritis, sleep apnea and respiratory problems, and some types of cancer (endometrial, breast, prostate, and colon). In addition, obesity is also associated with complications of pregnancy, menstrual irregularities, hirsutism, stress incontinence, and psychological disorders (e.g., depression) (40, 147, 169, 172).

It should be no surprise that obesity is linked to an increased morbidity due to cardiovascular disease and some types of cancers. However, being overweight is not. Overweight was associated with a lower mortality from all causes, including cardiovascular disease (68). This information provides special urgency to promote strategies, including doing physical activity on a regular basis, to reduce the chance of a person moving from the overweight to the obese category. Let's take a more detailed look at obesity.

Obesity

If we use a BMI of ≥30 as a classification for obesity, the prevalence of obesity in U.S. adults increased from 15% in the 1976–1980 reporting period, to 23.3% in 1988–1994, to 30.9% in 1999–2000, to 32.2% in 2004 and to 33.8% for 2007–08 (67, 152). When you include those who are classified as overweight (BMI 25.0–29.9), the prevalence of overweight and obesity was 68.0%. Consequently, more than two-thirds of the U.S. adult population is overweight, and one-third is obese. In addition, some ethnic groups were overrepresented. More than half of non-Hispanic Black women aged 40 years and older were obese, and almost 80% were overweight (67). The good news is that the prevalence of obesity is not increasing at the same rate as it was 10 years ago.

All obesity is not the same. Studies suggest that not only is the relative body fatness related to an increased risk of CVD, but the distribution of that fatness must also be considered. Individuals with a large waist circumference compared to hip circumference have a higher risk of CVD and sudden death (200, 201). These data suggest that in addition to skinfold or underwater weighing estimates of body density, measurements of waist and hip circumferences should also be obtained (121, 122). Ratios of waist to hip circumference >0.95 for men and >0.8 for women are associated with the CVD risk factors of insulin resistance, high cholesterol, and hypertension, and such individuals are treated even if they are only borderline obese (19, 36, 43, 200). Given that the risk of these problems is associated with abdominal obesity, the guidelines mentioned previously (147) use only waist circumference and recommend values of 102 cm (40 in) and 88 cm (35 in) to be used for men and women, respectively, when classifying those at high risk. Recent reviews support the continued use of circumference measurements to assess health risk (190), but there is renewed interest in developing appropriate cutoff values for different racial groups since existing standards were derived primarily from Caucasian populations (96, 168, 205).

In addition to fat tissue distribution, there is a need to determine whether the obesity is due to an increase in the amount of fat in each fat cell (hypertrophic obesity), or to an increase in the number of fat

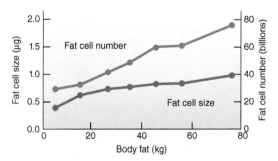

Figure 18.4   Relationship of fat cell size and fat cell number to total kilograms of body fat. Fat cell size is given in μg of fat, and fat cell number in billions of cells. The increase in body fatness beyond about 30 kg of fat is directly related to an increasing fat cell number; fat cell size remains relatively constant.

cells (hyperplastic obesity), or both (16, 17, 20). In moderate obesity where the mass of adipose tissue is less than 30 kg, the increase in fat cell size appears to be the primary means of storing the additional fat. Beyond that, the cell number is the variable most strongly related to the mass of adipose tissue (16, 92). This is shown in figure 18.4, where cell size increases up to about 30 kg of body fat, but does not significantly change thereafter. In contrast, the fat cell number is strongly related to the mass of adipose tissue (198, 199).

There are about 25 billion fat cells in a normal-weight individual versus 60 to 80 billion in the extremely obese (16, 92, 199). When a person undergoes dietary restriction, the size of the fat cells decreases but the number does not (16, 92). This high fat-cell number is believed to be related to the difficulty obese patients have in maintaining body weight after it has been lost (119). For example, a study was conducted to determine the pattern of weight loss, maintenance, and gain of groups classified as having obesity that is hyperplastic, hypertrophic, or both. Those with hyperplastic obesity or combined hyperplastic and hypertrophic obesity lost weight quickly, kept it off for only a short period of time, and regained it at a high rate. At this point we have seen that dieting does not change fat cell number, and that those who possess a high number of fat cells have difficulty maintaining a reduced body weight. The next question to consider is, when does the fat cell number increase?

In a longitudinal study of children during the first 18 months of life, the fat cell number did not increase during the first 12 months; the increase in cell size was entirely responsible for the increase in body fat. In contrast, the gain in body fat from 12 to 18 months was due entirely to an increase in fat cell number with cell size remaining stable (85). When

these data were plotted along with data from other studies, the results indicated that cell number increases throughout growth (85, 92). Given that physical activity and dietary intervention in extremely obese young children (8 years old) can slow the rate of growth in the fat cell number, and that the fat cell number is tied to the inability of obese children to lose their obesity as adults, the emphasis on treatment during childhood is obvious (86, 114). Unfortunately, in spite of our understanding of the problem, the prevalence of overweight and obesity in children and adolescents increased dramatically (from ~6% to ~15%)) between the late 1970s and 2000; however, the rate of increase has slowed between 2000 and 2007–08 for both 6–11 year olds (15.1% to 19.0%) and 12–19 year olds (14.8% to 18.1%) (151, 153). A major concern is that the prevalence of those at the high end of the BMI scale (97th percentile for BMI) continue to increase at a fast rate (151).The increase in overweight and obesity in children over the past 35 years carries with it a disease burden (e.g., type 2 diabetes), formerly reserved for those over age 40 and overweight. What causes obesity?

There is clearly no single cause of obesity. Obesity is related to both genetic and environmental variables. In 1965, Mayer (135) commented on the numerous studies showing that 70% to 80% of obese children had at least one obese parent, but concluded that it was difficult to interpret those data given the way cultural background interacts with genetics. In effect, the need to do hard physical work in some countries, or extreme social pressure against obesity (discussed later), might not allow a genetic predisposition to express itself. Garn and Clark (75) found a strong relationship between parental fatness and the fatness of children. They identified three categories of fatness on the basis of triceps skinfold: lean = <15th percentile; medium = 15th to 85th percentile, and obese = >85th percentile. The triceps skinfold thickness was related to parental fatness, being below average for the lean-dad/lean-mom pair and above average for the obese-dad/obese-mom pair. Although this might imply that a genetic link exists, when the investigators compared husbands to wives (usually no genetic tie), the relationship was similar to that for their children, suggesting either that there was a tendency of like to mate like, or that communal living exerts a major influence.

A slightly different approach to this question was taken when the body mass index of biological and adoptive parents were compared to the values of the adopted child as an adult. On the basis of a health questionnaire, they were classified as thin (≤4th percentile), median (50th percentile), overweight (92nd–96th percentile), and obese (>96th percentile). A stronger relationship existed between the BMI of the adoptee and that of the biological parent (207).

However, a subsequent review of this work pointed out that while the results were consistent with a genetic effect, it was not a very strong one (25). Other observations support the importance of the environment as a cause of obesity. In American women, obesity is inversely related to socioeconomic class: 30% for lower, 18% for middle, and 5% for the upper class (79). Further, women and adolescent girls have been shown to suffer the most direct discrimination because of this obesity (230). Clearly, although we may possess a genetic predisposition for obesity, a variety of social factors influence its appearance. Is there any way to determine the importance of each?

Bouchard (25) and colleagues have determined, on the basis of an analysis of the relationships between and among nine types of relatives (spouses, parent-child, siblings, uncle-nephew, etc.), that 25% of body fat and fat mass is tied to genetic factors, and 30% is due to cultural transmission. What is interesting is the components of energy expenditure that are influenced by genetic factors: (a) the amount of spontaneous physical activity, (b) resting metabolic rate, (c) thermic effect of food, and (d) relative rate of carbohydrate and fat oxidation. Further, when challenged with an excess of calories due to overeating, there is a genetic component related to the amount of weight gained and the proportion of that weight that is stored as fat or lean tissue. Given that information, it should be no surprise that physicians and scientists who work in this area believe that genetic factors are important causes of obesity (30, 89). However, as we will see, there is more to the story.

IN SUMMARY

- Obesity is associated with an increased mortality from cardiovascular disease and some types of cancer, but being overweight is not. Emphasis should be on maintaining or reducing weight in the overweight individual to decrease the chance of migration to the obese category.
- Obesity associated with fat mass in excess of 30 kg is due primarily to an increase in fat cell number, with fat cell hypertrophy being related to smaller degrees of obesity. Those with hyperplasia have a more difficult time losing weight and keeping it off.
- Genetic factors account for about 25% of the transmissible variance for fat mass and percentage of body fat; culture accounts for 30%.

Set Point and Obesity Obese individuals, as previously mentioned, have a great deal of difficulty maintaining a reduced weight. In fact, the tendency of a person to return to a certain weight suggests that there is a biological set point for body weight much

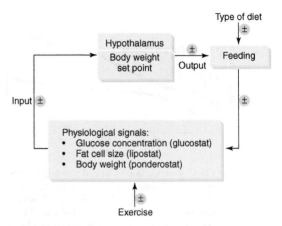

Figure 18.5 Physiological set point model for control of body weight by altering feeding behavior, showing the glucostatic (blood glucose), lipostatic (adipose tissue), and ponderostatic (weight) input to the hypothalamus. The signals from these latter mechanisms are compared against a "set point," and an appropriate increase or decrease in feeding behavior occurs. In this model, exercise can modify the input, and the type of diet can modify feeding behavior.

like the set points for any negative feedback biological control system. Although the hypothalamus contains centers associated with satiety and feeding behavior, we must remember that the *body weight set point is a concept, rather than a reality* (24). Figure 18.5 shows a physiological model of a body weight set point in which biological signals with regard to blood glucose (glucostatic signal), lipid stores (lipostatic signal), or weight on feet (ponderostatic signal) provide input to the hypothalamus (24). If the collective signals indicate low energy stores, food intake is stimulated until the source of the signal is diminished and the energy stores now equal the set point. Like any biological control system, if the set point were to be increased, body weight would increase to meet this new value. Exercise can modify the signals going to the hypothalamus, and the type of diet can also influence feeding behavior. In addition, drugs can be used to directly affect the neurotransmitters in the hypothalamus to alter feeding behavior (see Clinical Applications 18.4).

In contrast to this physiological model, Booth's cognitive set-point model (24) deals with the role the environment (culture, socioeconomic class, etc.) has on body weight. Figure 18.6 shows that relative to a personally selected "ideal" body weight set point, we are constantly receiving a variety of cognitive signals about how we look, body weight, clothing size, perception of effort, and concerns about health. A mismatch between the "ideal" set point and these perceptions leads to appropriate eating behavior. Exercise can modify the signals, and the type of diet can influence the feeding behavior. There is clear

CLINICAL APPLICATIONS 18.4

Drugs, Dietary Supplements, and Weight Loss

Obesity is such a big problem in this country that it is not surprising that people seek help wherever they can find it. In response to this need, a variety of dietary supplements and drugs have been offered to help obese people lose weight. A survey of adults regarding beliefs and practices about weight control found that 33.9% used dietary supplements for weight loss, and many thought such products were approved by the Food and Drug Administration (FDA). They aren't (160). In one major review, the following

dietary supplements were examined: chitosan, chromium picolinate, *Ephedra sinica*, *Garcinia cambogia*, glucomannan, guar gum, hydroxy-methylbutyrate, plantago psyllium, pyruvate, yerba maté, and yohimbe. Although the authors found some encouraging results, there was simply not enough evidence to recommend any specific dietary supplement for reducing body weight. The only exception was *E. sinica*- and ephedrine-containing supplements, both of which have been associated with adverse events (162).

Currently, only two drugs (orlistat and sibutramine) have been approved by the FDA to treat obesity over the long term, but both have undesirable side effects. Other drugs have been approved for short-term use (e.g., sympathomimetic drugs), but they also have potential adverse effects (82, 174). As of now, the following statement sums up the evidence (46, 162): The focus of any weight-loss (and maintenance) program should be on long-term diet and exercise behaviors.

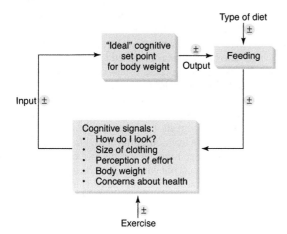

Figure 18.6 Cognitive set point for control of body weight by altering feeding behavior. A person's perception of "ideal" body weight is balanced against signals about how one looks, body weight, clothing size, and so on. Exercise can modify the input, and the type of diet can modify feeding behavior.

evidence that a high-fat diet results in an increase in caloric intake before satiety is reached—leading to weight gain in the long run (215). This set-point model is closely related to the behavior modification approach to diet, exercise, and weight control.

In a review of this topic, Levitsky (124) suggests that we might want to look at this issue as a "settling-point" theory rather than a "set-point" theory. This revision suggests that biology might set a range or zone of body weights, rather than a fixed weight. Within that zone, body weight may "settle" at a value determined by behaviors that are influenced by environmental and

cognitive stimuli. In effect, Levitsky's "settling point" theory attempts to integrate aspects of each of the two positions just mentioned. He suggests that if the body weight zone is large enough to allow a person to move between a hypertensive condition and normal blood pressure condition or between a type 2 diabetic and nondiabetic state, then additional attention must be directed at the environmental and cognitive factors that drive eating behavior.

IN SUMMARY

- Investigators have proposed a set-point theory to explain obesity given the tendency for people who diet to return to their former weight. Theories based on weight sensors (ponderostatic), the blood glucose concentration (glucostatic), and the mass of lipid (lipostatic) have been proposed.
- A behavioral set-point theory has been proposed that relies on the person making appropriate activity and dietary judgments when body weight, size, or shape does not match up with that person's ideal.

DIET, EXERCISE, AND WEIGHT CONTROL

The Framingham Heart Study showed that body weight increases as we age. A reasonable question to ask is whether this gain in weight was due to an increase in caloric intake. Interestingly, caloric intake decreased over the same age span (27). We are forced to conclude that energy expenditure decreased faster than the decrease in caloric intake, and as a result, weight gain occurred (22). This weight gain problem can be corrected by understanding and dealing with one or both sides of the energy balance equation. We will deal with the energy balance equation first, and then discuss how modifications in energy intake can affect weight loss. Finally, we will explore the variables on the energy expenditure side of the equation.

Energy and Nutrient Balance

Weight gain occurs when there is a chronic increase in caloric intake, compared to energy expenditure. A net gain of about 3,500 kcal is needed to add 1 lb (454 grams) of adipose tissue. We are all familiar with the energy balance equation:

Change in energy stores = energy intake − energy expenditure

What is implied by this equation is that an excess energy intake of 250 kcal/day will cause body weight to increase 1 pound in 14 days (250 kcal/day × 14 day = 3,500 kcal = 1 pound). At the end of one year the person will have gained about 24 pounds. As reasonable as this equation may appear, we know that a weight gain of that magnitude will not occur. The equation is a "static" energy balance equation that does not consider the effect that the weight gain will have on energy expenditure (208).

The energy balance equation can be expressed in a manner to account for the dynamic nature of energy balance in biological systems:

Rate of change of = rate of change of − rate of change of
energy stores   energy intake   energy expenditure

When body weight increases as a result of a chronically elevated energy intake, there is a compensatory increase in the amount of energy used at rest, as well as during activity when that heavier body weight is carried about. At some point, then, the additional 250 kcal/d of energy intake will be balanced by a higher rate of energy expenditure brought about by the higher body weight. Body weight will stabilize at a new and higher value, but it will be more like 3.5 pounds, rather than 24 pounds, higher (208).

IN SUMMARY

■ The dynamic energy balance equation correctly expresses the dynamic nature of changes in energy intake and body weight. An increase in energy intake leads to an increase in body weight; in turn, energy expenditure increases to eventually match the higher energy intake. Body weight is now stable at a new and higher value.

Nutrient Balance Investigators have taken this issue of energy balance one step further in an attempt to understand the causes of obesity. The dynamic energy balance equation can be subdivided into its components, representing the three major nutrients to generate nutrient-balance equations:

Rate of change of = rate of change of − rate of change of
protein stores   protein intake   protein oxidation

Rate of change of = rate of change of − rate of change of
carbohydrate   carbohydrate   carbohydrate
stores   intake   oxidation

Rate of change of = rate of change of − rate of change of
fat stores   fat intake   fat oxidation

If a person maintains balance for each of these nutrients—that is, what is taken in is expended—then energy balance is achieved. Nutrient balance is not a problem for protein and carbohydrate. The daily protein intake is used to maintain existing tissue protein, hormones, and enzymes. If more is taken in than is needed, the "extra" is oxidized for metabolic needs, and fat mass is not increased. The same is true for carbohydrates. Ingested carbohydrates are used to fill liver and muscle glycogen stores; the excess is oxidized and is not converted to fat (1, 18, 88). Carbohydrate intake promotes its own oxidation. This is a relatively new idea that has major ramifications for our understanding of nutrient and energy balance. The evidence seems to be quite convincing that *de novo* lipogenesis from carbohydrates (the making of new lipids from other nutrients) is of only minor consequence in humans. Simply, carbohydrates are either stored as carbohydrates or oxidized; they do not add *directly* to adipose tissue mass. This leaves fat.

In contrast to carbohydrate and protein, fat intake is not automatically balanced by fat oxidation. When "extra" fat is added to the diet, the same amounts of carbohydrate, fat, and protein are oxidized as before; the extra fat is stored in adipose tissue. Fat intake *does not* promote its own oxidation. Fat oxidation is determined primarily by the difference between total energy expenditure and the amount of energy ingested in the form of carbohydrate and protein. Consequently, if one wishes to keep the size of the adipose tissue stores constant (i.e., maintain body weight), one should not eat more fat than one can oxidize (64–66, 106, 107, 208). In this regard, when individuals are placed on a short-term, high-fat diet, the use of exercise (compared to rest) shortens the time needed to achieve fat balance (48). One last point: Alcohol intake is balanced by its own oxidation, but in the process, it suppresses fat oxidation. In this sense, the calories from alcohol should be included with that provided by fat (66).

In chapter 4 you were introduced to the concept of the respiratory quotient (RQ = $\dot{V}CO_2/\dot{V}O_2$) as an indicator of the fuel oxidized during exercise. An RQ of 1.0 indicates that 100% of the energy is derived from carbohydrates, and an RQ of 0.7 indicates that 100% of the energy comes from fat. An RQ of 0.85 indicates that a 50%/50% mixture of carbohydrate and fat was used. This RQ concept has been extended to the foods we ingest, and it is called the Food Quotient, or FQ. The FQ is defined as the ratio of the CO_2 produced to the O_2 consumed during the oxidation of a representative sample of the diet (65). The following equations are used to calculate FQ:

■ O_2 consumption (L/day) = (0.966 × protein intake) + (2.019 × fat intake) + (0.829 × carbohydrate intake), and

■ CO_2 production (L/day) = (0.774 × protein intake) + (1.427 × fat intake) + (0.829 × carbohydrate intake),

where intake of protein, fat, and carbohydrate is expressed in grams/day (81). The reason for describing this is that the FQ concept can be used with the RQ concept to determine if an individual is in nutrient balance (106, 107). Figure 18.7 presents this concept, and the following comments summarize its content:

■ When RQ = FQ, the person is in nutrient and energy balance; the RQ/FQ ratio is 1.0.

■ When RQ > FQ, the person is not oxidizing as much fat as was consumed (positive energy balance), and some fat has been stored in adipose tissue; the RQ/FQ ratio is >1.0.

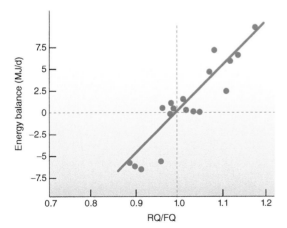

Figure 18.7 Relationship between respiratory quotient (RQ)-to-food quotient (FQ) ratio and energy balance in humans. Each point represents values for a given subject measured over a 24-hour period. (From E. Jéquier. 1992. Calorie balance versus nutrient balance. In *Energy Metabolism: Tissue Determinants and Cellular Corollaries*, eds. J. M. Kinney and H. N. Tucker, p. 131. New York: Raven.)

■ When RQ < FQ, the person used more fat than was consumed (negative energy balance), and some of the fat stores were used; the RQ/FQ ratio is <1.0.

This concept is helpful in discussing weight control, because one could improve nutrient and energy balance with regard to fat by either reducing the amount of fat in the diet (increasing the FQ), or doing exercise to use more fat (decreasing the RQ). We will now discuss both of these options.

IN SUMMARY

■ Nutrient balance exists for both protein and carbohydrate. Excess intake is oxidized and is not converted to fat.
■ Excess fat intake does not drive its own oxidation; the excess is stored in adipose tissue. Achieving fat balance is an important part of weight control.
■ The ratio of the Food Quotient (FQ) to the Respiratory Quotient (RQ) provides good information about the degree to which an individual is in nutrient balance.

Diet and Weight Control

A good diet provides the necessary nutrients and calories to provide for tissue growth and regeneration and to meet the daily energy requirements of work and play. In our society we are fortunate to have a variety of foods to meet these needs. However, we tend to consume more than the recommended amount of fat, which is believed to be related to our country's obesity problem. The focus on dietary fat is twofold:

■ Fat contains more than twice the number of calories per gram as carbohydrate and can contribute to a positive energy balance.

■ It is difficult to achieve nutrient balance for fat when it represents a large fraction of caloric intake.

The hypothesis that the FQ of the diet is an important aspect of weight control revolves around the factors driving energy intake. There is a mandatory need for carbohydrate oxidation by the nervous system, and we are driven to eat what is used (64, 91). If we eat a high-fat diet, we will take in a considerable amount of fat while consuming the necessary carbohydrates to refill the carbohydrate stores. This fat is stored and body weight will increase. As mentioned earlier, as body weight increases, daily energy expenditure increases until an energy balance is achieved at a new and higher body weight. The fat-balance concept is consistent with this. Flatt (64) proposes that the increase in adipose tissue mass that accompanies weight gain increases the mobilization of free fatty acids, shifting the RQ to a lower value, and bringing it into balance with the FQ. In this sense, the elevation of body weight and fat mass due to a high fat/calorie diet is a compensatory mechanism that results in weight maintenance.

However, while we focus on the FQ/RQ concept, we should not forget that calories count in any weight-loss or weight-maintenance program. For example, studies in which subjects were switched from a high-fat to a low-fat diet, *while maintaining a constant caloric intake*, showed no change in energy expenditure or body weight (91, 123, 180, 215). In addition, in conditions in which a negative caloric balance was imposed to achieve weight loss, the composition of the diet (high-fat vs. low-fat) did not matter (90). In this sense, one should not get carried away with the high-carbohydrate diet and consume calories in excess of what is needed (66). In fact, when a variety of popular diets (Atkins, Ornish, Weight Watchers, and Zone) were compared over the course of one year, each modestly reduced body weight, with no difference between diets. It should be no surprise that the best predictor of weight loss was the degree to which individuals adhered to the diet—no matter which one (52, 71, 150, 181). Given these facts, why should diet composition matter in terms of weight control and obesity?

Quite simply, diets with a high fat-to-carbohydrate ratio are associated with obesity (144). When subjects are given free access to food, more calories are consumed when one eats a high-fat diet than when one eats a high-carbohydrate diet (23, 210). The high-carbohydrate content may contribute to satiety better than the high-fat diet, resulting in an earlier termination of eating (175). The nutrient balance (RQ = FQ) concept helps focus our attention on the need for a high-carbohydrate/low-fat diet to achieve and maintain a healthy level of body fatness. This diet is also consistent with what is needed to have normal cholesterol levels and sufficient carbohydrate for physical performance (see chapter 23). However, there is renewed interest in the diet-composition issue, not just related to weight loss, but also to weight control (maintenance). Three different reviews suggest that a high protein (25% to 30%) diet, coupled with moderate carbohydrate (35% to 50%) and fat (25% to 35%), should be studied in a systematic way to evaluate its effect on risk factors, feelings of satiety and hunger, and the fat-free mass (2, 183, 206). One of the *Dietary Guidelines for Americans* was to balance the food you eat with physical activity—maintain or improve your weight. Recommendations to accomplish this include the following:

- To maintain body weight in a healthy range, balance calories from foods and beverages with calories expended.

- To prevent gradual weight gain over time, make small decreases in food and beverage

calories and increase physical activity. We will see more on physical activity in a later section.

One last point before leaving this topic: As we mentioned earlier in the chapter, data on energy intake is assessed by twenty-four-hour recall or food records. However, one has to be cautious when interpreting these data as part of a weight-loss program. Research suggests that these methods may result in a considerable underestimation of caloric intake, especially in obese individuals (21, 53, 125, 141, 216). This, of course, would create a misdirection in looking for the cause of the obesity problem. It should be no surprise then that careful energy balance studies are done in highly controlled laboratory situations.

In the Institute of Medicine (100) recommendations that set appropriate levels of energy intakes for different levels of physical activity, the experts used data from doubly labeled water (DLW) rather than dietary recall. The DLW method measures total energy expenditure in free-living individuals, without the need for the person to remember what he or she had eaten. In the DLW method, the subject ingests a drink containing two isotopes of water: $H_2^{18}O$ and ^2H_2O. Urine or blood samples are obtained over a period of 7 to 21 days to evaluate the disappearance of ^2H_2O (relates to water flux) and $H_2^{18}O$ (reflects water flux plus the CO_2 production rate). The difference between the two rates gives information about total energy expenditure (rate of CO_2 production) and represents an improvement over earlier approaches that relied solely on dietary recall information.

IN SUMMARY

- Diets with a high fat-to-carbohydrate ratio are linked to obesity. Nutrient balance for fat can be most easily achieved with a low-fat diet (high FQ).
- Calories do count, and they must be considered in any diet aimed at achieving or maintaining a weight-loss goal.

Energy Expenditure and Weight Control

The other side of the energy balance equation involves the expenditure of energy and includes the basal metabolic rate, thermogenesis (shivering and nonshivering), and exercise. We will examine each of these relative to its role in energy balance.

Basal Metabolic Rate Basal metabolic rate (BMR) is the rate of energy expenditure measured under standardized conditions (i.e., immediately after rising, 12 to 18 hours after a meal, in a supine position in a thermoneutral environment). Because of the difficulty of achieving these conditions during routine measurements, investigators have measured **resting metabolic rate (RMR)** instead. In this latter procedure, the subject reports to the lab about 4 hours after eating a light meal, and after a period of time (30 to 60 minutes) the metabolic rate is measured (145). Given the low level of oxygen uptake measured for BMR or RMR (200 to 400 ml · min^{-1}), a variation of only ±20 to 40 ml · min^{-1} represents a potential ±10% error. In the following discussion both BMR and RMR will be discussed interchangeably, except where a specific contrast must be made for clarification.

The BMR is important in the energy balance equation because it represents 60% to 75% of total energy expenditure in the average sedentary person (163). The BMR is proportional to the fat-free mass, and after age 20 it decreases approximately 2% and 3% per decade in women and men, respectively. Women have a significantly lower BMR at all ages, due primarily to their lower fat-free mass (49, 57, 158, 235). Consistent with this, when RMR is expressed per unit of fat-free mass, there is no gender difference. At any body weight the RMR decreases about 0.01 kcal/min for each 1% increase in body fatness (158). Although this may appear to be insignificant, this small difference can become meaningful in the progressive increase in weight gain over time. For example, a 5% difference in body fatness at the same body weight results in a difference of 0.05 kcal · min^{-1}, or 3 kcal · hr^{-1}, which is equal to 72 kcal · d^{-1}. It must be emphasized that the percentage of body fat makes only a small contribution to the BMR. This was confirmed in a study examining the relationship of body composition to BMR; fat mass did not improve the prediction of BMR based on the fat-free mass alone (49).

As mentioned earlier, part of the variation in BMR is due to a genetic predisposition to be higher or lower (25). The range (±3 SD) in normal BMR values is about ±21% from the average value, and such variation helps to explain the observation that some have an easier time at maintaining body weight than others. If an average adult male has a BMR of 1,500 kcal · d^{-1}, those at +3 SD can take in an additional 300 kcal · d^{-1} (21% of 1,500 kcal) to maintain weight, whereas others at the low end of the range (−3 SD) would have to take in 300 fewer kcals (57, 76).

The fat-free mass is not the only factor influencing the BMR. In 1919, Benedict et al. (15) showed that prolonged dieting (reduction from about 3,100 kcal to 1,950 kcal) was associated with a 20% decrease in the BMR expressed per kilogram of body weight. This observation was confirmed in the famous Minnesota Starvation Experiment (113), and is shown in figure 18.8. In this figure the BMR is expressed as

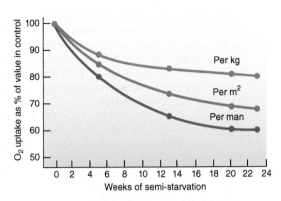

Figure 18.8 Decrease in basal metabolic rate during 24 weeks of semi-starvation.

a percent of the value measured before the period of semi-starvation. The percent decrease in BMR is larger "per man" because of the loss of lean tissue (as well as fat tissue); however, when the value is expressed per kilogram of body weight or per unit of surface area (m^2), the BMR is still shown to be reduced. A decrease in the concentration of one of the thyroid hormones (T$_3$) and a reduced level of sympathetic nervous system activity have been implicated in this lower BMR due to caloric restriction (26). What these data mean is that during a period of low caloric intake, the energy production of the tissues decreases in an attempt to adapt to the lower caloric intake and reduce the rate of weight loss. This is an appropriate adaptation in periods of semi-starvation, but is counterproductive in weight-reduction programs. This information bears heavily on the use of low-calorie diets as a primary means of weight reduction (56, 70, 225, 228).

The BMR is also responsive to periods of overfeeding. In the dieting experiment of Benedict et al. (15) mentioned earlier, when the subjects were allowed a day of free eating, the BMR was elevated on the following day. Further, in long-term (14 to 20 days) overfeeding to cause obesity, increases in resting and basal metabolic rates have been recorded. In essence, during the dynamic phase of weight gain (going from a lower to a higher weight), more calories are required per kg of body weight to maintain the weight gain than to simply maintain normal body weight (76, 194). This increased heat production due to an excess caloric intake, called **thermogenesis,** will be discussed in the next section. However, before leaving this discussion of the BMR, we need to mention the effect of exercise.

There is no doubt that the resting metabolic rate is elevated following exercise. The questions relate to how much and how long it is elevated, and to what extent it contributes to total daily energy expenditure (31, 164). A review of this topic indicates that controversies still exist even though the questions have been studied for over 100 years (145). At the heart of the matter is the measure of the metabolic rate that is taken as the baseline in these experiments. Should it be the BMR? The RMR? Molé (145) suggests that we need to create a new measurement called the Standard Metabolic Rate that would take into consideration the day-to-day fluctuations in normal physical activity, dietary intake, added exercise, and body composition. In support of these concerns it has been shown that trained subjects had a higher RMR than untrained subjects only when they did heavy exercise and consumed sufficient calories to maintain energy balance (37). This suggests that the higher RMR in trained individuals is not due to chronic adaptations associated with training, but more to the higher energy flux associated with the training and diet. This is consistent with other studies showing that the RMR, expressed per kg of fat-free mass, is similar for trained and untrained individuals, and that resistance and endurance training do not affect the value (34, 35). Aside from helping to maintain or increase the lean body mass and the RMR, exercise training may favorably impact nutrient balance. Two studies, using strength training, showed a significant decrease in the 24-hour (218) and sleeping (223) metabolic rate RQ values, signifying an increased use of fat. This is consistent with achieving nutrient balance and energy balance over time (241).

IN SUMMARY

- The BMR represents the largest fraction of total energy expenditure in sedentary persons. The BMR decreases with age, and women have lower BMR values than men.
- The fat-free mass is related to both the gender difference and to the decline in BMR with age. A reduction in caloric intake by dieting or fasting can reduce the BMR, while physical activity is important in maintaining it.

Thermogenesis Core temperature is maintained at about 37° C by balancing heat production with heat loss. Under thermoneutral conditions, the BMR (RMR) provides the necessary heat, but under cold environmental conditions, the process of shivering is actuated and 100% of the energy required for involuntary muscle contraction appears as heat to maintain core temperature. In addition, some animals (including newborn humans) produce heat by a process called nonshivering thermogenesis, involving brown adipose tissue. This type of adipose tissue is rich in mitochondria and increases heat production in response to norepinephrine (NE). Thyroid hormones, especially T_3, may either directly affect this process or act in a permissive manner to facilitate the action of NE (26, 27, 105). Heat production is increased by

uncoupling oxidative phosphorylation; that is, oxygen is used without ATP formation, so the energy contained in NADH and FADH appears directly as heat. Those individuals with large quantities of brown adipose tissue have a greater capacity to "throw off" calories in the form of heat rather than store them in adipose tissue. It has been hypothesized that variations in brown adipose tissue might be related to the ease or difficulty with which one gains weight.

Thermogenesis involves more than brown adipose tissue. The heat generated due to the food we consume accounts for about 10% to 15% of our total daily energy expenditure; this is called the *thermic effect of food* (27, 163). Generally, this is determined by having a subject ingest a test meal (700–1,000 kcal), and the elevation in the metabolic rate is measured following the meal. This portion of our daily energy expenditure is influenced by genetic factors (25, 163), is lower in obese than in lean individuals (110, 187), and is influenced by the level of spontaneous activity and the degree of insulin resistance (209). However, because it represents such a small part of the overall daily energy expenditure, it is not a good predictor of subsequent obesity.

In individuals who have been on a diet (underfeeding), just one day of overfeeding leads to an increase in the next day's BMR. The BMR then quickly returns to the level consistent with the low-caloric intake specified in the diet (15). It is as if the body is throwing off extra heat to maintain body weight during this period of relative overfeeding. This phenomenon has also been observed in the chronic overfeeding of human subjects. In Garrow's (77) and Danforth's (51) reviews of these overfeeding studies, the subjects showed an unexplained heat production associated with chronic excess caloric intakes. The elevations of the BMR have been explained on the basis of an increase in the mass of brown adipose tissue (mentioned earlier), and the involvement of other **energy wasteful systems.** These latter systems include a change in the Na^+/K^+ pump activity, or "futile cycles" in which the equivalent of one ATP is lost in each turn of the cycle (26, 27). An example of a futile cycle is when an ATP is used to convert fructose 6-phosphate to fructose 1,6-diphosphate, which, in the next step, is converted back to fructose 6-phosphate. In situations in which heat, but no ATP, is produced, the resting oxygen consumption would have to be higher to maintain the normal ATP-consuming systems. Whatever the mechanism by which this dietary thermogenesis is induced, via brown fat or by futile cycles, it must be made clear that, like the BMR, there are marked differences in how individuals respond to an increased dietary intake. Clearly, those who have a normally high BMR and are very responsive to a large caloric excess would have an easier time staying at normal weight than those who do not.

IN SUMMARY

- Thermogenesis (heat generation) is associated with the ingestion of meals (thermic effect of feeding), brown adipose tissue, and "futile cycles."
- The thermic effect of food represents a small part of total energy expenditure and is not predictive of obesity.

Physical Activity and Exercise Physical activity constitutes the most variable part of the energy expenditure side of the energy balance equation, being 5% to 40% of the daily energy expenditure (41, 163). There are those who have sedentary jobs and who do little physical activity during their leisure time. Others may have strenuous jobs, or expend 300 to 1,000 kcal during their leisure time every day or two. Just how important is physical activity in weight control? Epidemiological evidence suggests an inverse association between physical activity and body weight, with body fat being more favorably distributed in those who are physically active (55). One study examined the relationship of body fatness to the different components of energy expenditure. Figure 18.9 shows that body fatness was inversely related to "nonbasal" (primarily that associated with physical activity) energy expenditure. In this sense, the level of physical activity is a permissive factor for obesity (173, 184). Consistent with this, recent studies showed an inverse relationship between BMI and

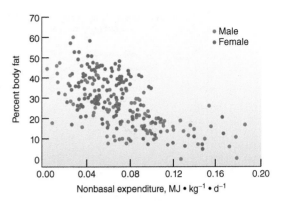

Figure 18.9 Relationship between body fatness and nonbasal energy expenditure is highly significant (P < 0.01); for females it is $r = -0.83$, for males $r = -0.55$.

accumulated daily walking (measured by pedometer). Those accumulating more than 10,000 steps per day were more likely to be in the "normal" BMI range (93, 213). For those wondering if a diet calorie is the same as an exercise calorie, see Clinical Applications 18.5.

Appetite The classic animal study describing the role of exercise on appetite was conducted by Mayer and colleagues (136). Figure 18.10 shows that when female rats exercised for 20 to 60 minutes per day (sedentary range), the caloric intake actually decreased slightly and the animals lost weight. Over the durations of 1 to 6 hours of activity the caloric

CLINICAL APPLICATIONS 18.5

A Calorie Is a Calorie

From a weight-loss perspective, a caloric deficit that results from an increase in energy expenditure through physical activity is equivalent to that due to a decrease in caloric intake. However, as Ross et al. (178) point out, leading authorities (147) state that the addition of exercise makes only a modest contribution to weight loss. How can this be the case, given the equivalency of the caloric deficit induced by either diet or exercise? Ross et al. (178) show that in the majority of weight-loss studies in which a diet treatment was compared to an exercise treatment, the energy deficit caused by exercise was only a fraction of that caused by diet. In

this situation, it is not surprising that weight loss due to diet was greater than that due to exercise; however, the weight loss due to exercise was as expected. The exercise-induced weight loss, 30% of that due to diet, was equivalent to the caloric deficit associated with the exercise (28% of that due to diet). Ross et al. (177) did a controlled experiment designed to achieve a 700 kcal/day energy deficit due to either exercise alone or diet alone. Both groups lost 16.5 lbs over 12 weeks—exactly what was expected from the 58,800 kcal deficit (700 kcal/day times 84 days). However, the exercise group lost more total fat, thus preserving mus-

cle. These results were supported in a more recent study that compared subjects who underwent a 6-month 25% caloric restriction with those who had a 12.5% caloric restriction plus an exercise intervention equal to a 12.5% reduction in caloric intake (171). Both groups lost the same amount of weight, similar to what was mentioned earlier. There is little question that a calorie of aerobic exercise is really equal to a calorie of diet restriction as far as change in body weight is concerned; however, the exercise intervention yields results (e.g., increase in $\dot{V}O_2$ max) that cannot be realized by a diet-alone approach to weight loss (171).

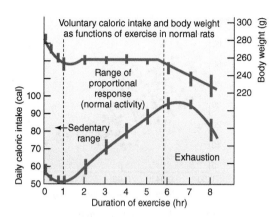

Figure 18.10 Pattern of caloric intake for rats versus the durations of exercise. When rats do little or no exercise, caloric intake exceeds what is needed and body weight increases (see top-left part of figure). However, over a broad range of physical activity, caloric intake increases proportional to the activity, and body weight (top line) remains constant.

intake increased proportionately and body weight was maintained, but at a level below that of the sedentary rat. Durations in excess of 6 hours were associated with a relative decrease in caloric intake and body weight (exhaustion). Twenty-five years after this study, Katch et al. (112) showed that in male rats accomplishing the same amount of work, those exercising at the higher intensity had a greater depression in appetite and weight gain than those at the lower intensity, with both groups being lower than the sedentary animals. In contrast, female rats tend to respond to increasing exercise intensity with an increase in appetite (156).

Mayer and colleagues (137) also studied the relationship of exercise to caloric intake on mill workers in West Bengal, India. Figure 18.11 shows a pattern of response similar to Mayer et al.'s (136) study on rats. In the activity classifications from light to very heavy work, caloric intake increased proportionately so that body weight was not different among the various groups. However, in the sedentary classification, caloric intake was as high as for the very heavy work classification, and body weight was higher than the other groups. This suggests that a minimal level of exercise is needed to help regulate appetite. This study has been cited over the years as a primary supporting piece of evidence showing exercise to be important in the regulation of appetite. However, in 1978 Garrow (76) questioned the analysis of the data at the sedentary end of the scale where the group called "Clerks I" had a body weight similar to the more active groups, *but consumed about 400 kcal/day more* than those in the light work category. This analysis of the data would support a conclusion opposite that of

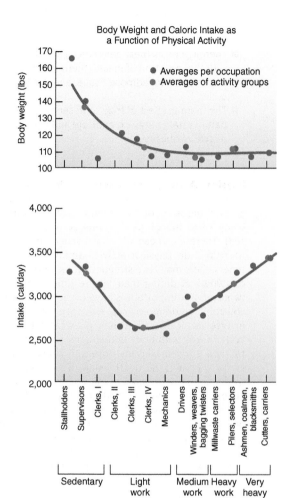

Figure 18.11 Pattern of caloric intake versus occupational activity in humans. For occupations ranging from light work to very heavy work, there is a balance between caloric intake and physical activity such that body weight remains constant. For sedentary occupations, caloric intake (see left side of lower figure) exceeds needs and body weight is higher than expected (see left side of top figure).

Mayer et al. (137). It should be clear that there would have to be some proportional increase in appetite as subjects increased physical activity; otherwise, an athlete would gradually waste away during the course of a competitive season! However, when an exercise program is introduced to obese and/or sedentary individuals, appetite does not appear to increase. In Wilmore's (239) and Titchenal's (214) reviews of such exercise intervention studies, appetite did not increase in proportion to energy expenditure, suggesting a net loss of appetite. In summary, in male animals, exercise decreases appetite in proportion to exercise intensity, whereas in female animals,

A LOOK BACK—IMPORTANT PEOPLE IN SCIENCE

Jean Mayer, Ph.D., D.Sc. Recognized the Problems of Overweight and Obesity

Jean Mayer (pronounced Zhahn my-YAIR) (1920–1993) was one of the most well-known scientists in the twentieth century in the field of nutrition. He received his B.S. and M.S. degrees at the University of Paris in the late 1930s, but his progress to the Ph.D. was interrupted by World War II. He served in the French army, was captured by German troops, and escaped from a prison camp. He then served with distinction in the French underground and fought with the Free French and Allied forces across Europe, for which he was recognized with numerous military decorations. Following the war he studied at Yale University for his Ph.D. in physiological chemistry. He later attended the Sorbonne where he received the D.Sc. in physiology.

Dr. Mayer taught and did research at Harvard University from 1950 to 1975 during which time his classical studies on physical activity, appetite, and body weight (reported in this chapter) were done. During this time he played a major role in the United Nations' fight against hunger and malnutrition in third-world countries in Africa; he also highlighted the problems of hunger and poverty in the United States, which resulted in the food stamp program and an expanded lunch program for schoolchildren.

In 1976 he became the president of Tufts University and was a prime mover in developing the first graduate school in nutrition, New England's only veterinary school, and the USDA Human Nutrition Research Center on Aging at Tufts. He co-founded the Sackler School of Graduate Biomedical Sciences and the Center for Environmental Management.

Dr. Mayer published more than 750 scientific papers and numerous articles for popular magazines, and had a syndicated weekly newspaper column on nutrition that was published in 150 newspapers. He also published numerous books, including *Overweight: Causes, Cost and Control* in 1968. Many might be surprised by the title of that 1968 book given the fact that the late 1960s and early 1970s are used as a "reference point" (for how little obesity there was in the adult and childhood populations) when we talk about the current prevalence of overweight and obesity. However, it is simply a reflection of how far he was ahead of his time in recognizing the overweight and obesity problem and the importance of physical activity. It is unfortunate that we did not listen.

Source: http://www.bookrags.com/biography/jean-mayer/

---

exercise stimulates appetite. Generally, in humans, caloric intake is regulated in proportion to energy expenditure over a broad range of exercise intensities and durations to help maintain body weight, but when exercise is introduced to a formerly sedentary population, a net decrease in appetite results. See A Look Back—Important People in Science for an individual who had a major impact on nutrition and health in the twentieth century.

Body Composition Although exercise may help regulate appetite to maintain body weight, exercise has an independent effect on the composition of that weight. This has been shown in both animal and human studies. In general, male rats that participate in regular exercise have lower body weights, less lean body mass, and very little body fat compared to their sedentary control litter mates. In contrast, female rats tend to respond to exercise training with an increase in appetite such that they are as heavy as the sedentary group, with a lower fat weight and a higher lean weight (155). Oscai et al. (157) have shown that, in addition to these general changes in body composition due to exercise, exercise or food restriction in rats results in fewer and smaller fat cells. This observation is supported by Hager et al.'s (86) finding that

in a group of 8-year-old obese girls, a diet/activity program was instrumental in reducing the rate of gain in fat cell number.

The advantage of using exercise compared to caloric restriction alone in weight-loss programs is that the composition of the weight that is lost is more fat tissue than lean tissue. In both animal (157) and human (36, 39, 58) studies using dietary restriction alone, lean body mass loss can equal 30% to 40% of the weight loss. Exercise plus diet results in less lean body mass loss and a proportionately greater fat loss (157). In addition, the preferential mobilization of fat from visceral adipose tissue results in an improved body fat distribution and risk factor profile (179, 229). However, it must be remembered that body composition changes take place slowly in human exercise studies, and the magnitude of the change is small. Wilmore's 1983 summary (239) of exercise and body composition studies showed the average decrease in percentage of body fat to be only 1.6% with fitness programs ranging in duration from 6 to 104 weeks. This old observation was recently confirmed in a collection of well-designed randomized controlled trials in which subjects participated in various physical activity interventions for a duration of 8 to 12 months. In general, and to no one's surprise, those doing the

CLINICAL APPLICATIONS 18.6

Successful Losers—How Much Exercise Is Needed to Keep the Weight Off?

There is general agreement that most U.S. adults need more physical activity. The question is, how much? The systematic increase in the prevalence of obesity over the past 25 years has provided a strong incentive to address this issue and, to some extent, we are making progress.

In chapter 16 we presented the U.S. *Physical Activity Guidelines'* recommendation that all adults should do at least 150 minutes of moderate-intensity or 75 minutes of vigorous-intensity physical activity per week (see Suggested Readings). There is clear evidence that this amount of physical activity results in significant health benefits. This is a minimal recommendation, with clear support that "more is better." So, doing 300 minutes per week of moderate-intensity or 150 minutes per week of vigorous-intensity physical activity results in additional benefits, including maintaining or losing weight. This is consistent with both the 2002 Institute of Medicine (IOM) report (100), and the most recent ACSM position stand on the issue of physical activity and weight (4), in which they recommend:

■ 150–250 min/wk of moderate-intensity physical activity to prevent weight gain

■ >250 min/wk of moderate-intensity physical activity to achieve significant weight loss, and
■ >250 minutes per week of moderate-intensity physical activity may be needed to prevent weight regain after weight lost

Regarding the last point, Dr. Rena Wing of the University of Pittsburgh and Dr. James Hill of the University of Colorado formed the National Weight Control Registry (NWCR) in 1993 to gain some insights into what made "successful losers"—individuals who lost weight and kept it off. To be included in the registry, individuals had to have lost substantial weight (≥13.6 kg [30 lb]) and kept it off for at least one year. Some of the findings follow (211):

■ The average weight loss of the registrants was 33.6 kg, and they kept the weight off for an average of 5.2 years, which placed most in the normal (57.9%) or overweight (29.9%) BMI range.
■ About 88% limit foods high in fat and sugar, 44% limit the amount of food consumed, and 44% count calories.
■ A total of 75% of registrants expend more than 1,000 kcal/week, and 54% expend more

than 2,000 kcal/week (about 200 min/wk of moderate-intensity physical activity).

The NWCR has provided unique and helpful insights into what makes a successful loser. The seven key habits for long-term success at weight loss include (211):

1. High level of physical activity
2. Limit television watching—63% watch less than 10 hours a week
3. Low-calorie, low-fat diet—1,380 kcal/day, with less than 30% fat
4. Consistent diet—eat the same foods regularly
5. Breakfast consumption—at least 78% eat breakfast daily
6. High dietary restraint (good control over eating)
7. Self-monitoring—more than 50% weigh weekly and track their daily food intake

These characteristics are consistent with those in a recent review describing an ideal person who is a successful weight maintainer (60). Clearly, these messages from those who have been successful in maintaining weight loss have great value for both the professional and the client working toward that goal.

---

largest amount of physical activity had the greatest changes in percentage of body fat (101, 139, 203). However, those doing about 180 minutes per week of moderate-intensity aerobic physical activity (similar to current public health physical activity recommendations) experienced a decrease in percentage of fat of only 2.5% over this time period (101, 203).

IN SUMMARY

■ Humans increase appetite over a broad range of energy expenditure to maintain body weight; however, formerly sedentary individuals show a net loss of appetite when they undertake an exercise program.
■ When weight loss occurs with an exercise and diet program, less lean body mass is lost than when the same weight loss is achieved by diet alone.

Weight Loss vs. Weight Maintenance One point that needs to be stated at the outset is that exercise is not required to achieve weight loss. All that is necessary is a caloric deficit, the magnitude of which is easily controlled by diet (90). However, as mentioned previously, the use of exercise as a part of a weight-loss program might maintain a higher lean body mass and RMR, and result in an optimal body fatness at a higher body weight.

Although exercise might not be an essential ingredient in a weight-loss program, it is in a weight-maintenance program (204). A major, unresolved question is, how much? However, some of the general exercise recommendations for health and fitness presented in chapter 16 would be considered reasonable for weight-maintenance programs. The primary factor involved in energy expenditure is the total work accomplished, so low-intensity, long-duration exercise is as good as high-intensity, short-duration exercise in expending calories. For the sedentary, overweight person, moderate-intensity exercise is the proper choice because it can be done for longer periods of time in each exercise session and can be done each day. Recent, well-controlled physical activity interventions showed that regular participation in moderate-intensity physical activity of 180 minutes or more per week (with no dietary restriction) was associated with a weight loss of about 1 to 2 pounds over 8 to 12 months, indicating that the subjects were weight stable over that time (101, 139, 203). Although the magnitude of weight change is small, the message it conveys is very important: only 30 minutes or more of moderate-intensity physical activity per day is enough to prevent migration from one BMI level to the next—an important effect considering the prevalence of overweight and obesity in our society. However, as we saw in chapter 16, "more is better" when it comes to physical activity and health, including maintaining a healthy body weight.

Further, at moderate intensities, free fatty acids are mobilized from the periphery to provide the majority of the fuel used and help with maintaining fat balance (176). This does not mean that "fat-burning" is restricted to low-intensity activities. Individuals interested in more vigorous activity ($\sim$65% $\dot{V}O_2$ max) that can increase $\dot{V}O_2$ max can also reap the benefits of high rates of calorie and fat use (176). Finally, even though carbohydrate makes up a large fraction of the energy supply during high-intensity exercise ($\sim$85% $\dot{V}O_2$ max) (176), training programs using intermittent high-intensity exercise have been shown to cause a greater reduction in skinfold thickness than programs conducted at the target heart rate

range (217). Although there is considerable interest in the role exercise plays in fat oxidation after exercise, results are inconsistent (13, 140). It is clear that virtually any form of exercise contributes to fat loss and the maintenance of body weight. The important thing is to just do it. See Clinical Applications 18.6 for information on "successful losers."

IN SUMMARY

- Moderate-intensity physical activity is an appropriate choice for most Americans to achieve health-related and weight-loss goals.
- Vigorous-intensity physical activity is effective in expending calories and achieving health-related fitness, performance, and weight-loss goals.

For weight-loss considerations, the caloric cost of an activity should be listed as the net cost (that above resting), because the gross cost of the activity includes energy already associated with resting metabolism. Table 18.6 shows the net energy cost per kg for walking and running 1 mile. In chapter 1, the net cost per m $\cdot$ min^{-1} of horizontal travel was 0.1 ml $\cdot$ kg^{-1} $\cdot$ min^{-1} for walking (up to about 3.75 mph), and 0.2 ml $\cdot$ kg^{-1} $\cdot$ min^{-1} for jogging or running. This translates to about 0.77 kcal per kg per mile for walking (0.1 ml $\cdot$ kg^{-1} $\cdot$ min^{-1} times 1,609 m $\cdot$ mile^{-1} times .0048 kcal per ml O_2), and 1.53 kcal per kg per mile for jogging or running. If a 60-kg person wished to expend 250 kcal by walking, a distance of 5.4 miles would have to be covered (250 kcal ÷ [60 kg × 0.77 kcal $\cdot$ kg^{-1} $\cdot$ mile^{-1}]); the

TABLE 18.6 Net Caloric Cost Per Mile for Walking, Jogging, and Running

Walking							
Mph	2	2.5	3	3.5	4	4.5	5
Meters/min	54	67	80	94	107	121	134
Net cost kcal $\cdot$ kg^{-1} $\cdot$ mile^{-1}	.77	.77	.77	.77	.96	1.15	1.38

Jogging/Running							
Mph	3	4	5	6	7	8	9
Meters/min	80	107	134	160	188	215	241
Net cost kcal $\cdot$ kg^{-1} $\cdot$ mile^{-1}	1.53	1.53	1.53	1.53	1.53	1.53	1.53

Note: Multiply by body weight in kilograms to obtain the number of kilocalories used per mile.

From E.T. Howley and B. D. Franks, *Health/Fitness Instructor's Handbook*, 2d ed. Copyright © 1992 Human Kinetics Publishers, Inc., Champaign, IL. Used by permission.

TABLE 18.7 Estimated Net Energy Expenditure at 70% of $\dot{V}O_2$ Max During One Hour of Activity

$\dot{V}O_2$ Max (METs) (kcal · kg^{-1} · hr^{-1})	Net Energy Expenditure at 70% $\dot{V}O_2$ Max (kcal · kg^{-1} · min^{-1})	BODY WEIGHT (KG) 50 (kcal · hr^{-1})	70	90
20	13.0	650	910	1,170
18	11.6	580	812	1,044
16	10.2	510	714	918
14	8.8	440	616	792
10	6.0	300	420	540
8	4.6	230	322	414
6	3.2	160	224	287

From E. T. Howley and B. D. Franks, *Health/Fitness Instructor's Handbook*, 2d ed. Copyright © 1992 Human Kinetics Publishers, Inc., Champaign, IL. Used by permission.

distance would be only 2.7 miles if jogged. If the person walks at relatively high walking speeds, the caloric cost is higher than for the slower walking speeds, and a shorter distance would have to be walked to expend the same number of calories. As mentioned earlier, because it is the total amount of work that is important in weight loss, the total distance walked or jogged does not have to be done at any one time.

In selecting activities to achieve weight-loss goals, one must be careful not to overestimate the energy expenditure. If a table of values of the caloric cost of activities lists climbing stairs as requiring 15 kcal · min^{-1}, one must realize that this is an impossible goal to achieve aerobically for those with a maximal oxygen uptake of less than 3 liters · min^{-1}. Further, while an average value may be stated in such tables, some activities (e.g., swimming) have extreme variations in the energy required for the task. To deal realistically with this problem, Sharkey (192) provides a means of estimating the caloric expenditure associated with exercise for people of different fitness levels. If a person has a $\dot{V}O_2$ max equal to 10 METs, the appropriate range of exercise intensities to be in the THR zone would be 6 to 8 METs (60% to 80% $\dot{V}O_2$ max). Since 1 MET is 1 kcal · kg^{-1} · hr^{-1} (in addition to

3.5 ml · kg^{-1} · min^{-1}), this subject would be working in the range of 6 to 8 kcal · kg^{-1} · hr^{-1}. If the person weighs 70 kg and exercises for 30 minutes at 7 kcal · kg^{-1} · hr^{-1}, the person would expend a total of 245 kcal (70 kg × 7 kcal · kg^{-1} · hr^{-1} × 0.5 hr). The net caloric expenditure would be about 210 kcal. Table 18.7 summarizes the estimated energy expenditure associated with exercise training for those with different $\dot{V}O_2$ max values (95). It should be clear that as the person loses weight, the number of kcal used per fixed workout decreases, along with a decrease in the BMR. The combined effect of these two elements on the expenditure side of the weight-balance equation is that there will be a slowing of the rate of weight loss over time.

IN SUMMARY

- Although 150 minutes/week of moderate-intensity physical activity is associated with clear and significant health gains, more may be necessary to prevent weight gain (150–250 minutes/week) or prevent weight regain after weight loss (>250 minutes/week).

STUDY QUESTIONS

1. Summarize the range of carbohydrate, fat, and protein intakes recommended by the Institute of Medicine.
2. What is the difference between an RDA standard and a Daily Value?
3. Is there any risk in taking fat-soluble vitamins in large quantities? Explain.
4. Which two minerals are believed to be inadequate in women's diets?
5. Relative to coronary heart disease, why is there a major focus on dietary fat?

6. Generate a one-week menu using the MyPlate website. How do the choices compare to those in the DASH eating plan?
7. Identify and describe the following methods of measuring body composition: isotope dilution, potassium-40, ultrasound, bioelectrical impedance analysis, dual energy X-ray absorptiometry, skinfold thickness, and underwater weighing.
8. Contrast the four-component and two-component models of body composition assessment.

9. What is the principle of underwater weighing? Why should a different body density equation be used for children, in contrast to adults?

10. Given: a 20-year-old college male, 180 lb, 28% fat. What is his target body weight to achieve 17% fat?

11. In terms of the resistance to weight reduction, contrast obesity due to hypertrophy with obesity due to hyperplasia of fat cells.

12. Is obesity more related to genetics or the environment?

13. If a person consumes 120 kcal per day in excess of need, what weight gain does the static energy balance equation predict compared to the dynamic energy balance equation?

14. What does nutrient balance mean and how is the ratio of the RQ to FQ used to determine nutrient balance?

15. Contrast a physiological set point with a behavioral set point related to obesity.

16. What happens to the BMR when a person goes on a low-calorie diet?

17. What recommendations would you give about the use of diet alone versus a combination of diet and exercise to achieve a weight-loss goal?

18. What is thermogenesis and how might it be related to a weight gain?

19. What is the effect of exercise on appetite and body composition?

20. In contrast to the general physical activity recommendation for achieving significant health benefits, how much physical activity may be needed to prevent weight gain or maintain weight once it has been lost?

SUGGESTED READINGS

Heyward, V. H., and D. R. Wagner. 2004. *Applied Body Composition Assessment*. 2nd ed. Champaign, IL: Human Kinetics.

Roche, A. F., S. B. Heymsfield, and T. G. Lohman, (eds). 2005. *Human Body Composition*. 2nd ed. Champaign, IL: Human Kinetics.

U.S. Department of Health and Human Services. 2008. *2008 Physical Activity Guidelines for Americans*. Washington, D.C: Author.

U.S. Department of Agriculture, 2010. 2010 *Dietary Guidelines for Americans* (http://www.health.gov/dietaryguidelines/)

Wardlaw, G. M. and A. M. Smith. 2011. *Contemporary Nutrition*. 8th ed. New York: McGraw-Hill Companies.

REFERENCES

1. **Acheson KJ, Schutz Y, Bessard T, Flatt JP, and Jequier E.** Carbohydrate metabolism and de novo lipogenesis in human obesity. *The American Journal of Clinical Nutrition* 45: 78–85, 1987.

2. **Adam-Perrot A, Clifton P, and Brouns F.** Low-carbohydrate diets: nutritional and physiological aspects. *Obes Rev* 7: 49–58, 2006.

3. **AHA Committee Report.** Rationale of the diet-heart statement of the American Heart Association. *Nutrition Today* 1982.

4. **American College of Sports Medicine.** Appropriate physcial activity intervention strategies for weight loss and prevention of weight regain for adults. *Medicine and Science in Sports and Exercise* 41: 459–471, 2009.

5. **American College of Sports Medicine.** Exercise and physical activity for the older adult. *Medicine and Science in Sports and Exercise* 41: 1510–1530, 2009.

6. **American College of Sports Medicine.** Physcial activity and bone health. *Medicine and Science in Sports and Exercise* 36: 1985–1996, 2004.

7. **American College of Sports Medicine.** The female athlete triad. *Medicine and Science in Sports and Exercise* 39: 1867–1882, 2007.

8. **American Dietetic Association.** Position of the American Dietetic Association: health implications of dietary fiber. *Journal of the American Dietetic Association* 102: 993–1000, 2002.

9. **American Alliance for Health Physical Education Recreation and Dance.** *Physical Best*. Reston: AAHPERD, 1988.

10. **Azadbakht L, Mirmiran P, Esmaillzadeh A, Azizi T, and Azizi F.** Beneficial effects of dietary approaches to stop hypertension eating plan on features of the metabolic syndrome. *Diabetes Care* 28: 2823–2831, 2005.

11. **Bailey RL, Dodd KW, Goldman JA, Gahche JJ, Dwyer JT, Moshfegh AJ, Sempos CT, and Picciano MF.** Estimation of total usual calcium and vitamin D intakes in the United States. *Journal of Nutrition* 140: 817–822, 2010.

12. **Barnard RJ, Roberts CK, Varon SM, and Berger JJ.** Diet-induced insulin resistance precedes other aspects of the metabolic syndrome. *J Appl Physiol* 84: 1311–1315, 1998.

13. **Barwell ND, Malkova D, Leggate M, and Gill JMR.** Individual responsiveness to exercise-induced fat loss is associated with change in resting substrate utilization. *Metabolism Clinical and Experimental* 58: 1320–1328, 2009.

14. **Behnke AR, Welham WC, and Feen BG.** The specific gravity of healthy men: body weight volume as an index of obesity. *Journal of the American Medical Association* 118: 495–498, 1942.

15. **Benedict F.** *Human Vitality and Efficiency Under Prolonged Restricted Diet*. The Carnegie Institution of Washington, 1919.

16. **Björntorp P.** Number and size of adipose tissue fat cells in relation to metabolism in human obesity. *Metabolism: Clinical and Dxperimental* 20: 703–713, 1971.

17. **Björntorp P, Bengtsson C, Blohme G, Jonsson A, Sjöström L, Tibblin E, Tibblin G, and Wilhelmsen L.** Adipose tissue fat cell size and number in relation to metabolism in randomly selected middle-aged men and women. *Metabolism: Clinical and Experimental* 20: 927–935, 1971.

18. **Björntorp P, and Sjöstrom L.** Carbohydrate storage in man: speculations and some quantitative considerations. *Metabolism: Clinical and Experimental* 27: 1853–1865, 1978.

19. **Björntrop P.** Regional patterns of fat distribution. *Annals of Internal Medicine* 103: 994–995, 1985.

20. **Björntrop P.** The fat cell: a clinical view. In: *Recent Advances in Obesity Research: II,* edited by Bray G. Westport: Technomic, 1978, p. 153–168.

21. **Black AE, Goldberg GR, Jebb SA, Livingstone MB, Cole TJ, and Prentice AM.** Critical evaluation of energy intake data using fundamental principles of energy physiology: evaluating the results of published surveys. *European Journal of Clinical Nutrition* 45: 583–599, 1991.

22. **Blair SN, and Nichaman MZ.** The public health problem of increasing prevalence rates of obesity and what should be done about it. *Mayo Clinic Proceedings* 77: 109–113, 2002.

23. **Blundell JE, Burley VJ, Cotton JR, and Lawton CL.** Dietary fat and the control of energy intake: evaluating the effects of fat on meal size and postmeal satiety. *The American Journal of Clinical Nutrition* 57: 772S–777S; discussion 777S–778S, 1993.

24. **Booth DA.** Acquired behavior controlling energy intake and output. In: *Obesity,* edited by Stunkard AJ. Philadelphia: W. B. Saunders, 1980, p. 101–143.

25. **Bouchard C.** Heredity and the path to overweight and obesity. *Medicine and Science in Sports and Exercise* 23: 285–291, 1991.

26. **Bray GA.** Effect of caloric restriction on energy expenditure in obese patients. *Lancet* 2: 397–398, 1969.

27. **Bray GA.** The energetics of obesity. *Medicine and Science in Sports and Exercise* 15: 32–40, 1983.

28. **Bray GA, and Atkinson RL.** New weight guidelines for Americans. *The American Journal of Clinical Nutrition* 55: 481–483, 1992.

29. **Bray GA, Nielsen SJ, and Popkin BM.** Consumption of high fructose corn syrup in beverages may play a role in the epidemic of obesity. *Amercian Journal of Clinical Nutrition* 79: 537–543, 2004.

30. **Bray GA, York B, and DeLany J.** A survey of the opinions of obesity experts on the causes and treatment of obesity. *The American Journal of Clinical Nutrition* 55: 151S–154S, 1992.

31. **Brehm BA.** Elevation of metabolic rate following exercise: implications for weight loss. *Sports Medicine (Auckland, NZ)* 6: 72–78, 1988.

32. **Brodie DA.** Techniques of measurement of body composition. Part I. *Sports Medicine (Auckland, NZ)* 5: 11–40, 1988.

33. **Brodie DA.** Techniques of measurement of body composition. Part II. *Sports Medicine (Auckland, NZ)* 5: 74–98, 1988.

34. **Broeder CE, Burrhus KA, Svanevik LS, and Wilmore JH.** The effects of aerobic fitness on resting metabolic rate. *The American Journal of Clinical Nutrition* 55: 795–801, 1992.

35. **Broeder CE, Burrhus KA, Svanevik LS, and Wilmore JH.** The effects of either high-intensity resistance or endurance training on resting metabolic rate. *The American Journal of Clinical Nutrition* 55: 802–810, 1992.

36. **Brozek J, Grande F, Anderson JT, and Keys A.** Densitometric analysis of body composition: revision of some quantitative assumptions. *Annals of the New York Academy of Sciences* 110: 113–140, 1963.

37. **Bullough RC, Gillette CA, Harris MA, and Melby CL.** Interaction of acute changes in exercise energy expenditure and energy intake on resting metabolic rate. *The American Journal of Clinical Nutrition* 61: 473–481, 1995.

38. **Buskirk ER.** Underwater weighing and body density: a review of procedures. In: *Techniques for Measuring Body Composition,* edited by J. Brozek J, and Henschel A. National Research Council, 1961.

39. **Buskirk ER, Thompson RH, Lutwak L, and Whedon GD.** Energy balance of obese patients during weight reduction: influence of diet restriction and exercise. *Annals of the New York Academy of Sciences* 110: 918–940, 1963.

40. **Calle EE, Thun MJ, Petrelli JM, Rodriguez C, and Heath CW, Jr.** Body-mass index and mortality in a prospective cohort of U.S. adults. *The New England Journal of Medicine* 341: 1097–1105, 1999.

41. **Calles-Escandon J, and Horton ES.** The thermogenic role of exercise in the treatment of morbid obesity: a critical evaluation. *The American Journal of Clinical Nutrition* 55: 533S–537S, 1992.

42. **Cameron JR, and Sorenson J.** Measurement of bone mineral in vivo: an improved method. *Science (New York, NY)* 142: 230–232, 1963.

43. **Campaigne BN.** Body fat distribution in females: metabolic consequences and implications for weight loss. *Medicine and Science in Sports and Exercise* 22: 291–297, 1990.

44. **Centers for Disease Control and Prevention.** Trends in intake of energy and macronutrients—United States 1971–2000. *Morbidity & Mortality Weekly Report* 53: 80–82, 2004.

45. **Cha SH, Wolfgang M, Tokutake Y, Chohnan S, and Lane MD.** Differential effects of central fructose and glucose on hypothalamic malonyl-CoA and food intake. *Proceedings of the National Academy of Sciences* 105: 16871–16875, 2008.

46. **Clarkson PM.** The skinny on weight loss supplements & drugs. *ACSM's Health and Fitness Journal* 2: 18–55, 1999.

47. **Coniglio JG.** Fat. In: *Nutrition Reviews' Present Knowledge in Nutrition.* Washington, D.C.: The Nutrition Foundation, 1984, p. 79–89.

48. **Cooper JA, Watras AC, Shriver T, Adams AK, and Schoeller DA.** Influence of dietary fatty acid composition and exercise on changes in fat oxidation from a high-fat diet. *Journal of Applied Physiology* 109: 2010.

49. **Cunningham JJ.** Body composition as a determinant of energy expenditure: a synthetic review and a proposed general prediction equation. *The American Journal of Clinical Nutrition* 54: 963–969, 1991.

50. **Dahlquist A.** Carbohydrates. In: *Nutrition Reviews' Present Knowledge in Nutrition.* Washington, D.C.: The Nutrition Foundation, 1984, p. 116–130.

51. **Danforth E.** Undernutrition contrasted to overnutrition. In: *Recent Advances in Obesity Research: II,* edited by Bray G. Westport: Technomic, 1978, p. 229–236.

52. **Dansinger ML, Gleason JA, Griffith JL, Selker HP, and Schaefer EJ.** Comparison of the Atkins, Ornish, Weight Watchers, and Zone diets for weight loss and heart disease risk reduction: a randomized trial. *JAMA* 293: 43–53, 2005.

53. **De Vries JH, Zock PL, Mensink RP, and Katan MB.** Underestimation of energy intake by 3-d records compared with energy intake to maintain body weight in 269 nonobese adults. *The American Journal of Clinical Nutrition* 60: 855–860, 1994.

54. **Dempster P, and Aitkens S.** A new air displacement method for the determination of human body composition. *Medicine and Science in Sports and Exercise* 27: 1692–1697, 1995.

55. **DiPietro L.** Physical activity, body weight, and adiposity: an epidemiologic perspective. *Exercise and Sport Sciences Reviews* 23: 275–303, 1995.

56. **Donnelly JE, Jakicic J, and Gunderson S.** Diet and body composition: effect of very low calorie diets and exercise. *Sports Medicine* (Auckland, NZ) 12: 237–249, 1991.

57. **DuBois EF.** Basal energy, metabolism at various ages: man. In: *Metabolism: Clinical and Experimental*, edited by Altman PL, and Dittmer DS. Bethesda: Federation of American Societies for Experimental Biology, 1968.

58. **Durnin JV.** Possible interaction between physical activity, body composition, and obesity in man. In: *Recent Advances in Obesity Research:* II, edited by Bray G. Westport: Technomic, 1978, p. 237–241.

59. **Eastwood M.** Dietary fiber. In: *Nutrition Reviews' Present Knowledge in Nutrition*. Washington, D.C.: The Nutrition Foundation, 1984, p. 156–175.

60. **Ebbeling CB, Leidig MM, Feldman HA, Lovesky MM, and Ludwig DS.** Effects of a low-glycemic load vs low-fat diet in obese young adults: a randomized trial. JAMA 297: 2092–2102, 2007.

61. **Ellis KJ, Shypailo RJ, Pratt JA, and Pond WG.** Accuracy of dual-energy x-ray absorptiometry for body-composition measurements in children. *The American Journal of Clinical Nutrition* 60: 660–665, 1994.

62. **Ernst ND, and Levy RI.** Diet and cardiovascular disease. In: *Nutrition Reviews' Present Knowledge in Nutrition*. Washington, D.C.: The Nutrition Foundation, 1984, p. 724–739.

63. **Finberg L.** Clinical assessment of total body water. In: *Body-Composition Assessments in Youth and Adults*, edited by Roche AF. Columbus: Ross Laboratories, 1985.

64. **Flatt JP.** Dietary fat, carbohydrate balance, and weight maintenance. *Annals of the New York Academy of Sciences* 683: 122–140, 1993.

65. **Flatt JP.** Importance of nutrient balance in body weight regulation. *Diabetes/Metabolism Reviews* 4: 571–581, 1988.

66. **Flatt JP.** Use and storage of carbohydrate and fat. *American Journal of Clinical Nutrition* Suppl. 61: 952S–959S, 1995.

67. **Flegal KM, Carroll MD, Ogden CL, and Curtin LR.** Prevalence and trends in obesity among US adults, 1999–2008. JAMA 303: 235–241, 2010.

68. **Flegal KM, Graubard BI, Williamson DF, and Gail MH.** Cause-specific excess deaths associated with underweight, overweight, and obesity. JAMA 298: 2028–2037, 2007.

69. **Fogli-Cawley JJ, Dwyer JT, Saltzman E, McCullough ML, Troy LM, Meigs JB, and Jacques PF.** The 2005 Dietary Guidelines for Americans and risk of the metabolic syndrome. *The American Journal of Clinical Nutrition* 86: 1193–1201, 2007.

70. **Foster GD, Wadden TA, Feurer ID, Jennings AS, Stunkard AJ, Crosby LO, Ship J, and Mullen JL.** Controlled trial of the metabolic effects of a very-low-calorie diet: short- and long-term effects. *The American Journal of Clinical Nutrition* 51: 167–172, 1990.

71. **Franz MJ, VanWormer JJ, Crain AL, Boucher JL, Histon T, Caplan W, Bowman JD, and Pronk NP.** Weight-loss outcomes: a systematic review and meta-analysis of weight-loss clinical trials with a minimum 1-year follow-up. J Am Diet Assoc 107: 1755–1767, 2007.

72. **Gao X, Wilde PE, Lichtenstein AH, and Tucker KL.** The 2005 USDA Food Guide Pyramid is associated with more adequate nutrient intakes within energy constraints than the 1992 Pyramid. *The Journal of Nutrition* 136: 1341–1346, 2006.

73. **Garfinkle PE, and Garner DM.** *Anorexia Nervosa*. New York: Brunner/Mazel, 1982.

74. **Garn SM.** Radiographic analysis of body composition. In: *Techniques for Measuring Body Composition*, edited by J. Brozek J, and Henschel A. National Research Council, 1961.

75. **Garn SM, and Clark DC.** Trends in fatness and the origins of obesity ad hoc committee to review the ten-state nutrition survey. *Pediatrics* 57: 443–456, 1976.

76. **Garrow JS.** *Energy Balance and Obesity in Man*. New York: Elsevier North-Holland, 1978.

77. **Garrow JS.** The regulation of energy expenditure in man. In: *Recent Advances in Obesity Research:* II, edited by Bray G. Westport: Technomic, 1978, p. 200–210.

78. **Going S, Williams D, and Lohman T.** Aging and body composition: biological changes and methodological issues. *Exercise and Sport Sciences Reviews* 23: 411–458, 1995.

79. **Goldblatt PB, Moore ME, and Stunkard AJ.** Social factors in obesity. JAMA 192: 1039–1044, 1965.

80. **Goldman RF, and Buskirk ER.** Body volume measurement by underwater weighing: description of a method. In: *Techniques for Measuring Body Composition*, edited by J. Brozek J, and Henschel A. National Research Council, 1961.

81. **Goris AHC, and Westerterp KR.** Postabsorptive respiratory quotient and food quotient-an analysis in lean and obese men and women. *European Journal of Clinical Nutrition* 54: 546–550, 2000.

82. **Greenway FL, and Bray GA.** Combination drugs for treating obesity. *Current Diabetes Reports* 10: 108–115, 2010.

83. **Guthrie HA, and Picciano MF.** *Human Nutrition*. St. Louis: Mosby, 1995.

84. **Guyton AG.** Body fat and adipose tissue cellularity in infants: a longitudinal study. *Metabolism: Clinical and Experimental* 26: 607–614, 1977.

85. **Guyton AG.** *Textbook of Medical Physiology*. Philadelphia: W. B. Saunders, 1981.

86. **Hager A, Sjorstrom L, Arvidsson B, Bjorntorp P, and Smith U.** Adipose tissue cellularity in obese school girls before and after dietary treatment. *The American Journal of Clinical Nutrition* 31: 68–75, 1978.

87. **Hallberg L.** Iron. In: *Nutrition Reviews' Present Knowledge in Nutrition*. Washington, D.C.: The Nutrition Foundation, 1984, p. 459–478.

88. **Hellerstein MK, et al.** Measurement of de novo hepatic lipogenesis in humans using stable isotopes. *The American Society for Clinical Investigation, Inc* 87: 1841–1852, 1991.

89. **Herrera BM, and Lindgren CM.** The genetics of obesity. *Current Diabetes Reports* 10: 498–505, 2010.

90. **Hill J.** Obesity treatment: can diet composition play a role? *American College of Physicians* 119: 694–697, 1993.

91. **Hirsch J.** Role and benefits of carbohydrate in the diet: key issues for future dietary guidelines. *American Journal of Clinical Nutrition* Suppl. 61: 996S–1000S, 1995.

92. **Hirsch J, and Knittle JL.** Cellularity of obese and nonobese human adipose tissue. *Federation Proceedings* 29: 1516–1521, 1970.

93. **Hornbuckle LM, Bassett DR, Jr., and Thompson DL.** Pedometer-determined walking and body composition variables in African-American women. *Medicine and Science in Sports and Exercise* 37: 1069–1074, 2005.

94. **Houtkooper LB, and Going SB.** *Body Composition: How Should It Be Measured? Does It Affect Performance?* Barrington: Gatorade Sports Science Institute, 1994.

95. **Howley ET, and Don Franks B.** *Health/Fitness Instructor's Handbook.* Champaign: Human Kinetics, 1992.

96. **Huxley R, Mendis S, Zheleznyakov E, Reddy S, and Chan J.** Body mass index, waist circumference and waist:hip ratio as predictors of cardiovascular risk—a review of the literature. *European Journal of Clinical Nutrition* 64: 16–22, 2010.

97. **Institute of Medicine.** *Dietary Reference Intakes for Calcium and Vitamin D.* Washington, D.C.: National Academy of Sciences, 2010.

98. **Institute of Medicine.** *Dietary Reference Intakes for Water, Potassium, Sodium, Chloride, and Sulfate.* Washington, D.C.: National Academies Press, 2004.

99. **Institute of Medicine.** *Dietary Reference Intakes for Energy, Carbohydrate, Fiber, Fat, Fatty Acids, Cholesterol, Protein, and Amino Acids.* Washington, D.C.: National Academies Press, 2002.

100. **Institute of Medicine.** *Dietary Reference Intakes for Energy, Carbohydrate, Fiber, Fat, Fatty Acids, Cholesterol, Protein, and Amino Acids.* Washington, D.C.: National Academies Press, 2002.

101. **Irwin ML, Yasui Y, Ulrich CM, Bowen D, Rudolph RE, Schwartz RS, Yukawa M, Aiello E, Potter JD, and McTiernan A.** Effect of exercise on total and intra-abdominal body fat in postmenopausal women: a randomized controlled trial. *JAMA* 289: 323–330, 2003.

102. **Jackson AS, and Pollock ML.** Generalized equations for predicting body density of men. *The British Journal of Nutrition* 40: 497–504, 1978.

103. **Jackson AS, and Pollock ML.** Practical assessment of body composition. *The Physician and Sportsmedicine* 13: 76–90, 1985.

104. **Jackson AS, Pollock ML, and Ward A.** Generalized equations for predicting body density of women. *Medicine and Science in Sports and Exercise* 12: 175–181, 1980.

105. **James WP, and Trayhurn P.** Thermogenesis and obesity. *British Medical Bulletin* 37: 43–48, 1981.

106. **Jéquier E.** Body weight regulation in humans: the importance of nutrient balance. *News in Physiological Sciences* 8: 273–276, 1993.

107. **Jéquier E.** Calorie balance versus nutrient balance. In: *Energy Metabolism: Tissue Determinants and Cellular Corollaries,* edited by Kinney JM, and Tucker HN. New York: Raven, 1992, p. 123–137.

108. **Johnston FE, and Malina RM.** Age changes in the composition of the upper arm in Philadelphia children. *Human Biology: An International Record of Research* 38: 1–21, 1966.

109. **Jones DW.** Dietary sodium and blood pressure. *Hypertension* 43: 932–935, 2004.

110. **Jung RT, Shetty PS, James WP, Barrand MA, and Callingham BA.** Reduced thermogenesis in obesity. *Nature* 279: 322–323, 1979.

111. **Katch FI.** Assessment of lean body tissues by radiography and bioelectrical impedance. In: *Body-Composition Assessment in Youths and Adults,* edited by Roche AF. Columbus: Ross Laboratories, 1985.

112. **Katch VL, Martin R, and Martin J.** Effects of exercise intensity on food consumption in the male rat. *The American Journal of Clinical Nutrition* 32: 1401–1407, 1979.

113. **Keys A.** *The Biology of Human Starvation.* Minneapolis: The University of Minnesota Press, 1950.

114. **Knittle JL.** Obesity in childhood: a problem in adipose tissue cellular development. *The Journal of Pediatrics* 81: 1048–1059, 1972.

115. **Kopp W.** The atherogenic potential of dietary carbohydrate. *Preventive Medicine* 42: 336–342, 2006.

116. **Krebs NF, Himes JH, Jacobson D, Nicklas TA, Guilday P, and Styne D.** Assessment of child and adolescent overweight and obesity. *Pediatrics* 120: S193–S228, 2007.

117. **Krebs-Smith SM, and Kris-Etherton P.** How does MyPyramid compare to other population-based recommendations for controlling chronic disease? *J Am Diet Assoc* 107: 830–837, 2007.

118. **Kris-Etherton P, Daniels SR, Eckel RH, Engler M, Howard BV, Krauss RM, Lichtenstein AH, Sacks F, St Jeor S, Stampfer M, Eckel RH, Grundy SM, Appel LJ, Byers T, Campos H, Cooney G, Denke MA, Howard BV, Kennedy E, Krauss RM, Kris-Etherton P, Lichtenstein AH, Marckmann P, Pearson TA, Riccardi G, Rudel LL, Rudrum M, Sacks F, Stein DT, Tracy RP, Ursin V, Vogel RA, Zock PL, Bazzarre TL, and Clark J.** Summary of the scientific conference on dietary fatty acids and cardiovascular health: conference summary from the nutrition committee of the American Heart Association. *Circulation* 103: 1034–1039, 2001.

119. **Krotkiewski M, Sjostrom L, Bjorntorp P, Carlgren G, Garellick G, and Smith U.** Adipose tissue cellularity in relation to prognosis for weight reduction. *International Journal of Obesity* 1: 395–416, 1977.

120. **Lane MD, and Cha SH.** Effect of glucose and fructose on food intake via malonyl-CoA signaling in the brain. *Biochemical and Biophysical Research Communications* 382: 1–5, 2009.

121. **Lapidus L, Bengtsson C, Larsson B, Pennert K, Rybo E, and Sjostrom L.** Distribution of adipose tissue and risk of cardiovascular disease and death: a 12 year follow up of participants in the population study of women in Gothenburg, Sweden. *British Medical Journal (Clinical Research Ed)* 289: 1257–1261, 1984.

122. **Larsson B, Svardsudd K, Welin L, Wilhelmsen L, Bjorntorp P, and Tibblin G.** Abdominal adipose tissue distribution, obesity, and risk of cardiovascular disease and death: 13 year follow up of participants in the study of men born in 1913. *British Medical Journal (Clinical Research Ed)* 288: 1401–1404, 1984.

123. **Leibel RL, Hirsch J, Appel BE, and Checani GC.** Energy intake required to maintain body weight is not affected by wide variation in diet composition. *The American Journal of Clinical Nutrition* 55: 350–355, 1992.

124. **Levitsky DA.** Putting behavior back into feeding behavior: a tribute to George Collier. *Appetite* 38: 143–148, 2002.

125. **Lichtman SW, Pisarska K, Berman ER, Pestone M, Dowling H, Offenbacher E, Weisel H, Heshka S, Matthews DE, and Heymsfield SB.** Discrepancy between self-reported and actual caloric intake and exercise in obese subjects. *The New England Journal of Medicine* 327: 1893–1898, 1992.

126. **Lohman T, Houtkooper LB, and Going S.** Body fat meaurement goes high-tech. *ACSM's Health & Fitness Journal* 1: 30–35, 1997.

127. **Lohman TG.** *Advances in Body Composition Assessment.* Champaign: Human Kinetics, 1992.

128. **Lohman TG.** Applicability of body composition techniques and constants for children and youths. In: *Exercise and Sport Sciences Reviews,* edited by Pandolf KB. New York: Macmillan, 1986, p. 325–357.

129. **Lohman TG.** Assessment of body composition in children. *Pediatric Exercise Science* 1: 19–30, 1989.

130. **Lohman TG.** Body composition methodology in sports medicine. *The Physician and Sportsmedicine* 10: 47–58, 1982.

131. **Lohman TG.** Skinfolds and body density and their relation to body fatness: a review. *Human Biology: An International Record of Research* 53: 181–225, 1981.

132. **Lohman TG.** The use of skinfold to estimate body fatness in children and youth. *Journal of the Alliance for Health, Physical Education, Recreation and Dance* 58: 98–102, 1987.

133. **Lohman TG, and Going SB.** Multicomponent models in body composition research: Opportunities and pitfalls. In: *Human Body Composition*, edited by Ellis KJ, and Eastman JD. New York: Plenum Press, 1993, p. 53–58.

134. **Lohman TG, Slaughter MH, Boileau RA, Bunt J, and Lussier L.** Bone mineral measurements and their relation to body density in children, youth and adults. *Human Biology: An International Record of Research* 56: 667–679, 1984.

135. **Mayer J.** Genetic factors in human obesity. *Annals of the New York Academy of Sciences* 131: 412–421, 1965.

136. **Mayer J, Marshall NB, Vitale JJ, Christensen JH, Mashayekhi MB, and Stare FJ.** Exercise, food intake and body weight in normal rats and genetically obese adult mice. *The American Journal of Physiology* 177: 544–548, 1954.

137. **Mayer J, Roy P, and Mitra KP.** Relation between caloric intake, body weight, and physical work: studies in an industrial male population in West Bengal. *The American Journal of Clinical Nutrition* 4: 169–175, 1956.

138. **Mazess RB, Barden HS, Bisek JP, and Hanson J.** Dual-energy x-ray absorptiometry for total-body and regional bone-mineral and soft-tissue composition. *The American Journal of Clinical Nutrition* 51: 1106–1112, 1990.

139. **McTiernan A, Sorensen B, Irwin ML, Morgan A, Yasui Y, Rudolph RE, Surawicz C, Lampe JW, Lampe PD, Ayub K, and Potter JD.** Exercise effect on weight and body fat in men and women. *Obesity* (Silver Spring, Md) 15: 1496–1512, 2007.

140. **Melanson EL, Gozansky WS, Barry DW, MacLean PS, Grunwald GK, and Hill JO.** When energy balance is maintained exercise does not induce negative fat balance in lean sedentary, obese sedentary, or lean enduranced-trainined individuals. *Journal of Applied Physiology* 107: 1847–1856, 2009.

141. **Mertz W, Tsui JC, Judd JT, Reiser S, Hallfrisch J, Morris ER, Steele PD, and Lashley E.** What are people really eating? The relation between energy intake derived from estimated diet records and intake determined to maintain body weight. *The American Journal of Clinical Nutrition* 54: 291–295, 1991.

142. **Metropolitan Life Insurance Company.** New weight standards for men and women. *Statistical Bulletin Metropolitan Life Insurance Company.* 40: 1–4, 1959.

143. **Millard-Stafford ML, Collins MA, Evans EM, Snow TK, Cureton KJ, and Rosskopf LB.** Use of air displacement plethysmography for estimating body fat in a four-component model. *Medicine and Science in Sports and Exercise* 33: 1311–1317, 2001.

144. **Miller WC.** Diet composition, energy intake, and nutritional status in relation to obesity in men and women. *Medicine and Science in Sports and Exercise* 23: 280–284, 1991.

145. **Mole PA.** Impact of energy intake and exercise on resting metabolic rate. *Sports Medicine* (Auckland, NZ) 10: 72–87, 1990.

146. **Morrow JR, Jr., Jackson AS, Bradley PW, and Hartung GH.** Accuracy of measured and predicted residual lung volume on body density measurement. *Medicine and Science in Sports and Exercise* 18: 647–652, 1986.

147. **National Institutes of Health.** Clinical guidelines on the identification, evaluation, and treatment of overweight and obesity in adults. *Obesity Research* 6 (Suppl 2): 1998.

148. **National Research Council.** *Diet and Health.* Washington, D.C.: National Academy Press, 1989.

149. **National Research Council.** *Recommended Dietary Allowances.* Washington, D.C.: National Academy Press, 1989.

150. **Nordmann AJ, Nordmann A, Briel M, Keller U, Yancy WS, Jr., Brehm BJ, and Bucher HC.** Effects of low-carbohydrate vs low-fat diets on weight loss and cardiovascular risk factors: a meta-analysis of randomized controlled trials. *Archives of Internal Medicine* 166: 285–293, 2006.

151. **Ogden CL, Carroll MD, Curtin LR, Lamb MM, and Flegal KM.** Prevalence of high body mass index in US children and adolescents, 2007–2008. *JAMA* 303: 242–249, 2010.

152. **Ogden CL, Carroll MD, Curtin LR, McDowell MA, Tabak CJ, and Flegal KM.** Prevalence of overweight and obesity in the United States, 1999–2004. *JAMA* 295: 1549–1555, 2006.

153. **Ogden CL, Flegal KM, Carroll MD, and Johnson CL.** Prevalence and trends in overweight among US children and adolescents, 1999–2000. *JAMA* 288: 1728–1732, 2002.

154. **Opperman AM, Venter CS, Oosthuizen W, Thompson RL, and Vorster HH.** Meta-analysis of the health effects of using the glycaemic index in meal-planning. *The British Journal of Nutrition* 92: 367–381, 2004.

155. **Oscai LB.** The role of exercise in weight control. In: *Exercise and Sport Sciences Reviews*, edited by Wilmore JH. New York: Academic Press, 1973, p. 103–120.

156. **Oscai LB, Mole PA, and Holloszy JO.** Effects of exercise on cardiac weight and mitochondria in male and female rats. *The American Journal of Physiology* 220: 1944–1948, 1971.

157. **Oscai LB, Spirakis CN, Wolff CA, and Beck RJ.** Effects of exercise and of food restriction on adipose tissue cellularity. *Journal of Lipid Research* 13: 588–592, 1972.

158. **Passmore R.** Energy metabolism at various weights: man. part II. resting: adults. In: *Metabolism: Clinical and Experimental*, edited by Altman PL, and Dittmer DS. Bethesda: Federation of American Societies for Experimental Biology, 1968, p. 344–345.

159. **Pietrobelli A, Heymsfield SB, Wang ZM, and Gallagher D.** Multi-component body composition models: recent advances and future directions. *European Journal of Clinical Nutrition* 55: 69–75, 2001.

160. **Pillitteri JL, Shiffman S, Rohay JM, Harkins AM, Burton SL, and Wadden TA.** Use of dietary supplements for weight loss in the United States: results of a national survey. *Obesity (Silver Spring, Md)* 16: 790–796, 2008.

161. **Pittas AG, Roberts SB, Das SK, Gilhooly CH, Saltzman E, Golden J, Stark PC, and Greenberg AS.** The effects of the dietary glycemic load on type 2 diabetes risk factors during weight loss. *Obesity (Silver Spring, Md)* 14: 2200–2209, 2006.

162. **Pittler MH, and Ernst E.** Dietary supplements for body-weight reduction: a systematic review. *American Journal of Clinical Nutrition* 79: 529–536, 2004.

163. **Poehlman ET.** A review: exercise and its influence on resting energy metabolism in man. *Medicine and Science in Sports and Exercise* 21: 515–525, 1989.

164. **Poehlman ET, Melby CL, and Goran MI.** The impact of exercise and diet restriction on daily energy expenditure. *Sports Medicine* (Auckland, NZ) 11: 78–101, 1991.

165. **Pollock ML, and Wilmore JH.** *Exercise in Health and Disease.* Philadelphia: W. B. Saunders, 1990.

166. **Presta E, Casullo AM, Costa R, Slonim A, and Van Itallie TB.** Body composition in adolescents: estimation by total body electrical conductivity. *J Appl Physiol* 63: 937–941, 1987.

167. **Qi L, and Hu FB.** Dietary glycemic load, whole grains, and systemic inflammation in diabetes: the epidemiological evidence. *Current Opinion in Lipidology* 18: 3–8, 2007.

168. **Qiao Q, and Nyamdorj R.** Is the association of type II diabetes with waist circumference or waist:hip ratio stronger than that with body mass index? *European Journal of Clinical Nutrition* 64: 3–34, 2010.

169. **Rabkin SW, Mathewson FA, and Hsu PH.** Relation of body weight to development of ischemic heart disease in a cohort of young North American men after a 26 year observation period: the Manitoba Study. *The American Journal of Cardiology* 39: 452–458, 1977.

170. **Ratamess N.** Body composition status and assessment. In: ACSM's *Resource Manual for Guidelines for Exercise Testing and Prescription*, edited by Ehrman JK. Baltimore: Lippincott Williams & Wilkins, 2010, p. 264–281.

171. **Redman LM, Heilbronn LK, Martin CK, Alfonso A, Smith SR, and Ravussin E.** Effect of calorie restriction with or without exercise on body composition and fat distribution. *The Journal of Clinical Endocrinology and Metabolism* 92: 865–872, 2007.

172. **Rimm AA, and P. L. White.** Obesity: its risks and hazards. In *Obesity in America*, edited by U.S. Department of Health EaWNIH Publication No. 79–359, 1979.

173. **Rising R, Harper IT, Fontvielle AM, Ferraro RT, Spraul M, and Ravussin E.** Determinants of total daily energy expenditure: variability in physical activity. *The American Journal of Clinical Nutrition* 59: 800–804, 1994.

174. **Robinson JR, and Niswender KD.** What are the risks and benefits of current and emerging weight-loss medications? *Current Diabetes Reports* 9: 368–375, 2009.

175. **Rolls BJ.** Carbohydrates, fats, and satiety. *American Journal of Clinical Nutrition* Suppl. 61: 960S–967S, 1995.

176. **Romijn JA, Coyle EF, Sidossis LS, Gastaldelli A, Horowitz JF, Endert E, and Wolfe RR.** Regulation of endogenous fat and carbohydrate metabolism in relation to exercise intensity and duration. *The American Journal of Physiology* 265: E380–391, 1993.

177. **Ross R, Dagnone D, Jones PJ, Smith H, Paddags A, Hudson R, and Janssen I.** Reduction in obesity and related comorbid conditions after diet-induced weight loss or exercise-induced weight loss in men: randomized, controlled trial. *Ann Intern Med* 133: 92–103, 2000.

178. **Ross R, Freeman JA, and Janssen I.** Exercise alone is an effective strategy for reducing obesity and related comorbidities. *Exercise and Sport Sciences Reviews* 28: 165–170, 2000.

179. **Ross R, and Rissanen J.** Mobilization of visceral and subcutaneous adipose tissue in response to energy restriction and exercise. *The American Journal of Clinical Nutrition* 60: 695–703, 1994.

180. **Roust LR, Hammel KD, and Jensen MD.** Effects of isoenergetic, low-fat diets on energy metabolism in lean and obese women. *The American Journal of Clinical Nutrition* 60: 470–475, 1994.

181. **Sacks FM, Bray GA, Carey VJ, Smith SR, Ryan DH, Anton SD, McManus K, Champagne CM, Laranjo LMB, Leboff MS, Rood JC, de Jonge L, Greenway FL, Loria CM, Obarzanek E, and Williamson DA.** Comparison of weight-loss diets with different compositions of fat, protein and carbohydrates. *New England Journal of Medicine* 360: 859–873, 2009.

182. **Schoeller D.** Measurement of total body water: isotope dilution techniques. In: *Body-Composition Assessment in Youths and Adults*, edited by Roche AF. Columbus: Ross Laboratories, 1985, p. 24–29.

183. **Schoeller DA, and Buchholz AC.** Energetics of obesity and weight control: does diet composition matter? *J Am Diet Assoc* 105: S24–28, 2005.

184. **Schulz LO, and Schoeller DA.** A compilation of total daily energy expenditures and body weights in healthy adults. *The American Journal of Clinical Nutrition* 60: 676–681, 1994.

185. **Schutte JE, Townsend EJ, Hugg J, Shoup RF, Malina RM, and Blomqvist CG.** Density of lean body mass is greater in blacks than in whites. *J Appl Physiol* 56: 1647–1649, 1984.

186. **Segal KR, Burastero S, Chun A, Coronel P, Pierson RN, Jr., and Wang J.** Estimation of extracellular and total body water by multiple-frequency bioelectrical-impedance measurement. *The American Journal of Clinical Nutrition* 54: 26–29, 1991.

187. **Segal KR, Edano A, Blando L, and Pi-Sunyer FX.** Comparison of thermic effects of constant and relative caloric loads in lean and obese men. *The American Journal of Clinical Nutrition* 51: 14–21, 1990.

188. **Segal KR, Gutin B, Presta E, Wang J, and Van Itallie TB.** Estimation of human body composition by electrical impedance methods: a comparative study. *J Appl Physiol* 58: 1565–1571, 1985.

189. **Segal MS, Gollub E, and Johnson RJ.** Is the fructose index more relevant with regards to cardiovascular disease than the glycemic index? *European Journal of Nutrition* 46: 406–417, 2007.

190. **Seidell JC.** Waist circumference and waist/hip ratio in relation to all-cause mortality, cancer and sleep apnea. *European Journal of Clinical Nutrition* 64: 35–41, 2010.

191. **Services US Department of Health and Human Services.** DASH Eating Plan. Washington, D.C.: Author, 2006.

192. **Sharkey B.** *The Physiology of Fitness.* Champaign: Human Kinetics, 1984.

193. **Sheard NF, Clark NG, Brand-Miller JC, Franz MJ, Pi-Sunyer FX, Mayer-Davis E, Kulkarni K, and Geil P.** Dietary carbohydrate (amount and type) in the prevention and management of diabetes: a statement by the American Diabetes Association. *Diabetes Care* 27: 2266–2271, 2004.

194. **Sims EA, Danforth E, Jr., Horton ES, Bray GA, Glennon JA, and Salans LB.** Endocrine and metabolic effects of experimental obesity in man. *Recent Progress in Hormone Research* 29: 457–496, 1973.

195. **Sinning WE, Dolny DG, Little KD, Cunningham LN, Racaniello A, Siconolfi SF, and Sholes JL.** Validity of "generalized" equations for body composition analysis in male athletes. *Medicine and Science in Sports and Exercise* 17: 124–130, 1985.

196. **Sinning WE, and Wilson JR.** Validity of "generalized" equations for body composition analysis in women athletes. *Research Quarterly for Exercise Sport* 55: 153–160, 1984.

197. **Siri WE.** Body composition from fluid spaces and density: analysis of methods. In: *Techniques for Measuring Body Composition*, edited by Brozek J, and Henschel A. Washington, D.C.: National Academy of Sciences, 1961, p. 223–244.

198. **Siri WE.** Fat cells and body weight. In: *Obesity*, edited by Strunkard, JA. Philadelphia: W. B. Saunders, 1980, p. 72–100.

199. **Sjöström L, and Björntrop P.** Body composition and adipose tissue cellularity in human obesity. *Acta Media Scandinavica* 195: 201–211, 1974.

200. **Sjöström LV.** Morbidity of severely obese subjects. *The American Journal of Clinical Nutrition* 55: 508S–515S, 1992.

201. **Sjöström LV.** Mortality of severely obese subjects. *The American Journal of Clinical Nutrition* 55: 516S–523S, 1992.

202. **Slaughter MH, Lohman TG, Boileau RA, Horswill CA, Stillman RJ, Van Loan MD, and Bemben DA.** Skinfold equations for estimation of body fatness in children and youth. *Human Biology: An International Record of Research* 60: 709–723, 1988.

203. **Slentz CA, Duscha BD, Johnson JL, Ketchum K, Aiken LB, Samsa GP, Houmard JA, Bales CW, and Kraus WE.** Effects of the amount of exercise on body weight, body composition, and measures of central obesity: STRRIDE—a randomized controlled study. *Archives of Internal Medicine* 164: 31–39, 2004.

204. **Stefanick ML.** Exercise and weight control. *Exercise and Sport Sciences Reviews* 21: 363–396, 1993.

205. **Stevens J, Katz EG, and Huxley RR.** Associations between gender, age and waist circumference. *European Journal of Clinical Nutrition* 64: 6–15, 2010.

206. **Stiegler P, and Cunliffe A.** The role of diet and exercise for the maintenance of fat-free mass and resting metabolic rate during weight loss. *Sports Medicine (Auckland, NZ)* 36: 239-262, 2006.

207. **Stunkard AJ, Sorensen TI, Hanis C, Teasdale TW, Chakraborty R, Schull WJ, and Schulsinger F.** An adoption study of human obesity. *The New England Journal of Medicine* 314: 193–198, 1986.

208. **Swinburn B, and Ravussin E.** Energy balance or fat balance? *The American Journal of Clinical Nutrition* 57: 766S–770S; discussion 770S–771S, 1993.

209. **Tataranni PA, Larson DE, Snitker S, and Ravussin E.** Thermic effect of food in humans: methods and results from use of a respiratory chamber. *The American Journal of Clinical Nutrition* 61: 1013–1019, 1995.

210. **Thomas CD, Peters JC, Reed GW, Abumrad NN, Sun M, and Hill JO.** Nutrient balance and energy expenditure during ad libitum feeding of high-fat and high-carbohydrate diets in humans. *The American Journal of Clinical Nutrition* 55: 934–942, 1992.

211. **Thomas JG, Bond DS, Hill JO, and Wing RR.** The national weight control registry. *ACSM's Health & Fitness Journal* 15: 8–12, 2011.

212. **Thompson CA, and Thompson PA.** Healthy lifestyle and cancer prevention. *ACSM's Health & Fitness Journal* 12: 18–26, 2008.

213. **Thompson DL, Rakow J, and Perdue SM.** Relationship between accumulated walking and body composition in middle-aged women. *Medicine and Science in Sports and Exercise* 36: 911–914, 2004.

214. **Titchenal CA.** Exercise and food intake:what is the relationship? *Sports Medicine (Auckland, NZ)* 6: 135–145, 1988.

215. **Tremblay A.** Dietary fat and body weight set point. *Nutrition Reviews* 62: S75–77, 2004.

216. **Tremblay A, Seale J, Almeras N, Conway J, and Moe P.** Energy requirements of a post obese man reporting a low energy intake at weight maintenance. *The American Journal of Clinical Nutrition* 54: 506–508, 1991.

217. **Tremblay A, Simoneau JA, and Bouchard C.** Impact of exercise intensity on body fatness and skeletal muscle metabolism. *Metabolism: Clinical and Experimental* 43: 814–818, 1994.

218. **Treuth MS, Hunter GR, Weinsier RL, and Kell SH.** Energy expenditure and substrate utilization in older women after strength training: 24-h calorimeter results. *J Appl Physiol* 78: 2140–2146, 1995.

219. **U.S. Department of Agriculture.** *Dietary Guidelines for Americans.* Washington, D.C.: Author, 2005.

220. **U.S. Department of Agriculture.** *Dietary Guidelines for Americans.* Washington, D.C.: Author, 2010.

221. **U.S. Department of Health and Human Services.** *2008 Physical Activity Guidelines for Americans.* Washington, D.C.: Author, 2008.

222. **U.S. Senate Select Committee on Nutrition and Human Needs.** *Eating in America: Dietary Goals for the U.S.* Washington, D.C.: U.S. Government Printing Office, 1977.

223. **Van Etten LM, Westerterp KR, and Verstappen FT.** Effect of weight-training on energy expenditure and substrate utilization during sleep. *Medicine and Science in Sports and Exercise* 27: 188–193, 1995.

224. **Van Itallie T.** Clinical assessment of body fat content in adults: potential role of electrical impedance methods. In: *Body-Composition Assessment in Youths and Adults*, edited by Roche AF. Columbus: Ross Laboratories, 1985, p. 5–8.

225. **Van Itallie TB.** Conservative approaches to treatment. In: *Obesity in America*, edited by Bray G. Department of Health, Education, and Welfare. NIH Publication No. 79–359, 1979.

226. **Van Loan MD, Keim NL, Berg K, and Mayclin PL.** Evaluation of body composition by dual energy x-ray absorptiometry and two different software packages. *Medicine and Science in Sports and Exercise* 27: 587–591, 1995.

227. **Van Marken Lichtenbelt WD, et al.** Validation of bio-electrical-impedance measurements as a method to estimate body-water compartments. *American Journal of Clinical Nutrition* 60: 159–166, 1994.

228. **Vasselli JR, Cleary MP, and Van Itallie TB.** Obesity. In: *Nutrition Reviews' Present Knowledge in Nutrition.* Washington, D.C.: The Nutrition Foundation, 1984, p. 35–36.

229. **Wabitsch M, Hauner H, Heinze E, Muche R, Bockmann A, Parthon W, Mayer H, and Teller W.** Body-fat distribution and changes in the atherogenic risk-factor profile in obese adolescent girls during weight reduction. *The American Journal of Clinical Nutrition* 60: 54–60, 1994.

230. **Wadden TA, and Stunkard AJ.** Social and psychological consequences of obesity. *Ann Intern Med* 103: 1062–1067, 1985.

231. **Wagner DR, and Heyward VH.** Techniques of body composition assessment: a review of laboratory and field methods. *Research Quarterly for Exercise and Sport* 70: 135–149, 1999.

232. **Ward A, Pollock ML, Jackson AS, Ayres JJ, and Pape G.** A comparison of body fat determined by underwater weighing and volume displacement. *The American Journal of Physiology* 234: E94–96, 1978.

233. **Wardlaw GM, and Smith AM.** *Contemporary Nutrition.* New York: McGraw-Hill, 2011.

234. **Weinberger MH.** Sodium and blood pressure 2003. *Current Opinion in Cardiology* 19: 353–356, 2004.

235. **Weinsier RL, Schutz Y, and Bracco D.** Reexamination of the relationship of resting metabolic rate to fat-free mass and to the metabolically active components of fat-free mass in humans. *The American Journal of Clinical Nutrition* 55: 790–794, 1992.

236. **Willett WC, Stampfer M, Manson J, and VanItallie T.** New weight guidelines for Americans: justified or injudicious? *The American Journal of Clinical Nutrition* 53: 1102–1103, 1991.

237. **Willett WC, Stampfer M, Manson J, and VanItallie T.** Reply to G. A. Bray and R. L. Atlinson. *American Journal of Clinical Nutrition* 55: 482–483, 1992.

238. **Williams MH.** *Nutrition for Health, Fitness, & Sport.* New York: McGraw-Hill, 2010.

239. **Wilmore JH.** Body composition in sport and exercise: directions for future research. *Medicine and Science in Sports and Exercise* 15: 21–31, 1983.

240. **Wright J.** Dietary intake of ten key nutrients for public health, United States: 1999–2000. Advance data from vital and health statistics. No. 334. National Center for Health Statistics, 2003.

241. **Zurlo F, Lillioja S, Esposito-Del Puente A, Nyomba BL, Raz I, Saad MF, Swinburn BA, Knowler WC, Bogardus C, and Ravussin E.** Low ratio of fat to carbohydrate oxidation as predictor of weight gain: study of 24-h RQ. *The American Journal of Physiology* 259: E650–657, 1990.

Exercise Prescriptions for Health and Fitness

In chapter 14 we discussed a variety of risk factors related to cardiovascular and other diseases. Physical inactivity had long been considered only a secondary risk factor in the development of CHD—that is, an inactive lifestyle would increase a person's risk for CHD only if other primary risk factors were present. However, as explained in chapter 14, this is no longer the case. Numerous studies (43, 45, 55, 65) suggest that physical inactivity is a primary risk factor for coronary heart disease (CHD), similar to smoking, hypertension, and high serum cholesterol. These studies also show that regular vigorous physical activity is instrumental in reducing the risk of CHD in those who smoke or are hypertensive (38, 44). Based on this growing body of evidence, the American Heart Association (AHA) recognized physical inactivity as a primary or major risk factor (6). Finally, epidemiological studies show that increases in physical activity (46) and fitness (8) are associated with a reduced death rate from all causes as well as from CHD. This means that physical activity should be used along with other therapies to reduce the risk of CHD in those possessing other risk factors. Consequently, there is little disagreement that regular physical activity is a necessary part of a healthy lifestyle (74). The only question is, how much?

Before we answer this question we need to distinguish among the terms *physical activity*, *exercise*, and *physical fitness*. **Physical activity (PA)** is defined as any form of muscular activity. Therefore physical activity results in the expenditure of energy proportional to muscular work and is related to physical fitness. **Physical fitness** is defined as a set of attributes that people have or develop that relate to the ability to perform physical activity. **Exercise** represents a subset of physical activity that is planned, with a goal of improving or maintaining fitness (12). These distinctions, while subtle, are important to understand in our discussion of the role of physical activity as a part of a healthy lifestyle. For example, there is no question that a planned exercise program will improve $\dot{V}O_2$ max, and that a higher $\dot{V}O_2$ max is associated with a lower death rate (9). However, we must emphasize that physical activity, including that done at a moderate intensity, is beneficial. The reduction in the risks of CHD due to the latter types of activity may be mediated through changes in the distribution of cholesterol or an increase in fibrinolysis (clot dissolving) activity (24). It should be no surprise that the American College of Sports Medicine, in the ACSM's *Guidelines for Exercise Testing and Prescription*, and *Physical Activity and Health: A Report of the Surgeon General*, state the need for increased participation in moderate-intensity exercise (e.g., brisk walking) throughout the life span (2, 74). Such a recommendation is consistent with exposing the general population to low-risk physical activity to achieve health-related benefits aimed at reducing cardiovascular and metabolic diseases. In contrast to this general recommendation for everyone, there is a need to follow a variety of guidelines in prescribing moderate to strenuous exercise that is aimed at improving $\dot{V}O_2$ max. We will address both concerns in this chapter. For information on training for performance, see chapter 21.

IN SUMMARY

- Physical inactivity has been classified as a primary risk factor for coronary heart disease.
- Regular participation in physical activity can reduce the overall risk for those who smoke or who are hypertensive.
- Those who increase their physical activity and/or cardiorespiratory fitness have a lower death rate from all causes compared to those who remain sedentary.

PRESCRIPTION OF EXERCISE

The concern about the proper **dose** of exercise needed to bring about a desired **effect (response)** is similar to the physician's need to know the type and quantity of a drug, as well as the time frame over which it must be taken, to cure a disease. Clearly, there is a difference in what is needed to cure a headache compared to what is needed to cure tuberculosis. In the same way there is no question that the dose of physical activity needed to achieve high-level running performance is different from that required to improve a health-related outcome (e.g., lower blood pressure) or fitness (e.g., an increase in $\dot{V}O_2$ max). This dose-response relationship for medications is described in figure 16.1 (20).

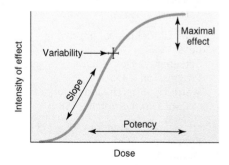

Figure 16.1 The relationship between the dose of a drug (expressed as the log of the dose) and the effect. Data from L. S. Goodman and A. Gilman, eds., 1975, *The Pharmacological Basis of Therapeutics*. New York: Macmillan Publishing Company.

- *Potency.* The potency of a drug is a relatively unimportant characteristic of a drug in that it makes little difference whether the effective dose of a drug is 1 μg or 100 mg as long as it can be administered in an appropriate dosage. Applied to exercise, walking 4 miles is as effective in expending calories as running 2 miles.

- *Slope.* The slope of the curve gives some information about how much of a change in effect is obtained from a change in dose. Some physiological measures change quickly for a given dose of exercise, while some health-related effects require the application of exercise over many months to see a desired outcome.

- *Maximal effect.* The maximal effect (efficacy) of a drug varies with the type of drug. For example, morphine can relieve pain of all intensities, while aspirin is effective against only mild to moderate pain. Similarly, strenuous exercise can cause an increase in $\dot{V}O_2$ max as well as modify risk factors, while light-to-moderate exercise can change risk factors with a smaller impact on $\dot{V}O_2$ max (an important point we will return to later).

- *Variability.* The effect of a drug varies between individuals—and within individuals, depending on the circumstances. The intersecting brackets in figure 16.1 indicate the variability in the dose required to bring about a particular effect, and the variability in the effect associated with a given dose. For example, gains in $\dot{V}O_2$ max due to endurance training show considerable variation, even when the initial $\dot{V}O_2$ max value is controlled for (17). See A Closer Look 13.1 for more on the issue of variability.

- *Side effect.* A last point worth mentioning that can also be applied to our discussion of exercise prescription is that no drug produces a single effect. The spectrum of effects might include adverse (side) effects that limit the usefulness of the drug. For exercise, the side effects might include increased risk of injury.

In contrast to drugs that individuals stop taking when a disease is cured, there is a need to engage in some form of physical activity throughout one's life to experience the health-related and fitness effects.

Dose-Response

The exercise dose is usually characterized by the intensity, frequency, duration, and type of activity. The intensity can be described in terms of:

- % $\dot{V}O_2$ max,
- % maximal heart rate,

- rating of perceived exertion, and
- the lactate threshold.

The frequency could include:

- the number of days per week and
- the number of times per day.

The duration of exercise for each exercise session can be given as the:

- number of minutes of exercise,
- total kilocalories (kcal) expended, and
- total kcal expended per kilogram body weight.

The type of exercise relates to whether resistance exercises or cardiovascular endurance exercises are used in the training program. For the latter, we would also distinguish among the effects of walking vs. jogging/running vs. swimming. Although we know a considerable amount about the role that each of these variables may play in a gain in $\dot{V}O_2$ max, we are learning more each year about the minimum or optimal quantities of each variable related to health outcomes (37, 72, 73).

The response (effect) generated by a particular dose of exercise can include changes in $\dot{V}O_2$ max, resting blood pressure, insulin sensitivity, body weight (percent fat), and depression. Haskell (23, 24) provided an important insight into how we should rethink our understanding of cause and effect when we study how a dose of physical activity is related to the responses, physical fitness and health. Physical activity could bring about favorable changes by:

- improving fitness (especially cardiovascular fitness), thereby improving health, or
- improving fitness and health simultaneously and separately, or
- improving fitness, but not a specific health outcome, or
- improving some specific health outcome, but not fitness.

It has become clear that improvements in a variety of health-related concerns are not dependent on an increase in $\dot{V}O_2$ max. This is important and provides a transition to our next section.

- An exercise dose reflects the interaction of the intensity, frequency, and duration of exercise.
- The cause of the health-related response may be related to an improvement in $\dot{V}O_2$ max or may act through some other mechanism, making health-related outcomes and gains in $\dot{V}O_2$ max independent of each other.

Physical Activity and Health

The issue of the proper dose of exercise to bring about a desired effect is a crucial one in the prescription of exercise for both prevention and rehabilitation. Over the past two decades we have learned that the proper dose differs greatly, depending on the outcome. For example, an improvement in some health-related variable (e.g., resting blood pressure) might be accomplished with an exercise intensity lower than that required to achieve an increase in $\dot{V}O_2$ max. In addition, the frequency with which the exercise must be taken to have the desired effect varies with the intensity and the duration of the session (see later discussion).

Certain physiological variables respond very quickly to a "dose" of exercise. For example, we have shown how rapidly the sympathetic nervous system, blood lactate, and heart rate (see chapter 13) adapt to exercise training, taking only days to see changes in response. In contrast to these rapid responses to exercise training, a variety of physiological variables, such as the capillary number, change more slowly (62). Similarly, when Haskell describes the potential association between physical activity and health, he distinguishes between short-term (acute) and long-term (training) responses (23). The following terms are used to describe the patterns of responses in the weeks following the initiation of a dose of exercise:

- acute responses—occur with one or several exercise bouts but do not improve further
- rapid responses—benefits occur early and plateau
- linear—gains are made continuously over time
- delayed—occur only after weeks of training

The need for such distinctions can be seen in figure 16.2, which shows proposed dose-response relationships between physical activity, defined as minutes of exercise per week at 60% to 70% of maximal work capacity, and a variety of physiological responses (34): (1) blood pressure and insulin sensitivity are most responsive to exercise, (2) changes in $\dot{V}O_2$ max and resting heart rate are intermediate, and (3) serum lipid changes such as high-density lipoprotein (HDL) are delayed. For an update on dose-response issues, see Clinical Applications 16.1.

By this time it should be clear that it is difficult to provide a single exercise prescription that addresses all issues related to prevention and/or treatment of various diseases. However, in spite of this difficulty, there was a pressing need to spell out a general public health physical activity recommendation to improve the health status of all U.S. adults. In 1995 the American College of Sports Medicine and the Centers for Disease Control and Prevention (CDC) responded to this need. Their guidelines were based on a comprehensive review of the literature dealing

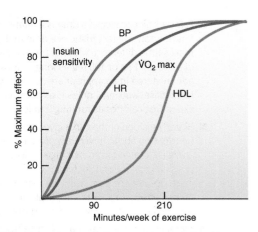

Figure 16.2 Proposed dose-response relationships between amount of exercise performed per week at 60% to 70% maximum work capacity and changes in several variables. Blood pressure (BP) and insulin sensitivity (curve to the left side) appear to be most sensitive to exercise. Maximum oxygen consumption ($\dot{V}O_2$ max) and resting heart rate, which are parameters of physical fitness (middle curve), are next in sensitivity, and lipid changes such as high-density lipoprotein (HDL) (right-hand curve) are least sensitive.

with the health-related aspects of physical activity (47). Their recommendation was that every U.S. adult should accumulate 30 minutes or more of moderate-intensity (3–6 METs) physical activity on most, preferably all, days of the week. This recommendation was based on the finding that caloric expenditure and total time of physical activity are associated with reduced cardiovascular disease and mortality. Further, doing the activity in intermittent bouts as short as 10 minutes was a suitable way of meeting the 30-minute goal (5, 47, 74).

In 2007 the ACSM and AHA released an update to this 1995 public health physical activity guideline, and in 2008 the first edition of the U.S. *Physical Activity Guidelines* was released (2008). Both guidelines supported the original statement, but attempted to provide more clarity about the roles of moderate versus strenuous physical activity in meeting the recommendation (25, 72). Because of the similarity between the two, we will present only the U.S. *Physical Activity Guidelines*.

- Individuals can realize the health-related benefits of physical activity by doing between 150 and 300 minutes of moderate-intensity physical activity per week, or 75 to 150 minutes of vigorous intensity physical activity per week, or some combination of the two.
  - 150 minutes of moderate-intensity physical activity or 75 minutes of vigorous intensity physical activity is the minimum goal.

CLINICAL APPLICATIONS 16.1

Dose-Response: Physical Activity and Health

In 2001 the results of a special symposium that examined whether a dose-response relationship existed between physical activity and a variety of health outcomes were published (37). At the end of the decade, another systematic review of the literature (73) was conducted on this same topic prior to the publication of the first set of national physical activity guidelines (2008 U.S. *Physical Activity Guidelines*). The more recent review supported the vast majority of the findings in the earlier report. Regular participation in physical activity was associated with:

- lower rates of all-cause mortality, total cardiovascular disease (CVD), and coronary heart disease incidence and mortality;
- increased weight loss, and reduced amount of weight regain after weight loss;
- a lower incidence of obesity, type 2 diabetes, and metabolic syndrome;
- a lower risk of colon and breast cancer;
- an improvement in the ability of older adults to do activities of daily living;
- reduced risk of falls in older adults at risk of falling;
- a reduction in depression and cognitive decline in adults and older adults; and
- favorable changes in cardiovascular risk factors, including blood pressure and blood lipid profile.

In general, the review found that:

- the volume of physical activity done was the most important

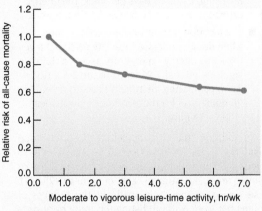

FIGURE 16.3 Dose-response of physical activity related to all-cause mortality. From: U.S. Department of Health and Human Services. Physical Activity Guidelines Advisory Committee Report 2008, Fig. G1.3, p. G1-19. http://www.health.gov/paguidelines/committeereport.aspx.

variable tied to health outcomes;
- the risk of many chronic diseases was reduced about 20% to 40% by regular participation in physical activity (see later discussion for how much physical activity); and
- a dose-response relationship existed for most health outcomes, meaning that "more is better." See figure 16.3 as an example for the health outcome, death from all causes.

That last finding, "more is better," had to be balanced by the increased risk of adverse outcomes when too much was done or when the exercise was a major change from what was currently being done. See more on this in Exercise Prescription for CRF.

The inability to establish a clear dose-response relationship between physical activity and some health outcomes was linked to lack of appropriate studies; methods of measuring physical activity not being sensitive enough to accurately characterize the "dose"; the small effect of physical activity on some health outcomes; uncontrolled factors such as genetic variability; and simultaneous changes in body weight, which confounded the data analysis. Clearly, there is a great need for additional, well-designed studies that use more sophisticated measurements of physical activity on a larger and more diverse population to be able to describe whether a dose-response relationship exists between physical activity and a specific health outcome.

- The range of physical activity (150–300 minutes) indicates that more health-related benefits are realized by doing additional activity (i.e., more is better).
- Physical activity can be done in multiple intermittent bouts (e.g., 10 minutes each) to meet the goal.

The health-related gains associated with physical activity are realized when the volume of PA is between about 500 and 1000 MET-min per week (72). Moderate-intensity PA is defined as absolute intensities of 3.0 to 5.9 METs, and vigorous intensity PA is defined as intensities of 6.0 METs or more.

- For example, walking at 3 mph requires ~3.3 METs, an activity at the low end of the moderate-intensity range. If the person walks at this speed for 30 minutes, an energy expenditure of 99 MET-min (3.3 METs times

30 min) is achieved. If done 5 days per week, the volume of PA is 495 MET-min per week.

- If an individual were to jog at 5 mph (~8 METs) for 25 minutes, the PA volume would be 200 MET-min. If done 3 days per week, the energy expenditure would be 600 MET-min per week.
- The fact that it takes about twice the time when doing moderate-intensity PA to achieve the same energy expenditure as when doing vigorous-intensity PA leads to the 2:1 ratio when comparing the time it takes to meet the PA guidelines for these different intensities (150 vs. 75 min).

In addition, the new guidelines recommended resistance training (at least 1 set, or 8–12 reps, of 8–10 exercises) on two or more days per week to improve or maintain muscular strength and endurance (25, 72). These new guidelines only spell out the number of minutes per week, without listing the number of days per week to exercise. That does not mean that one should do the 150 minutes of moderate-intensity physical activity on one day and rest for 6 days. For reasons that will be discussed later, spreading out the physical activity and exercise over the course of the week makes it easier to schedule and reduces the risk of adverse events (72). Even though there is an emphasis on moderate-intensity PA, because this is the type of activity most frequently done by adults (e.g., a brisk walk), much can be gained from participation in vigorous-intensity PA (see Clinical Applications 16.2).

IN SUMMARY

- To realize the health-related benefits of physical activity, adults should do between 150 and 300 minutes of moderate-intensity physical activity per week, or 75 to 150 minutes of vigorous intensity physical activity per week, or some combination of the two.
- Resistance training (8–10 exercises, 8–12 reps) should be done on 2 or more nonconsecutive days per week).

GENERAL GUIDELINES FOR IMPROVING FITNESS

An increase in moderate-intensity physical activity is an important goal for reducing health-related problems in sedentary individuals. These benefits occur at a point where the overall risk associated with physical activity is relatively small. However, even though the risk of cardiac arrest in habitually active men is higher during vigorous activity, the overall (rest + exercise) risk of cardiac arrest in vigorously active men is only

40% of the risk in sedentary men (64). A growing body of evidence indicates that achievement of an average-to-high level of cardiorespiratory fitness ($\dot{V}O_2$ max) confers additional health benefits, as well as increasing one's ability to engage in a broad range of recreational activities. The purpose of this section is to review the general guidelines for exercise programs aimed at increasing $\dot{V}O_2$ max. In chapter 13 the concepts of overload and specificity were presented relative to the adaptations that take place with different training programs. Although these principles apply here, it is important to remember that little exercise is needed to achieve a health-related effect. This stands in marked contrast to the intensity of exercise needed to achieve performance goals (see chapter 21).

IN SUMMARY

- In previously sedentary subjects, small changes in physical activity result in a large number of health benefits with only minimal risk.
- Strenuous exercise increases the risk of a heart attack during the activity, but reduces the overall (rest + exercise) risk of such an event.
- Moderate to high levels of cardiorespiratory fitness confers additional health benefits and increases one's ability to engage in recreational activities.

Screening

The first thing to do, if not already done in the evaluation of CRF, is to carry out some form of health status screening to decide who should begin an exercise program and who should obtain further consultation with a physician (see chapter 15 for details). The risk of cardiovascular complications during exercise is directly related to the degree of pre-existing cardiac disease. In young people the risk of sudden death is about 1/133,000 and 1/769,000 per year in men and women, respectively, due primarily to congenital or acquired heart disease. In adults the risk is one per year for every 15,000 to 18,000 individuals (2).

Progression

The emphasis in any health-related exercise program, for those who are sedentary, is to do too little rather than too much. By starting slowly and progressing from the easily accomplished activities to those that are more difficult, the chance of causing muscle soreness and of aggravating old injuries is reduced (72). The emphasis on moderate-intensity activities, such as walking at 3 to 4 mph, early in the fitness program is consistent with this recommendation, and the participant must be educated not to move too quickly

CLINICAL APPLICATIONS 16.2

Achieving Health-Related Outcomes: Is Vigorous Exercise Better than Moderate Activity?

There has been an ongoing debate over this question since the ACSM/CDC released their public health PA recommendation in 1995, with its emphasis on moderate-intensity PA. Prior to that, the emphasis was on vigorous-intensity exercise as described in the classic position stands of the ACSM (1). It must be noted that although moderate-intensity PA was emphasized, the 1995 statement also indicated that more exercise was better and encouraged vigorous exercise. Therefore, the question remains, is vigorous-intensity PA better than moderate-intensity PA for health-related outcomes?

Swain and Franklin (67) addressed this question in a systematic review of the literature examining the relationship of PA to the incidence of coronary heart disease (CHD) and risk factors for CHD. It was important in this review that the total energy expenditure associated with the PA was controlled for to allow a fair comparison of moderate-intensity versus vigorous-intensity PA (since for any duration of vigorous PA, more energy would be expended compared to moderate-intensity PA). Their findings follow:

- The vast majority of epidemiological studies observed a greater reduction in the risk of cardiovascular disease with vigorous-intensity PA ($\geq$6 METs) than with moderate-intensity PA (3–5.9 METs). In addition, more favorable risk factor profiles were found for those doing vigorous-intensity vs. moderate-intensity PA.

- Clinical intervention studies showed, generally, greater improvements in diastolic blood pressure, glucose control, and cardiorespiratory fitness after vigorous-intensity PA, compared to moderate-intensity PA. However, there was no difference between the two intensity

categories for improvements in systolic blood pressure, the blood lipid profile, or loss of body fat.

Clearly, more health-related benefits are realized, independent of the larger gains in $\dot{V}O_2$ max, through participating in vigorous-intensity exercise. O'Donovan et al. (42) supported these findings by showing that even when training groups are doing vigorous-intensity exercise, the higher the intensity the better the impact on CHD risk factors. In addition, regular participation in vigorous-intensity PA was shown to be associated with less sick leave, whereas moderate-intensity PA appeared to have no effect (56). This raises other questions: What is moderate-intensity PA? Vigorous-intensity PA?

Public health PA recommendations define moderate-intensity PA as being equal to an energy expenditure of 3–5.9 METs, but surprising as it may seem, moderate-intensity exercise may actually be vigorous-intensity PA for a large segment of the population.

Figure 16.4 shows the relative intensity for two fixed exercises (walking at 3 or 4 mph) to vary considerably across the range of $\dot{V}O_2$ max values (31, 73). Consequently, individuals with low $\dot{V}O_2$ max values who are doing moderate-intensity physical activity (3–5.9 METs) may actually be working at a relative intensity equivalent to vigorous exercise (60–84% $\dot{V}O_2$ max), consistent with achieving gains in $\dot{V}O_2$ max. This example emphasizes the need to consider measures of the relative exercise intensity (e.g., % HR max, %$\dot{V}O_2$ max) when developing PA programs, rather than relying solely on the absolute intensities (e.g., METs). Therefore, "moderate" activities, coupled with the lower threshold of training in deconditioned individuals, may be sufficient to elevate the metabolic rate and heart rate to the appropriate levels needed to achieve the various fitness ($\dot{V}O_2$ max) and health benefits that were a part of the original ACSM fitness recommendation.

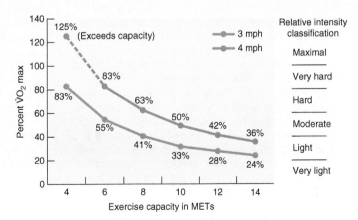

FIGURE 16.4 The relative exercise intensity for walking at 3.0 mph (3.3 METs) and 4.0 mph (5.0 METs) expressed as a percent of $\dot{V}O_2$ max for adults with an exercise capacity ranging from 4 to 14 METs. From: U.S. Department of Health and Human Services. Physical Activity Guidelines Advisory Committee Report 2008. Figure D.1; p. D-7. http://www.health.gov/paguidelines/committeereport.aspx.

into the more demanding activities. When the person can walk about two miles without fatigue, the progression to a walk-jog and jogging program is a reasonable recommendation (32).

Warm-Up, Stretch, and Cool-Down, Stretch

Prior to the actual activity used in the exercise session, a variety of very light exercises and stretches are done to improve the transition from rest to the exercise state. The emphasis at the onset of an exercise session is to gradually increase the level of activity until the proper intensity is reached. Stretching exercises to increase the range of motion of the joints involved in the activity, as well as specific stretches to increase the flexibility of the lower back, are included in the warm-up. At the end of the activity session, about 5 minutes of cool-down activities—slow walking and stretching exercises—are recommended to gradually return HR and BP toward normal. This part of the exercise session is viewed as important in reducing the chance of a hypotensive episode after the exercise session (32).

EXERCISE PRESCRIPTION FOR CRF

The exercise program includes dynamic, large muscle activities such as walking, jogging, running, swimming, cycling, rowing, and dancing. The CRF training effect of exercise programs is dependent on the proper frequency, duration, and intensity of the exercise sessions. The ACSM recommends three to five sessions per week, for 20 to 60 minutes per session, at an intensity of about 40/50% to 84% heart rate reserve (HRR) or oxygen uptake reserve ($\dot{V}O_2R$) (2). This relative intensity range accommodates both moderate intensity (40–59% HRR) and vigorous intensity (60–84% HRR). The term, % $\dot{V}O_2R$, is being used in place of the traditional % $\dot{V}O_2$ max, but for those of average to high fitness, the terms are quite similar (see later discussion). The combination of duration and intensity should result in the expenditure of about 200 to 300 kcal per session. A 75-kg person accumulating 600 MET-min/week of PA expends about 750 kcal/week, indicating a consistency between the U.S. *Physical Activity Guidelines* recommendation and the older ACSM position stands (1) and their *Guidelines* (2). This program is consistent with achieving weight-loss goals and reducing the risk factors associated with CHD (2, 26, 49-51, 74). See A Look Back—Important People in Science for information on someone who had a major impact on exercise testing and prescription.

Frequency

Improvements in CRF increase with the frequency of exercise sessions, with two sessions being the minimum, and the gains in CRF leveling off after three to four sessions per week (2, 75). Gains in CRF can be achieved with a 2-day-per-week program, but the intensity has to be higher than the 3-day-per-week program, and participants might not achieve weight-loss goals (50). In addition, the high-intensity exercise associated with a 2-day per-week frequency may not be appropriate for previously sedentary individuals. The schedule of 3 to 4 days per week includes a day off between sessions and reduces the scheduling problems associated with planned exercise programs. Figure 16.5 shows that higher frequencies are associated with higher rates of injuries (16, 52).

Duration

The duration has to be viewed together with intensity, in that the total work accomplished per session (200–300 kcal) is an important variable associated with improvements in CRF after the minimal threshold of intensity is achieved (2). A good example showing the role that duration plays (at constant exercise intensity) in the increase in CRF is a recent study by Church et al. (16). Sedentary, postmenopausal overweight or obese women were randomly assigned into either a control group or one of three moderate-intensity (~50% $\dot{V}O_2$ peak) physical activity groups to achieve an energy expenditure of 4, 8, or 12 kcal/kg per week. The increase in $\dot{V}O_2$ peak was 4.2%, 6%, and 8.2% in these groups, respectively, indicating a dose-response relationship with exercise duration (16). This is important, given that many sedentary persons can more easily accomplish an exercise session of low intensity and long duration than the reverse, and achieve the health-related benefits of physical activity with minimal risk. Obviously, if the participants choose to exercise at higher intensities, it would take less time to achieve an energy expenditure goal. For example, an 80-kg (176-lb) person walking at about 3.5 mph would consume O_2 at the rate of 1 liter per minute. Given 5 kcal per liter of O_2, the person is using 5 kcal $\cdot$ min^{-1}, and 60 minutes of walking would be required to expend 300 kcal. As the intensity of exercise increases, the duration needed to expend 300 kcal decreases. Given that "lack of time" is often cited as a principal reason for not exercising, doing vigorous-intensity PA would help address that problem. Figure 16.5 shows that doing strenuous exercise (75% $\dot{V}O_2$ max) for more than 30 minutes per session increases the risk of orthopedic problems.

A LOOK BACK—IMPORTANT PEOPLE IN SCIENCE

Michael L. Pollock, Ph.D., Laid the Foundation for Exercise Prescription

Michael L. Pollock received his Ph.D. at the University of Illinois under the direction of Dr. Thomas K. Cureton (see chapter 0's A Look Back—Important People in Science). In so many ways, Dr. Pollock built on Dr. Cureton's commitment to fitness, but raised it to a much higher level. Mike Pollock's research laid the foundation for much of the quantitative aspects of exercise prescription that were established in the 1970s and are little changed today. When we read about the optimal intensity, frequency, and duration of exercise to achieve fitness goals and health benefits, we have Dr. Pollock to thank for providing the foundation for much of that. In 1972 he published a chapter, "Quantification of Endurance Training Programs," in the first volume of *Exercise and Sports Sciences Reviews*. This chapter led the way for the

American College of Sports Medicine's first position stand in 1978: "Recommended Quantity and Quality of Exercise for Developing and Maintaining Fitness," of which Dr. Pollock was the lead author. His research on the importance of strength training was instrumental in including resistance training in a later revision of that position stand. In addition, Mike Pollock's name is attached to one of the most popular equations for converting the sum of skinfolds into percentage of body fat. The fact that these equations are still used on a daily basis, many years after their development, speaks well of the quality of his work in so many areas.

Dr. Pollock also had a major impact on the development, maturation, and recognition of cardiopulmonary exercise testing and training. His research publications and textbooks (*Heart Disease and Rehabilitation* and *Exercise in Health and Disease*) in this area provided clear guidance for the delivery of safe and effective

exercise programs in the cardiopulmonary rehabilitation environment (see Suggested Readings for a textbook written in his honor: *Pollock's Textbook of Cardiovascular Disease and Rehabilitation*). He was a founding member of the American Association of Cardiovascular and Pulmonary Rehabilitation (AACVPR) and was the founder of the *Journal of Cardiopulmonary Rehabilitation*. In addition to these valuable contributions, Dr. Pollock served as President of the American College of Sports Medicine.

Mike Pollock accomplished all this work while suffering (quietly) from ankylosing spondylitis—a degenerative inflammatory disease that impairs the mobility of the spinal column. He died of a stroke in 1998, but his legacy is with us each day we do exercise testing, write an exercise prescription, and talk about "how much exercise is enough?"

Note: Special thanks to Barry Franklin and William Haskell for information for this box.

Figure 16.5 Effects of increasing the frequency, duration, and intensity of exercise on the increase in $\dot{V}O_2$ max in a training program. This figure demonstrates the increasing risk of orthopedic problems due to exercise sessions that are too long or conducted too many times per week. The probability of cardiac complications increases with exercise intensity beyond that recommended for improvements in cardiorespiratory fitness.

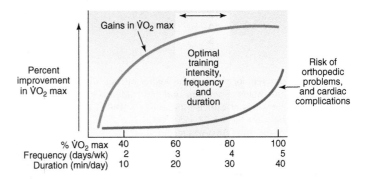

Intensity

Intensity describes the overload on the cardiovascular system that is needed to bring about a training effect. It should be no surprise that the intensity threshold for a CRF training effect is lower for the less fit and higher for the more fit. Swain and Franklin (68) found that the threshold for an improvement in $\dot{V}O_2$ max was only 30% of oxygen uptake reserve ($\dot{V}O_2R$) for those with $\dot{V}O_2$ max values less than 40 ml $\cdot$ kg^{-1} $\cdot$ min^{-1}, and only 46% $\dot{V}O_2R$ for those with a $\dot{V}O_2$ max greater than 40 ml $\cdot$ kg^{-1} $\cdot$ min^{-1}. However, in general, they

found that higher-intensity exercise was better for increasing $\dot{V}O_2$ max. As mentioned at the beginning of this section, the range of exercise intensities associated with an increase in $\dot{V}O_2$ max is 40/50% to 84% $\dot{V}O_2R$, which is similar to 40/50% to 84% $\dot{V}O_2$ max for people of average or better fitness (see Clinical Applications 16.3). However, for most people, 60% to 80% $\dot{V}O_2$ max seems to be a range sufficient to achieve CRF goals (32). It appears that for this information to be useful, the exercise leader has to know the energy requirements ($\dot{V}O_2$) of all the fitness activities so that a correct match can be made between the activity and

CLINICAL APPLICATIONS 16.3

Prescribing Exercise Intensity by the $\dot{V}O_2$ Reserve ($\dot{V}O_2R$) Method

Historically, the intensity portion of an exercise prescription was given as a % $\dot{V}O_2$ max, percent of maximal HR, or percent of the HR reserve (HRR). The linear relationship between HR and $\dot{V}O_2$ allowed the former to predict the latter. In this regard, some preferred the use of the HRR method because the percent values used in the calculation of the target heart rates were believed to be similar to the % $\dot{V}O_2$ max values (i.e., 60% HRR = 60% $\dot{V}O_2$ max). Research by Swain and colleagues (69, 70) questioned that close association, especially for subjects at the low end of the fitness scale. They found that the % HRR was more closely linked to the % $\dot{V}O_2R$ (the difference between maximal $\dot{V}O_2$ and

resting $\dot{V}O_2$) than to % $\dot{V}O_2$ max. This approach has been adopted in all of ACSM's position stands on the quantity and quality of exercise needed for fitness (1), and their *Guidelines for Exercise Testing and Prescription* (2). As Swain points out (66), the calculation of the % $\dot{V}O_2R$ is similar to that of the HHR. For example, the target $\dot{V}O_2$ of a person with a $\dot{V}O_2$ max of 35 ml · kg⁻¹· min⁻¹ who works at 60% HRR is:

Target $\dot{V}O_2$ = (0.60)(35 ml · kg⁻¹ · min⁻¹
  − 3.5 ml · kg⁻¹ · min⁻¹)
  + 3.5 ml · kg⁻¹ · min⁻¹

Target $\dot{V}O_2$ = 18.9 ml · kg⁻¹ · min⁻¹
  + 3.5 ml · kg⁻¹ · min⁻¹

Target $\dot{V}O_2$ = 22.4 ml · kg⁻¹ · min⁻¹

The advantage of this approach is that the % HRR and % $\dot{V}O_2R$ values are directly coupled over the entire range of fitness ($\dot{V}O_2$ max values) and exercise intensities, but it is most useful for those at the low end of the scale, where large discrepancies exist between % HRR and % $\dot{V}O_2$ max (66, 69, 70). On the other hand, for those with average to high fitness levels, the difference between the % $\dot{V}O_2$ max and % $\dot{V}O_2R$ is not very great. The following table gives a brief summary of the expected % $\dot{V}O_2$ max values across a broad range of $\dot{V}O_2$ max values (in METs) when exercise intensities are set at a % HRR:

$\dot{V}O_2$ max (METs)	40% HRR	50% HRR	60% HRR	70% HRR	80% HRR
	Percent $\dot{V}O_2$ Max at Different Percent Heart Rate Reserve (HRR) and Cardiorespiratory Fitness ($\dot{V}O_2$ Max) Values				
18	43.3	52.8	62.2	71.7	81.1
16	43.8	53.1	62.5	71.9	81.3
14	44.3	53.6	62.9	72.1	81.4
12	45.0	54.2	63.3	72.5	81.7
10	46.0	55.2	64.3	73.0	82.5
8	47.5	56.3	65.0	73.8	82.5
6	50.0	58.3	66.7	75.0	83.3

As you can see, for those at the high end of the fitness spectrum and at higher intensities of exercise, the difference between the % HRR and % $\dot{V}O_2$ max is not too great. This was recently shown to be the case for the elite cyclist, where for intensities greater than 75% of maximum, there was no difference between % HRR, % $\dot{V}O_2R$ or % $\dot{V}O_2$ max (40). However, for those at the low end of the fitness scale (e.g., 6

METs), there is a large (e.g., 10%) difference between the % $\dot{V}O_2$ max and % HRR at 40% HRR.

Special Notes

- When using an exercise heart rate value to estimate the % $\dot{V}O_2$ max or % $\dot{V}O_2R$ at which the individual is working, the error is about ±6% (i.e., 60% HRR = 60 ± 6% $\dot{V}O_2R$)

for two-thirds of the population when the measured maximal heart rate is known.
- If we use an age-predicted maximal heart rate to set the target heart rate range, the error involved in estimating the maximal heart rate value (one standard deviation is ± 11 b · min⁻¹) adds to the error in estimating % $\dot{V}O_2$ max or % $\dot{V}O_2R$.

the participant. Fortunately, because of the linear relationship between exercise intensity and HR, the exercise intensity can be set by using the HR values equivalent to 60% to 80% $\dot{V}O_2$ max. The range of heart rate values associated with the exercise intensity needed to have a CRF training effect is called the **target heart rate (THR) range.** How do you determine the THR range?

Direct Method   Figure 16.6 shows the HR response of a twenty-year-old subject during a maximal GXT on a treadmill. The subject's $\dot{V}O_2$ max was 12 METs, so that 60% and 80% $\dot{V}O_2$ max is equal to about 7.2 and 9.6 METs, respectively. A line is drawn from each of these work rates up to the HR/$\dot{V}O_2$ line, and over to the y-axis where the HR values equivalent to these work rates are obtained. These HR values, 138

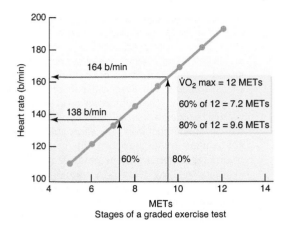

Figure 16.6 Target heart rate range determined from the results of an exercise stress test. The heart rate values measured at work rates equal to 60% and 80% $\dot{V}O_2$ max constitute the THR range.

to 164 b · min⁻¹, represent the THR range, the proper intensity for a CRF training effect (1, 32).

Indirect Methods The THR range can also be estimated by some simple calculations, knowing that the relationship between HR and $\dot{V}O_2$ is linear. The heart rate reserve, or Karvonen, method of calculating a THR range has three simple steps (35, 36):

1. Subtract resting HR from maximal HR to obtain HR reserve (HRR).
2. Take 60% and 80% of the HRR.
3. Add each HRR value to resting HR to obtain the THR range.

For example:

1. If a subject has a maximal HR of 200 b · min⁻¹ and a resting HR of 60 b · min⁻¹, then the HRR is 140 b · min⁻¹ (200 − 60).
2. 60% × 140 b · min⁻¹ = 84 b · min⁻¹ and 80% × 140 b · min⁻¹ = 112 b · min⁻¹
3. 84 b · min⁻¹ + 60 b · min⁻¹ = 144 b · min⁻¹
   112 b · min⁻¹ + 60 b · min⁻¹ = 172 b · min⁻¹
   The THR range is 144 to 172 b · min⁻¹.

This method gives reasonable estimates of the exercise intensity because 60% to 80% of the HRR is equal to about 60% to 80% $\dot{V}O_2$ max for those with average or high fitness (see Clinical Applications 16.3).

   The other indirect method of calculating the THR range is the *percentage of maximal* HR method. In this method you simply take 70% and 85% of maximal HR to obtain the THR range. In the following example, the subject has a maximal HR of 200 b · min⁻¹. The THR range for this person is 140 to 170 b · min⁻¹ (70% × 200 = 140 b · min⁻¹; 85% × 200 = 170 b · min⁻¹). Seventy percent of maximal HR is equal to

about 55% $\dot{V}O_2$ max, and 85% of maximal HR is equal to about 75% $\dot{V}O_2$ max, both within the intensity range needed for CRF gains (27–29, 39).

   The intensity of exercise can be prescribed by the direct method or by either of the indirect methods. Both of the indirect methods require knowledge of the maximal HR. If the maximal HR is measured during a maximal GXT, use it in the calculations. However, if you have to use the age-adjusted estimate of maximal HR (220 − age), remember the potential error, with the standard deviation of the estimate equal to ±11 b · min⁻¹. Tanaka, Monahan, and Seals (71) evaluated the validity of the classic "220 − age" equation to estimate maximal heart rate. They carried out an analysis of 351 published studies and cross-validated the findings with a well-controlled laboratory study. They found almost identical results using both approaches: HR max = 208 − 0.7 × age. This new equation yields maximal heart rate values that are 6 b · min⁻¹ lower for 20-year-olds and 6 b · min⁻¹ higher for 60-year-olds. A recent longitudinal study confirmed the above, with their equation being HR max = 207 − 0.7 × age (19). Although the new formulas yield better estimates of HR max *on average*, the investigators emphasize the fact that the estimated HR max for a given individual is still associated with a standard deviation of ±10 b · min⁻¹. Consequently, the estimated THR range is a guideline for exercise intensity and is meant to be used with other information (abnormal symptoms or signs) to determine if the exercise intensity is reasonable.

   In this regard, Borg's RPE scale can be used as an adjunct to HR in prescribing exercise intensity for apparently healthy individuals. The RPE range of 12 to 16 on the original Borg scale covers the range of exercise intensities similar to 40/50% to 84% HRR (1, 2, 7, 15, 21, 22, 53). The RPE scale is helpful because the participant learns to associate the THR range with a certain whole-body perception of effort, decreasing the need for frequent pulse rate measurements. The RPE scale has been shown to have a high test-retest reliability (14), and it is closely linked to the % $\dot{V}O_2$ max and lactate threshold, independent of the mode of exercise and fitness of the subject (30, 59, 63). Remember, the intensity threshold needed to achieve CRF goals is lower for the less fit, and vice versa.

IN SUMMARY

- A sedentary person needs to go through a health status screening before participating in exercise.
- Exercise programs for previously sedentary persons should start with moderate-intensity activities (walking), and the person should not progress until he or she can walk briskly for about 2 miles.

■ The optimal characteristics of an exercise program to increase $\dot{V}O_2$ max are intensity = 60% to 80% $\dot{V}O_2$ max; frequency = three to four times per week; duration = minutes needed to expend about 200 to 300 kcal.

■ The THR range, taken as 60% to 80% HRR, or 70% to 85% of maximal HR, is a reasonable estimate of the proper exercise intensity.

To determine if the subject is in the THR range during the activity, HR should be checked immediately after stopping, taking a 10-second pulse count within the first 15 seconds. The pulse can be taken at the radial artery or the carotid artery; if the latter is used, the participant should use only light pressure, since heavy pressure can actually slow the HR (32, 53).

The proper intensity, frequency, and duration of exercise needed to have a CRF training effect were discussed in the previous section. It is important that sedentary individuals start slowly before exercising at the recommended intensities specified in the THR range. The next section provides some directions on how to make that transition.

SEQUENCE OF PHYSICAL ACTIVITY

The old adage that you should "walk before you run" is consistent with the way exercise should be recommended to sedentary persons, be they young or old (72). After the person demonstrates an ability to do prolonged walking without fatigue, then controlled fitness exercises conducted at a reasonable intensity (THR) can be introduced. After that, and depending on the interest of the participant, a variety of fitness activities that are more game-like can be included. This section will deal with this sequence of activities that can lead to a fit life (32).

Walking

The primary activity to recommend to someone who has been sedentary for a long period of time is walking, or its equivalent if orthopedic problems exist. This recommendation is consistent with the introductory material on health benefits, and it deals with the issue of injuries associated with more strenuous physical activity. In addition, there is good reason to believe that some (many) individuals may use walking as their primary form of exercise. The emphasis at this stage is to simply get people active by providing an activity that can be done anywhere, anytime, and with anyone, young or old. In this way, the number of

possible interfering factors that can result in the discontinuance of the exercise is reduced.

The person should choose comfortable shoes that are flexible, offer a wide base of support, and have a fitted heel cup. There are a great number of "walking" shoes available, but a special pair of shoes is not usually required. The emphasis is on getting started; if walking becomes a "serious" activity, or leads to hiking, then the investment would be reasonable. If weather is not to interfere with the activity, then proper selection of clothing is necessary. The participant should wear light, loose-fitting clothing in warm weather, and layers of wool or polypropylene in cold weather. For those who cannot bear the extremes in temperature and humidity out of doors, various shopping malls provide a controlled environment with a smooth surface. Walkers should choose the areas in which they walk with care in order to avoid damaged streets, high traffic zones, and poorly lighted areas. Safety is important in any health-related exercise program (32, 72). A walking program is presented in table 16.1 (32). The steps are rather simple in that progression to the next stage does not occur unless the individual feels comfortable at the current stage. The HR should be recorded as described previously, but the emphasis is not on achieving the THR. Later on in the walking program if higher walking speeds are used, the THR zone will be attained. Remember that walking, in spite of not being very strenuous by the THR zone scale, when combined with long duration is an effective part of a weight-control and CHD risk factor reduction program (45, 54). Walking is an activity that many people find they can do every day, providing many opportunities to expend calories.

Jogging

Jogging begins when a person moves at a speed and form that results in a period of flight between foot strikes; this may be 3 or 4 mph, or 6 or 7 mph, depending on the fitness of the individual. As described in chapter 1, the net energy cost of jogging/running is about twice that of walking (at slow to moderate speeds) and requires a greater cardiovascular response. This is not the only reason for the jogging program to follow a walking program; there is also more stress on joints and muscles due to the impact forces that must be tolerated during the push off and landing while jogging (13).

The emphasis at the start of a jogging program is to make the transition from the walking program in such a way as to minimize the discomfort associated with the introduction of any new activity. This is accomplished by beginning with a jog-walk-jog program that eases the person into jogging by mixing in the lower energy cost and trauma associated with walking. The jogging speed is set according to the

TABLE 16.1	Walking Program			
Rules	Stage	Duration	Heart Rate	Comments
1. Start at a level that is comfortable for you.	1	15 min	_____	_____
	2	20 min	_____	_____
2. Be aware of new aches or pains.	3	25 min	_____	_____
	4	30 min	_____	_____
3. Don't progress to the next level if you are not comfortable.	5	30 min	_____	_____
	6	30 min	_____	_____
	7	35 min	_____	_____
4. Monitor your heart rate and record it.	8	40 min	_____	_____
	9	45 min	_____	_____
5. It would be healthful to walk at least every other day.	10	45 min	_____	_____
	11	45 min	_____	_____
	12	50 min	_____	_____
	13	55 min	_____	_____
	14	60 min	_____	_____

Reprinted, by permission, from B. D. Franks and E. T. Howley, 1989, *Fitness Leader's Handbook*, Champaign, IL: Human Kinetics Publishers, 136. This form may be copied by the fitness leader for distribution to participants.

THR, with the aim to stay at the low end of the THR zone at the beginning of the program. As the participant adapts to jogging, the HR response for any jogging speed will decrease, and jogging speed will have to be increased to stay in the THR zone. This is the primary marker that a training effect is taking place. Table 16.2 presents a jogging program with some simple rules to follow. Special attention is made to completing the walking program first, staying in the THR zone, and not progressing to the next level if the participant is not comfortable with the current level. Jogging is not for everyone, and for those who are obese, or have ankle, knee, or hip problems, it might be a good activity to avoid. Two activities that reduce such stress are cycling (stationary or outdoor) and swimming (32). More on exercise for special populations will be presented in chapter 17.

Games and Sports

As a person becomes accustomed to exercising in the THR range while jogging, swimming, or cycling, more uncontrolled activities can be introduced that require higher levels of energy expenditure, but do so in a more intermittent fashion. Games (paddleball, racquetball, squash), sports (basketball, soccer), and various forms of group exercise can keep a person's interest and make it more likely that the person will maintain a physically active life. These activities should be built on a walk-and-jogging base to reduce the chance that the participant will make poor adjustments to the activity. In addition, by having the habit of walking or jogging (swimming or cycling), the participant will still be able to maintain his or her

habit of physical activity when there is no one to play with or lead the class. In contrast to jogging, cycling, or swimming, it will be more difficult to stay in the THR range with these intermittent activities. It is more likely that the HR will move from below the threshold value to above the top end of the THR from time to time. This is a normal response to activities that are intermittent in nature. It must be stressed, however, that when playing games it is important that the participants have some degree of skill and be reasonably well matched. If one is much better than the other, neither will have a good workout (41).

STRENGTH AND FLEXIBILITY TRAINING

The focus in this chapter has been on training to improve cardiorespiratory fitness. However, both the ACSM position stand on fitness (1) and the recent update on the public health PA guidelines (25) recommend both strength and flexibility exercises as part of the complete fitness program. There is a growing body of evidence showing that resistance training has a variety of health benefits in addition to increasing or maintaining strength:

- Increases bone density and reduces risk of fractures
- Increases fat free mass and reduces percent fat
- Improves functional health
- Improves glucose metabolism, and
- Reduces risk of falls in seniors at risk of falling

TABLE 16.2 Jogging Program

Rules

1. Complete the Walking Program before starting this program.
2. Begin each session with walking and stretching.
3. Be aware of new aches and pains.
4. Don't progress to the next level if you are not comfortable.
5. Stay at the low end of your THR zone; record your heart rate for each session.
6. Do the program on a work-a-day, rest-a-day basis.

Stage 1 Jog 10 steps, walk 10 steps. Repeat five times and take your heart rate. Stay within THR zone by increasing or decreasing walking phase. Do 20–30 minutes of activity.

Stage 2 Jog 20 steps, walk 10 steps. Repeat five times and take your heart rate. Stay within THR zone by increasing or decreasing walking phase. Do 20–30 minutes of activity.

Stage 3 Jog 30 steps, walk 10 steps. Repeat five times and take your heart rate. Stay within THR zone by increasing or decreasing walking phase. Do 20–30 minutes of activity.

Stage 4 Jog 1 minute, walk 10 steps. Repeat three times and take your heart rate. Stay within THR zone by increasing or decreasing walking phase. Do 20–30 minutes of activity.

Stage 5 Jog 2 minutes, walk 10 steps. Repeat two times and take your heart rate. Stay within THR zone by increasing or decreasing walking phase. Do 30 minutes of activity.

Stage 6 Jog 1 lap (400 meters, or 440 yards) and check heart rate. Adjust pace during run to stay within the THR zone. If heart rate is still too high, go back to the Stage 5 schedule. Do 6 laps with a brief walk between each.

Stage 7 Jog 2 laps and check heart rate. Adjust pace during run to stay within the THR zone. If heart rate is still too high, go back to Stage 6 activity. Do 6 laps with a brief walk between each.

Stage 8 Jog 1 mile and check heart rate. Adjust pace during the run to stay within THR zone. Do 2 miles.

Stage 9 Jog 2 to 3 miles continuously. Check heart rate at the end to ensure that you were within THR zone.

In a recent study (61), muscular strength was associated with a lower cancer mortality risk in men, even after controlling for both adiposity and cardiorespiratory fitness. Collectively, these health-related findings point to the need for resistance training to be a part of a regular exercise program. Further, the combination of adequate flexibility and strength allows individuals to do the activities of daily living comfortably and safely. The ACSM recommendation emphasizes dynamic exercises done on a routine basis, but there is some debate about how much is enough (see Clinical Applications 16.4).

The Activity Pyramid provides a nice summary of the overall recommendations for health and fitness (see figure 16.7). It is beyond the scope of this text to go into detail regarding strength and flexibility programs aimed at improving or maintaining these fitness components. We recommend the Suggested Readings by Faigenbaum and McInnis, for muscular strength and endurance, and by Liemohn, for flexibility and low-back function, as good starting points.

IN SUMMARY

- A logical progression of physical activities is from walking to jogging to games. The progression addresses issues of intensity, as well as the risk of injury. For many, walking may be their only aerobic activity.
- Strength and flexibility activities should be included as a regular part of an exercise program.

ENVIRONMENTAL CONCERNS

It is important that the participant be educated about the effects of extreme heat and humidity, altitude, and cold on the adaptation to exercise. The THR range acts as a guide in that it provides feedback to the participant about the interaction of the environment and the exercise intensity. As the heat and humidity increase, there

CLINICAL APPLICATIONS 16.4

Strength Training: Single Versus Multiple Sets

In 1998 the ACSM recommended resistance training as a part of a well-rounded fitness program. The goals were to increase or maintain muscular strength and endurance, the fat-free mass, and bone mineral density (1). To accomplish this, the ACSM recommended:

- A minimum of one set of eight to ten exercises that conditions the major muscle groups,
- eight to twelve reps per set (ten to fifteen for older individuals), and
- two or more nonconsecutive sessions per week.

Although the position stand acknowledges that "multiple-set regimes may provide greater benefits," the review of literature supported the use of one set to achieve the health-related and fitness goals. This conclusion received additional support from a comprehensive review by Carpinelli and Otto (11), but not without reaction and reply to that reaction (10).

The debate was raised to a higher level when the ACSM published a second Position Stand in 2002 with a focus on progression models of resistance training for improving strength (4). This position stand recommended a variety of approaches to achieve strength goals, including using multiple sets. Since the appearance of that position stand, a number of systematic analyses of the research literature dealing with the issue of single set versus multiple sets have been published. They revealed the following:

- Prior to 1998 the evidence was split, and suggested that there was no difference in strength gains when a single set was compared to multiple sets. However, the use of small sample sizes, very short duration studies, and different methods

for measuring strength gains complicated the interpretation of the data. After 1998 most studies showed that multiple sets were better than single sets relative to strength gains, in both short- and long-term studies (18).
- Scientists re-examined all the literature on this topic by pooling the data from the various studies (to deal with the issues of small sample sizes and short duration studies). This analysis showed that multiple sets were better than single sets, and in the better-controlled studies the differences between the two were greater (57).
- Multiple sets were shown to be more effective in increasing strength in trained individuals and over long-duration training programs (76).

These review articles, as well as the most recent studies (33, 60), indicate that multiple sets are better than one set at increasing strength. However, "when maximal strength gain is not the principal goal of the training program, a single-set protocol may be sufficient to significantly improve upper- and lower-body strength as well as being time efficient" (18). This would appear to support both the "one-set" recommendation for improving and maintaining muscular fitness in the average individual as well as the "multiple set" recommendation for those interested in achieving higher strength goals.

The issue of dose-response was discussed earlier in this chapter relative to health-related outcomes and increases in $\dot{V}O_2$ max. For strength and conditioning programs, two recent comprehensive analyses of the literature suggest the following for *maximal gains* in strength:

- For untrained subjects: do four sets at 60% 1-RM, 3 days a week (58).
- For trained subjects: do four sets at 80% 1-RM, 2 days a week (58).
- For athletes: do eight sets at 85% 1-RM, 2 days a week (48).

This growing body of research prompted the American College of Sports Medicine to update its 2002 position standing on progression models in resistance training for healthy adults (3). What follows is a very brief summary of the position stand for gains in strength. Additional guidelines are provided in the position stand for gains in hypertrophy, power, and local muscular endurance.

- For novice (untrained individuals): loads should correspond to 60%–70% of 1-RM for 8–12 repetitions; do 1–3 sets at slow and moderate velocities of contraction, with at least 2–3 min rest between sets; train 2–3 days per week.
- For intermediate (~6 months training) individuals: loads should correspond to 60%–70% of 1-RM for 8–12 repetitions; use multiple sets with variations in volume and intensity over time; do at moderate velocities of contraction with 3–5 min rest between sets; train 3–4 days a week.
- For advanced (years of training) individuals: loads should correspond to 80%–100% of 1-RM; do multiple sets with variations in volume and intensity over time, using variable velocities of contraction (relative to intensity), with at least 2–3 min rest between sets; train 4–6 days a week.

---

is an increased need to circulate additional blood to the skin to dissipate the heat. As altitude increases, there is less oxygen bound to hemoglobin, and the person must pump more blood to the muscles to have the same

oxygen delivery. In both of these situations the HR response to a fixed work bout will be higher. To counter this tendency and stay in the THR range, the subject should decrease the work rate. Exercise in most cold

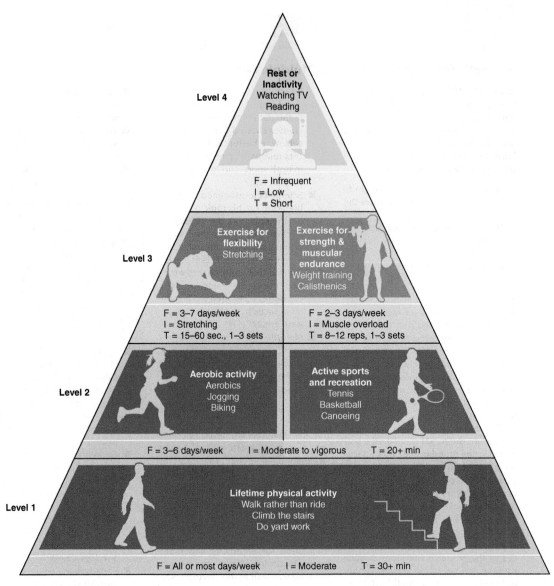

Figure 16.7   The physical activity pyramid.

environments can be refreshing and safe if a person plans in advance and dresses accordingly. However, there are some temperature/wind combinations that should be avoided because of the inability to adapt to them. As mentioned previously, some people simply plan exercise indoors (shopping malls, health spas, home exercise) during those occasions so that their routine is not interrupted. These environmental factors will be considered in more detail in chapter 24.

IN SUMMARY

- The THR acts as a guide to adjust exercise intensity in adverse environments such as high temperature and humidity, or altitude.
- A decrease in exercise intensity will counter the effects of high environmental temperature and humidity to allow one to stay in the target HR zone.

STUDY QUESTIONS

1. What are the practical implications of classifying physical inactivity as a primary risk factor?
2. From a public health standpoint, why is there so much attention paid to increasing a sedentary person's physical activity by a small amount rather than recommending strenuous exercise?
3. What is the risk of cardiac arrest for someone who participates in a regular physical activity program?
4. What is the difference between "exercise" and "physical activity"?
5. List the optimal frequency, intensity, and duration of exercise needed to achieve an increase in cardiorespiratory function.

6. For a person with a maximal heart rate of 180 b · min^{-1} and a resting heart rate of 70 b · min^{-1}, calculate a target heart rate range by the Karvonen method and the percent of maximal HR method.
7. Recommend an appropriate progression of activities for a sedentary person wanting to become fit.
8. Why is it important to monitor heart rate frequently during exercise in heat, in humidity, and at altitude?
9. What is the recommended resistance-training program for untrained adults?

SUGGESTED READINGS

American College of Sports Medicine. 2010. ACSM's *Resource Manual for Guidelines for Exercise Testing and Prescription*. 6th ed. Baltimore: Lippincott Williams & Wilkins.

Baechle, T. R., and R. W. Earle. 2008. *Essentials of Strength Training and Conditioning*. 3rd ed. Champaign, IL: Human Kinetics.

Durstine, J. L., G. E. Moore, M. J. LaMonte, and B. A. Franklin. 2008. *Pollock's Textbook of Cardiovascular Disease and Rehabilitation*. Champaign, IL: Human Kinetics.

Faigenbaum, A. D., and K. J. McInnis. 2007. Guidelines for muscular strength and endurance training. In *Health Fitness Instructor's Handbook*, 5th ed. E. T. Howley and B. D. Franks (eds). Champaign, IL: Human Kinetics.

Howley, E. T., and B. D. Franks. 2007. *Health Fitness Instructor's Handbook*. 5th ed. Champaign, IL: Human Kinetics.

Liemohn, W. P. 2007. Exercise prescription for flexibility and low-back function. In *Health Fitness Instructor's Handbook*. 5th ed. E. T. Howley and B. D. Franks (eds). Champaign, IL: Human Kinetics.

U.S. Department of Health and Human Services. 1996. *Physical Activity and Health: A Report of the Surgeon General*. Atlanta, GA: U.S. Department of Health and Human Services, Centers for Disease Control and Prevention, National Center for Chronic Disease Prevention and Health Promotion.

REFERENCES

1. **American College of Sports Medicine.** American College of Sports Medicine position stand: the recommended quantity and quality of exercise for developing and maintaining cardiorespiratory and muscular fitness, and flexibility in healthy adults. *Medicine and Science in Sports and Exercise* 30: 975–991, 1998.
2. **American College of Sports Medicine.** *Guidelines for Exercise Testing and Prescription*. Baltimore: Lippincott Williams & Wilkins, 2010.
3. **American College of Sports Medicine.** Progression models in resistance training for healthy adults. *Medicine and Science in Sports and Exercise* 41: 1510–1530, 2009.
4. **American College of Sports Medicine.** Progression models in resistance training for healthy adults. *Medicine and Science in Sports and Exercise* 34: 364–380, 2002.
5. **American College of Sports Medicine.** Summary statement: workshop on physical activity and public health. *Sports Medicine Bulletin* 28:7: 1993.
6. **American Heart Association.** Statement on exercise: benefits and recommendations for physical activity programs for all Americans. A statement for health professionals by the Committee on Exercise and Cardiac Rehabilitation of the Council on Clinical Cardiology, American Heart Association. *Circulation* 86: 340–344, 1992.
7. **Birk TJ, and Birk CA.** Use of ratings of perceived exertion for exercise prescription. *Sports Medicine (Auckland, NZ)* 4: 1–8, 1987.
8. **Blair SN, Kohl HW, III, Barlow CE, Paffenbarger RS, Jr., Gibbons LW, and Macera CA.** Changes in physical fitness and all-cause mortality: a prospective study of healthy and unhealthy men. *JAMA 273*: 1093–1098, 1995.

9. **Blair SN, Kohl HW, III, Paffenbarger RS, Jr., Clark DG, Cooper KH, and Gibbons LW.** Physical fitness and all-cause mortality: a prospective study of healthy men and women. *JAMA 262*: 2395–2401, 1989.
10. **Byrd R, Chandler TJ, Conley MS, Fry AC, Haff GG, Koch A, Hatfield F, Kirksey KB, McBride J, McBride T, Newton H, HS OB, Stone MH, Pierce KC, Plisk S, Ritchie-Stone M, and Wathen D.** Strength training: single versus multiple sets. *Sports Medicine (Auckland, NZ)* 27: 409–416, 1999.
11. **Carpinelli RN, and Otto RM.** Strength training: single versus multiple sets. *Sports Medicine (Auckland, NZ)* 26: 73–84, 1998.
12. **Caspersen CJ, Powell KE, and Christenson GM.** Physical activity, exercise, and physical fitness: definitions and distinctions for health-related research. *Public Health Reports* 100: 126–131, 1985.
13. **Cavanagh PR.** *The Running Shoe Book*. Mountain View: Anderson World, 1980.
14. **Ceci R, and Hassmen P.** Self-monitored exercise at three different RPE intensities in treadmill vs field running. *Medicine and Science in Sports and Exercise* 23: 732–738, 1991.
15. **Chow RJ, and Wilmore JH.** The regulation of exercise intensity by ratings of perceived exertion. *Journal of Cardiac Rehabilitation* 4: 382–387, 1984.
16. **Church TS, Earnest CP, Skinner JS, and Blair SN.** Effects of different doses of physical activity on cardiorespiratory fitness among sedentary, overweight or obese postmenopausal women with elevated blood pressure: a randomized controlled trial. *JAMA 297*: 2081–2091, 2007.

17. **Dionne FT, Turcotte L, Thibault MC, Boulay MR, Skinner JS, and Bouchard C.** Mitochondrial DNA sequence polymorphism, V̇O₂ max, and response to endurance training. *Medicine and Science in Sports and Exercise* 23: 177–185, 1991.

18. **Galvao DA, and Taaffe DR.** Single- vs. multiple-set resistance training: recent developments in the controversy. *Journal of Strength and Conditioning Research / National Strength & Conditioning Association* 18: 660–667, 2004.

19. **Gellish RL, Goslin BR, Olson RE, McDonald A, Russi GD, and Moudgil VK.** Longitudinal modeling of the relationship between age and maximal heart rate. *Medicine and Science in Sports and Exercise* 39: 822–829, 2007.

20. **Goodman LS, and Gilman A.** *The Pharmacological Basis of Therapeutics.* New York: Macmillan Publishing Company, Inc, 1975.

21. **Gutmann M.** Perceived exertion-heart rate relationship during exercise testing and training in cardiac patients. *Journal of Cardiac Rehabilitation* 1: 52–59, 1981.

22. **Hage P.** Perceived exertion: One measure of exercise intensity. *The Physician and Sportsmedicine* 9: 136–143, 1981.

23. **Haskell WL.** Dose-response issues from a biological perspective. In: *Physical Activity, Fitness, and Health*, edited by Bouchard C, Shephard RJ, and Stevens T. Champaign: Human Kinetics, 1994, p. 1030–1039.

24. **Haskell WL.** Physical activity and health: need to define the required stimulus. *The American Journal of Cardiology* 55: 4D–9D, 1985.

25. **Haskell WL, Lee IM, Pate RR, Powell KE, Blair SN, Franklin BA, Macera CA, Heath GW, Thompson PD, and Bauman A.** Physical activity and public health: updated recommendation for adults from the American College of Sports Medicine and the American Heart Association. *Medicine and Science in Sports and Exercise* 39: 1423–1434, 2007.

26. **Haskell WL, Montoye HJ, and Orenstein D.** Physical activity and exercise to achieve health-related physical fitness components. *Public Health Rep* 100: 202–212, 1985.

27. **Hellerstein H.** Principles of exercise prescription for normals and cardiac subjects. In: *Exercise Training in Coronary Heart Disease*, edited by Naughton JP, and Hellerstein HK. New York: Academic Press, 1973, p. 129–167.

28. **Hellerstein HK, and Ader R.** Relationship between percent maximal oxygen uptake (% max V̇O₂) and percent maximal heart rate (% MHR) in normals and cardiacs (ASHD). *Circulation* 43–44 (Suppl. II): 76, 1971.

29. **Hellerstein HK, and Franklin BA.** Exercise testing and prescription. In: *Rehabilitation of the Coronary Patient*, edited by Wenger NK, and Hellerstein HK. New York: Wiley, 1984, p. 197–284.

30. **Hetzler RK, Seip RL, Boutcher SH, Pierce E, Snead D, and Weltman A.** Effect of exercise modality on ratings of perceived exertion at various lactate concentrations. *Medicine and Science in Sports and Exercise* 23: 88–92, 1991.

31. **Howley ET.** Type of activity: resistance, aerobic and leisure versus occupational physical activity. *Medicine and Science in Sports and Exercise* 33: S364–369; discussion S419–320, 2001.

32. **Howley ET, and Franks BD.** *Health Fitness Instructor's Handbook.* Champaign: Human Kinetics, 2007.

33. **Humburg H, Baars H, Schroder J, Reer R, and Braumann KM.** 1-set vs. 3-set resistance training: a crossover study. *Journal of Strength and Conditioning Research/National Strength & Conditioning Association* 21: 578–582, 2007.

34. **Jennings GL, Deakin G, Korner P, Meredith I, Kingwell B, and Nelson L.** What is the dose-response relationship between exercise training and blood pressure? *Annals of Medicine* 23: 313–318, 1991.

35. **Karvonen J, and Vuorimaa T.** Heart rate and exercise intensity during sports activities: practical application. *Sports Medicine (Auckland, NZ)* 5: 303–311, 1988.

36. **Karvonen MJ, Kentala E, and Mustala O.** The effects of training on heart rate; a longitudinal study. *Annales Medicinae Experimentalis et Biologiae Fenniae* 35: 307–315, 1957.

37. **Kasaniemi YA, Danforth J, E., Jensen MD, Kopelman PG, Lefebvre P, and Reeder BA.** Dose-response issues concerning physical activity and health: an evidenced-based symposium. *Medicine and Science in Sports and Exercise* 33 (Supp): S351–358, 2001.

38. **Lee IM, Hsieh CC, and Paffenbarger RS, Jr.** Exercise intensity and longevity in men. The Harvard alumni health study. *JAMA* 273: 1179–1184, 1995.

39. **Londeree BR, and Ames SA.** Trend analysis of the % V̇O₂ max-HR regression. *Medicine and Science in Sports* 8: 123–125, 1976.

40. **Lounana J, Campion F, Noakes TD, and Medelli J.** Relationship between %HRmax, %HR reserve, % V̇O₂ max, and %V̇O₂ reserve in elite cyclists. *Medicine and Science in Sports and Exercise* 39: 350–357, 2007.

41. **Morgans L.** Heart rate responses during singles and doubles tennis competition. *The Physician and Sportsmedicine* 15: 67–74, 1987.

42. **O'Donovan G, Owen A, Bird SR, Kearney EM, Nevill AM, Jones DW, and Woolf-May K.** Changes in cardiorespiratory fitness and coronary heart disease risk factors following 24 wk of moderate- or high-intensity exercise of equal energy cost. *J Appl Physiol* 98: 1619–1625, 2005.

43. **Paffenbarger RS, and Hale WE.** Work activity and coronary heart mortality. *The New England Journal of Medicine* 292: 545–550, 1975.

44. **Paffenbarger RS, Hyde RT, and Wing AL.** Physical activity and physical fitness as determinants of health and longevity. In: *Exercise, Fitness and Health*, edited by Bouchard C, Shephard RJ, Stevens T, Sutton JR, and McPherson BD. Champaign: Human Kinetics, 1990, p. 33–48.

45. **Paffenbarger RS, Jr., Hyde RT, Wing AL, and Hsieh CC.** Physical activity, all-cause mortality, and longevity of college alumni. *The New England Journal of Medicine* 314: 605–613, 1986.

46. **Paffenbarger RS, Jr., Hyde RT, Wing AL, Lee IM, Jung DL, and Kampert JB.** The association of changes in physical-activity level and other lifestyle characteristics with mortality among men. *The New England Journal of Medicine* 328: 538–545, 1993.

47. **Pate RR, Pratt M, Blair SN, Haskell WL, Macera CA, Bouchard C, Buchner D, Ettinger W, Heath GW, King AC, et al.** Physical activity and public health: a recommendation from the Centers for Disease Control and Prevention and the American College of Sports Medicine. *JAMA* 273: 402–407, 1995.

48. **Peterson MD, Rhea MR, and Alvar BA.** Maximizing strength development in athletes: a meta-analysis to determine the dose-response relationship. *Journal of Strength and Conditioning Research / National Strength & Conditioning Association* 18: 377–382, 2004.

49. **Pollock ML.** How much exercise is enough? *The Physician and Sportsmedicine* 6: 50–64, 1978.

50. **Pollock ML, Broida J, Kendrick Z, Miller HS, Jr., Janeway R, and Linnerud AC.** Effects of training two days per week at different intensities on middle-aged men. *Medicine and Science in Sports* 4: 192–197, 1972.

51. **Pollock ML, Dimmick J, Miller HS, Jr., Kendrick Z, and Linnerud AC.** Effects of mode of training on cardiovascular function and body composition of adult men. *Medicine and Science in Sports* 7: 139–145, 1975.

52. **Pollock ML, Gettman LR, Milesis CA, Bah MD, Durstine L, and Johnson RB.** Effects of frequency and duration of training on attrition and incidence of injury. *Medicine and Science in Sports* 9: 31–36, 1977.

53. **Pollock ML, and Wilmore JH.** *Exercise in Health and Disease.* Philadelphia: W. B. Saunders, 1990.

54. **Porcari JP, Ebbeling CB, Ward A, Freedson PS, and Rippe JM.** Walking for exercise testing and training. *Sports Medicine (Auckland, NZ)* 8: 189–200, 1989.

55. **Powell KE, Thompson PD, Caspersen CJ, and Kendrick JS.** Physical activity and the incidence of coronary heart disease. *Annual Review of Public Health* 8: 253–287, 1987.

56. **Proper KI, van den Heuvel SG, De Vroome EM, Hildebrandt VH, and Van der Beek AJ.** Dose-response relation between physical activity and sick leave. *British Journal of Sports Medicine* 40: 173–178, 2006.

57. **Rhea MR, Alvar BA, and Burkett LN.** Single versus multiple sets for strength: a meta-analysis to address the controversy. *Research Quarterly for Exercise and Sport* 73: 485–488, 2002.

58. **Rhea MR, Alvar BA, Burkett LN, and Ball SD.** A meta-analysis to determine the dose response for strength development. *Medicine and Science in Sports and Exercise* 35: 456–464, 2003.

59. **Robertson RJ, Goss FL, Auble TE, Cassinelli DA, Spina RJ, Glickman EL, Galbreath RW, Silberman RM, and Metz KF.** Cross-modal exercise prescription at absolute and relative oxygen uptake using perceived exertion. *Medicine and Science in Sports and Exercise* 22: 653–659, 1990.

60. **Ronnestad BR, Egeland W, Kvamme NH, Refsnes PE, Kadi F, and Raastad T.** Dissimilar effects of one- and three-set strength training on strength and muscle mass gains in upper and lower body in untrained subjects. *Journal of Strength and Conditioning Research / National Strength & Conditioning Association* 21: 157–163, 2007.

61. **Ruiz JR, Sui X, Lobelo F, Lee D-C, Morrow JR, Jackson AW, Hébert JR, Mathews CE, Sjöström M, and Blair SN.** Muscular strength and adiposity as predictors of adulthood cancer mortality in men. *Cancer Epidemiology, Biomarkers & Prevention* 18: 1468–1476, 2009.

62. **Saltin B, and Gollnick PD.** Skeletal muscle adaptability: significance for metabolism and performance. In: *Handbook of Physiology-Section 10: Skeletal Muscle*, edited by Peachey LD, Adrian RH, and Geiger SR. Baltimore: Lippincott Williams & Wilkins, 1983.

63. **Seip RL, Snead D, Pierce EF, Stein P, and Weltman A.** Perceptual responses and blood lactate concentration: effect of training state. *Medicine and Science in Sports and Exercise* 23: 80–87, 1991.

64. **Siscovick DS, Weiss NS, Fletcher RH, and Lasky T.** The incidence of primary cardiac arrest during vigorous exercise. *The New England Journal of Medicine* 311: 874–877, 1984.

65. **Siscovick DS, Weiss NS, Fletcher RH, Schoenbach VJ, and Wagner EH.** Habitual vigorous exercise and primary cardiac arrest: effect of other risk factors on the relationship. *Journal of Chronic Diseases* 37: 625–631, 1984.

66. **Swain DP.** $\dot{V}O_2$ reserve-a new method for exercise prescription. *ACSM's Health and Fitness Journal* 3: 10–14, 1999.

67. **Swain DP, and Franklin BA.** Comparison of cardioprotective benefits of vigorous versus moderate intensity aerobic exercise. *The American Journal of Cardiology* 97: 141–147, 2006.

68. **Swain DP, and Franklin BA.** $\dot{V}O_{(2)}$ reserve and the minimal intensity for improving cardiorespiratory fitness. *Medicine and Science in Sports and Exercise* 34: 152–157, 2002.

69. **Swain DP, and Leutholtz BC.** Heart rate reserve is equivalent to %$\dot{V}O_2$ reserve, not to % $\dot{V}O_2$ max. *Medicine and Science in Sports and Exercise* 29: 410–414, 1997.

70. **Swain DP, Leutholtz BC, King ME, Haas LA, and Branch JD.** Relationship between % heart rate reserve and % $\dot{V}O_2$ reserve in treadmill exercise. *Medicine and Science in Sports and Exercise* 30: 318–321, 1998.

71. **Tanaka H, Monahan KD, and Seals DR.** Age-predicted maximal heart rate revisited. *Journal of the American College of Cardiology* 37: 153–156, 2001.

72. **U.S. Department of Health and Human Services.** 2008 Physcial activity guidelines for Americans. http://wwwhealthgov/paguidelines/guidelines/defaultaspx 2008.

73. **U.S. Department of Health and Human Services.** Physical Activity Guidelines Advisory Committee Report 2008. http://wwwhealthgov/paguidelines/committeereportaspx 2008.

74. **U.S. Department of Health and Human Services.** *Healthy People 2000: National Health Promotion and Disease Prevention Objectives.* U.S. Government Printing Office, 1990.

75. **Wenger HA, and Bell GJ.** The interactions of intensity, frequency and duration of exercise training in altering cardiorespiratory fitness. *Sports Medicine (Auckland, NZ)* 3: 346–356, 1986.

76. **Wolfe BL, LeMura LM, and Cole PJ.** Quantitative analysis of single- vs. multiple-set programs in resistance training. *Journal of Strength and Conditioning Research/ National Strength & Conditioning Association* 18: 35–47, 2004.

Exercise and the Environment

■ Objectives

By studying this chapter, you should be able to do the following:

1. Describe the changes in atmospheric pressure, air temperature, and air density with increasing altitude.

2. Describe how altitude affects sprint performances and explain why that is the case.

3. Explain why distance running performance decreases at altitude.

4. Draw a graph to show the effect of altitude on $\dot{V}O_2$ max and list the reasons for this response.

5. Graphically describe the effect of altitude on the heart rate and ventilation responses to submaximal work, and explain why these changes are appropriate.

6. Describe the process of adaptation to altitude and the degree to which this adaptation can be complete.

7. Explain why such variability exists among athletes in the decrease in $\dot{V}O_2$ max upon exposure to altitude, the degree of improvement in $\dot{V}O_2$ max at altitude, and the gains made upon return to sea level.

8. Describe the potential problems associated with training at high altitude and how one might deal with them.

9. Explain the circumstances that caused physiologists to reevaluate their conclusions that humans could not climb Mount Everest without oxygen.

10. Explain the role that hyperventilation plays in helping to maintain a high oxygen-hemoglobin saturation at extreme altitudes.

11. List and describe the factors influencing the risk of heat injury.

12. Provide suggestions for the fitness participant to follow to minimize the likelihood of heat injury.

13. Describe in general terms the guidelines suggested for running road races in the heat.

14. Describe the three elements in the heat stress index, and explain why one is more important than the other two.

15. List the factors influencing hypothermia.

16. Explain what the wind chill index is relative to heat loss.

17. Explain why exposure to cold water is more dangerous than exposure to air of the same temperature.

18. Describe what the "clo" unit is and how recommendations for insulation change when one does exercise.

19. Describe the role of subcutaneous fat and heat production in the development of hypothermia.

20. List the steps to follow to deal with hypothermia.

21. Explain how carbon monoxide can influence performance, and list the steps that should be taken to reduce the impact of pollution on performance.

By now it should be clear that performance is dependent on more than simply having a high $\dot{V}O_2$ max. In chapter 23, we saw the role of diet and body composition on performance, and in chapter 25 we will formally consider "ergogenic" or work-enhancing aids and performance. Sandwiched between these chapters is a discussion of how the environmental factors of altitude, heat, cold, and pollution can influence performance.

ALTITUDE

In the late 1960s, when the Olympic Games were scheduled to be held in Mexico City, our attention was directed at the question of how altitude (2,300 meters at Mexico City) would affect performance. Previous experience at altitude suggested that many performances would not equal former Olympic standards or, for that matter, the athlete's own personal record (PR) at sea level. On the other hand, some performances were actually expected to be better because they were conducted at altitude. Why? What happens to $\dot{V}O_2$ max with altitude? Can a sea-level resident ever completely adapt to altitude? We will address these and other questions after a brief review of the environmental factors that change with increasing altitude.

Atmospheric Pressure

The **atmospheric pressure** at any spot on earth is a measure of the weight of a column of air directly over that spot. At sea level the weight (and height) of that column of air is greatest. As one climbs to higher and higher altitudes, the height and, of course, the weight of the column are reduced. Consequently, atmospheric pressure decreases with increasing altitude, the air is less dense, and each liter of air contains fewer molecules of gas. Since the *percentages* of O_2,

CO_2, and N_2 are the same at altitude as at sea level, any change in the partial pressure of each gas is due solely to the change in the atmospheric or barometric pressure (see chapter 10). The decrease in the partial pressure of O_2 (PO_2) with increasing altitude has a direct effect on the saturation of hemoglobin and, consequently, oxygen transport. This lower PO_2 is called **hypoxia,** with **normoxia** being the term to describe the PO_2 under sea-level conditions. The term **hyperoxia** describes a condition in which the inspired PO_2 is greater than that at sea level (see chapter 25). In addition to the hypoxic condition at altitude, the air temperature and humidity are lower, adding potential temperature regulation problems to the hypoxic stress of altitude. How do these changes affect performance? To answer that question we will divide performances into short-term anaerobic performances and long-term aerobic performances.

Short-Term Anaerobic Performance

In chapters 3 and 19 we described the importance of the anaerobic sources of ATP in maximal performances lasting 2 minutes or less. If this information is correct, and we think it is, then the short-term anaerobic races shouldn't be affected by the low PO_2 at altitude, because O_2 transport to the muscles is not limiting performance. Table 24.1 shows this to be the case when the sprint performances of the 1968 Mexico City Olympic Games (~2,300 m) were compared to those in the 1964 Tokyo Olympic Games (sea level) (59). The performances improved in all but one case, in which the time for the 400-meter run for the women was the same. The reasons for the improvements in performance include the "normal" gains made over time from one Olympic Games to the next and the fact that the density of the air at altitude offers less resistance to movements at high speeds. Improvements in the 100-meter and 400-meter races for each increase

Olympic Games	Short Races: Men				Short Races: Women			
	100 m	*200 m*	*400 m*	*800 m*	*100 m*	*200 m*	*400 m*	*800 m*
1964 (Tokyo)	10.0 s	20.3 s	45.1 s	1 m 45.1 s	11.4 s	23.0 s	52.0 s	2 m 1.1 s
1968 (Mexico City)	9.9 s	19.8 s	43.8 s	1 m 44.3 s	11.0 s	22.5 s	52.0 s	2 m 0.9 s
% change*	+1.0	+2.5	+2.9	+0.8	+3.5	+2.2	0	+0.2

TABLE 24.1 Comparison of Performances in Short Races in the 1964 and 1968 Olympic Games

*+ sign indicates improvement over 1964 performance.

From E. T. Howley, "Effect of Altitude on Physical Performance," in G. A. Stull and T. K. Cureton, *Encyclopedia of Physical Education, Fitness and Sports: Training, Environment, Nutrition, and Fitness.* Copyright © 1980 American Alliance for Health, Physical Education, Recreation and Dance, Reston VA. Reprinted by permission.

of 1,000 meters in altitude have been estimated to be about 0.08 s and 0.06 s, respectively (9, 96). The issue of lower air resistance sparked controversy over Bob Beamon's fantastic performance in the long jump in the Mexico City Games (see A Closer Look 24.1).

Long-Term Aerobic Performance

Maximal performances in excess of 2 minutes are primarily dependent on oxygen delivery, and, in contrast to the short-term performances, are clearly affected by the lower PO_2 at altitude. Table 24.2 shows the results of the distance running events from 1,500 meters up through the marathon and the 50,000-meter walk, and as you can see, performance was diminished at all distances but the 1,500-meter run (59). This performance is worthy of special note, given that it was expected to be affected, as were the others. It is more than just of passing interest that the record setter was Kipchoge Keino, who was born and raised in Kenya at an altitude similar to that of Mexico City. Did he possess a special adaptation due to his birthplace? We will come back to this question in a later section. We would like to continue our discussion of

the effect of altitude on performance by asking, "Why did the performance fall off by as much as 6.2% in the long-distance races?"

- The atmospheric pressure, PO_2, air temperature, and air density decrease with altitude.
- The lower air density at altitude offers less resistance to high-speed movement, and sprint performances are either not affected or are improved.

Maximal Aerobic Power and Altitude

The decrease in distance running performance at altitude is similar to what occurs when a trained runner becomes untrained—it would clearly take longer to run a marathon! The similarity in the effect is related to a decrease in maximal aerobic power that occurs with detraining and with increasing altitude. Figure 24.1 shows that $\dot{V}O_2$ max decreases in a linear fashion, being about 12% lower at 2,400 meters (7,400 feet), 20% lower at 3,100 meters (10,200 feet), and 27% lower

A CLOSER LOOK 24.1

Jumping Through Thin Air

In the 1968 Olympic Games in Mexico City, Bob Beamon shattered the world record in the long jump with a leap of 29 feet 2.5 inches (8.90 m), 21.75 in (55 cm) longer than the existing world record. Because the record was achieved at altitude where air density is less than that at sea level, some questions were raised about the true magnitude of the achievement. Recent progress in biomechanics has made it

possible to determine just how much would have been gained by doing the long jump at altitude (124). The calculations had to consider the mass of the jumper, a drag coefficient based on the frontal area exposed to the air while jumping, and the difference in the air density between sea level and Mexico City. The result indicated that approximately 2.4 cm (less than an inch) would have been gained by doing the jump

at altitude where the air density is less. This confirmed the extraordinary nature of Beamon's performance. Scientists have tried to predict the effect of altitude on running performances by considering the opposing factors of lower air density and the reduced availability of oxygen (87). The latter factor is discussed relative to long-distance races.

TABLE 24.2	Comparison of Performances in Long Races in the 1964 and 1968 Olympic Games					
Olympic Games	Long Races: Men					
	1,500 m	*3,000 m*	*5,000 m*	*10,000 m*	*Marathon*	*50,000 m Walk*
1964 (Tokyo)	3 m 38.1 s	8 m 30.8 s	13 m 48.8 s	28 m 24.4 s	2 h 12 m 11.2 s	4 h 11 m 11.2 s
1968 (Mexico City)	3 m 34.9 s	8 m 51.0 s	14 m 05.0 s	29 m 27.4 s	2 h 20 m 24.6 s	4 h 20 m 13.6 s
% change*	+1.5	−3.9	−1.9	−3.7	−6.2	−3.6

*+ sign indicates improvement over 1964 performance.

From E. T. Howley, "Effect of Altitude on Physical Performance," in G. A. Stull and T. K. Cureton, *Encyclopedia of Physical Education, Fitness and Sports: Training, Environment, Nutrition, and Fitness.* Copyright © 1980 American Alliance for Health, Physical Education, Recreation and Dance, Reston VA. Reprinted by permission.

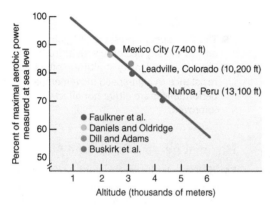

Figure 24.1 Changes in maximal aerobic power with increasing altitude. The sea-level value for maximal aerobic power is set to 100%. From E. T. Howley, "Effect of Altitude on Physical Performance," in G. A. Stull and T. K. Cureton, *Encyclopedia of Physical Education, Fitness and Sports: Training, Environment, Nutrition, and Fitness.* Copyright © 1980 American Alliance for Health, Physical Education, Recreation and Dance, Reston VA. Reprinted by permission.

at about 4,000 meters (13,100 feet) (15, 25, 28, 36). Although it should be no surprise that endurance performance decreases with such changes in $\dot{V}O_2$ max, why does $\dot{V}O_2$ max decrease?

Cardiovascular Function at Altitude Maximal oxygen uptake is equal to the product of the maximal cardiac output and the maximal arteriovenous oxygen difference, $\dot{V}O_2 = CO \times (CaO_2 - C\bar{v}O_2)$. Given this relationship, the decrease in $\dot{V}O_2$ max with increasing altitude could be due to a decrease in cardiac output and/or a decrease in oxygen extraction. It will become clear in the following paragraphs that oxygen extraction is a major factor causing a decrease in $\dot{V}O_2$ max at all altitudes, with decreases in maximal cardiac output contributing primarily at higher altitudes.

Maximal cardiac output is equal to the product of maximal heart rate and maximal stroke volume. In several studies the maximal heart rate was unchanged at altitudes of 2,300 meters (33, 92), 3,100 meters (45), and 4,000 meters (15), while changes in maximal stroke volume were somewhat inconsistent (64). If these two variables, maximal stroke volume and maximal heart rate, do not change much at these altitudes, then the decrease in $\dot{V}O_2$ max must be due to a difference in oxygen extraction.

Although oxygen extraction ($CaO_2 - C\bar{v}O_2$) could decrease due to a decrease in the arterial oxygen content (CaO_2) or an increase in the mixed venous oxygen content ($C\bar{v}O_2$), the primary cause is the desaturation of the arterial blood due to the low PO_2 at altitude. The lower atmospheric PO_2 causes the alveolar PO_2 to be lower. This reduces the pressure gradient for oxygen diffusion between the alveolus and the pulmonary capillary blood, thus lowering the arterial PO_2. As you recall from chapter 10, as the arterial PO_2 falls, there is a reduction in the volume of oxygen bound to hemoglobin. At sea level, hemoglobin is about 96% to 98% saturated with oxygen. However, at 2,300 meters and 4,000 meters, saturation falls to 88% and 71%, respectively. These decreases in the oxygen saturation of hemoglobin are similar to the reductions in $\dot{V}O_2$ max at these altitudes described earlier. Because maximal oxygen transport is the product of the maximal cardiac output and the arterial oxygen content, the capacity to transport oxygen to the working muscles at altitude is reduced due to desaturation, even though maximal cardiac output may be unchanged during acute exposures up to altitudes of 4,000 meters (64). However, it must be added that a variety of studies have shown a decrease in maximal heart rate at altitude. Although some of these decreases have been observed at altitudes of 3,100 meters (28) and 4,300 meters (33), it is more common to find lower maximal heart rates above altitudes of 4,300 meters. For example, compared to maximal HR at sea level, maximal HR was observed to be 24 to 33 beats/minute lower at 4,650 meters (15,300 feet) and 47 beats/minute lower at about 6,100 meters (20,000 feet) (48, 95). This depression in maximal heart rate is reversed by acute restoration of normoxia, or the use of atropine (48). This altitude-induced bradycardia suggests that myocardial hypoxia may trigger the slower heart rate to decrease the work and, therefore, the oxygen demand of the heart muscle.

As mentioned earlier, during an acute exposure to altitude, stroke volume during exercise is only slightly reduced, if at all. However, prolonged exposures to altitude results in a reduction in plasma volume that leads to a lower end diastolic volume and stroke volume (77). This means that $\dot{V}O_2$ max decreases at a faster rate at the higher altitudes due to the combined effects of the desaturation of hemoglobin and the decrease in maximal cardiac output.

This desaturation of arterial blood at altitude affects more than $\dot{V}O_2$ max. The cardiovascular responses to submaximal work are also influenced. Due to the fact that each liter of blood is carrying less oxygen, more liters of blood must be pumped per minute in order to compensate. This is accomplished through an increase in the HR response, since the stroke volume response is at its highest point already, or it is actually lower at altitude due to the hypoxia (2). This elevated HR response is shown in figure 24.2 (45). This has implications for more than the performance-based athlete. The average person who participates in an exercise program will have to decrease the intensity of exercise at altitude in order to stay in the target heart rate zone. Remember, the exercise prescription needed for a cardiovascular training effect includes a proper duration of exercise to achieve an appropriate total caloric expenditure (see chapter 16). If the intensity is too high, the person will have more difficulty achieving that goal.

Respiratory Function at Altitude In the introduction to this section we mentioned that the air is less dense at altitude. This means that there are fewer

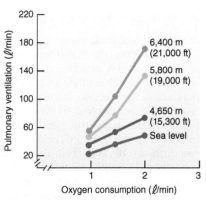

Figure 24.3 The effect of altitude on the ventilation response to submaximal exercise.

O_2 molecules per liter of air, and if a person wanted to consume the same number of liters of O_2, pulmonary ventilation would have to increase. At 5,600 meters (18,400 feet), the atmospheric pressure is one-half that at sea level, and the number of molecules of O_2 per liter of air is reduced by one-half; therefore, a person would have to breathe twice as much air to take in the same amount of O_2. The consequences of this are shown in figure 24.3, which presents the ventilation responses of a subject who exercised at work rates demanding about a $\dot{V}O_2$ of 1 to 2 L $\cdot$ min^{-1} at sea level and at three altitudes exceeding 4,000 meters. The pulmonary ventilation is elevated at all altitudes, reaching values of almost 180 L $\cdot$ min^{-1} at 6,400 meters (21,000 feet) (95). This extreme ventilatory response requires the respiratory muscles, primarily the diaphragm, to work so hard that fatigue may occur. We will see more on this in a later section dealing with the assault on Mount Everest.

IN SUMMARY

- Distance-running performances are adversely affected at altitude due to the reduction in the PO_2, which causes a decrease in hemoglobin saturation and $\dot{V}O_2$ max.
- Up to moderate altitudes (~4,000 meters) the decrease in $\dot{V}O_2$ max is due primarily to the decrease in the arterial oxygen content brought about by the decrease in atmospheric PO_2. At higher altitudes, the rate at which $\dot{V}O_2$ max falls is increased due to a reduction in maximal cardiac output.
- Submaximal performances conducted at altitude require higher heart rate and ventilation responses due to the lower oxygen content of arterial blood and the reduction in the number of oxygen molecules per liter of air, respectively.

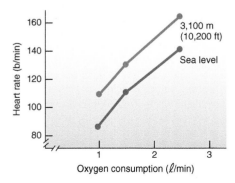

Figure 24.2 The effect of altitude on the heart-rate response to submaximal exercise.

Acclimatization to High Altitude

The low PO_2 at altitude triggers an increase in hypoxia inducible factor-1 (HIF-1) that is present in most cells of the body. HIF-1 activates genes associated with erythropoietin (EPO) production that is involved in red blood cell production, vascular endothelial growth factors that are involved in the generation of new blood vessels, and nitric oxide synthase that promotes the synthesis of nitric oxide that is involved in vasodilation (110). In the high altitude populations of the Andes in South America, the acclimatization response to the low PO_2 at altitude is to produce additional red blood cells to compensate for the desaturation of hemoglobin. In the mining community of Morococha, Peru, where people reside at altitudes above 4,540 meters, hemoglobin levels of $211 \text{ g} \cdot L^{-1}$ have been measured, in contrast to the normal $156 \text{ g} \cdot L^{-1}$ of the sea-level residents in Lima, Peru. This higher hemoglobin compensates rather completely for the low PO_2 at those altitudes (62):

Sea level: $156 \text{ g} \cdot L^{-1}$ times $1.34 \text{ ml } O_2 \cdot g^{-1}$ at 98% saturation = $206 \text{ ml} \cdot L^{-1}$

4,540 m: $211 \text{ g} \cdot L^{-1}$ times $1.34 \text{ ml } O_2 \cdot g^{-1}$ at 81% saturation = $224 \text{ ml} \cdot L^{-1}$

One of the best tests of the degree to which these high-altitude residents have adapted is found in the $\dot{V}O_2$ max values measured at altitude. Average values of 46 to $50 \text{ ml} \cdot kg^{-1} \cdot min^{-1}$ were measured on the altitude natives (65, 74–76), which compares favorably with sea-level natives in that country and in ours.

There is no question that any sea-level resident who makes a journey to altitude and stays a while will experience an acclimatization process that includes an increase in red blood cell number. However, the adaptation will probably never be as complete as seen in the permanent residents. This conclusion is drawn from a study that compared $\dot{V}O_2$ max values of several different groups: (a) Peruvian lowlanders and Peace Corps volunteers who came to altitude as adults, (b) lowlanders who came to altitude as children and spent their growing years at altitude, and (c) permanent altitude residents (36). The $\dot{V}O_2$ max values were $46 \text{ ml} \cdot kg^{-1} \cdot min^{-1}$ for the altitude residents and those who arrived there as children. In contrast, the lowlanders who arrived as adults and spent only 1 to 4 years at altitude had values of $38 \text{ ml} \cdot kg^{-1} \cdot min^{-1}$. This indicates that to have complete acclimatization, one must spend the developmental years at high altitude. This may help explain the surprisingly good performance of Kipchoge Keino's performance in the 1,500-meter run at the Mexico City Olympic Games mentioned earlier, because he spent his childhood at an altitude similar to that of Mexico City.

The elevated hemoglobin concentration of the Peruvian permanent altitude residents was believed to be the primary means by which humans adapted in order to live at high altitudes. That is no longer the case. It has become clear that those who live at high altitudes in Tibet have achieved that level of acclimatization by a different means compared to those who live in the Andes (71, 108, 116, 134). Tibetan residents adapt by increasing the oxygen saturation of hemoglobin, rather than the concentration of hemoglobin, which may be 30 g/L lower than Andeans living at comparable altitudes. Tibetan Sherpas' superior performance at extreme altitudes is linked, not to an exceptional $\dot{V}O_2$ max at altitude, but to better lung function, maximal cardiac output, and level of oxygen saturation of hemoglobin (110). The different types of adaptations observed in these populations is related to the natural selection of those with unique genes that promote either an increase in red blood cell production (e.g., Andean) or an increase in oxygen saturation (Tibetan) that is a result of an increase in nitric oxide in the lungs that promotes an increase in blood flow (116, 134).

IN SUMMARY

- Andeans adapt to high altitude by producing more red blood cells to counter the desaturation caused by the lower PO_2. Andean altitude residents who spent their growing years at altitude show a rather complete adaptation as seen in their arterial oxygen content and $\dot{V}O_2$ max values. Lowlanders who arrive as adults show only a modest adaptation.

- In contrast, Tibetan high altitude residents adapt by increasing the oxygen saturation of the existing hemoglobin, a result of increased blood flow to the lungs due to high nitric oxide levels.

Training for Competition at Altitude

It was clear to many of the middle- and long-distance runners who competed in the Olympic Trials or Games in 1968 that the altitude was going to have a detrimental effect on performance. Using $\dot{V}O_2$ max as an indicator of the impact on performance, scientists studied the effect of immediate exposure to altitude, the rate of recovery in $\dot{V}O_2$ max as the individual stayed at altitude, and whether $\dot{V}O_2$ max was higher than the pre-altitude value upon return to sea level. The results were interesting, not due to the general trends that were expected, but to the extreme variability in response among the athletes. For example, the decrease in $\dot{V}O_2$ max upon ascent to a 2,300-meter altitude ranged from 8.8% to 22.3% (92); at 3,090 meters it ranged from 13.9% to 24.4% (28); and at 4,000 meters the decrease ranged from 24.8% to 34.3% (15). One of the major conclusions that could be drawn from these data is that the best runner at sea level might not be the best at altitude if that person had the largest drop in $\dot{V}O_2$ max. Why such variability? Studies of this phenomenon suggest that the variability in the decrease in $\dot{V}O_2$ max across individuals relates to the degree to which athletes experience desaturation of arterial blood during maximal work (66, 72, 89). Chapter 10 described the effect that arterial desaturation has on $\dot{V}O_2$ max of superior athletes at sea level. If such desaturation can occur under sea-level conditions, then the altitude condition should have an additional impact, with the magnitude of the impact being greater on those who suffer some desaturation at sea level. Consistent with that, exposure to a simulated altitude of 3,000 meters resulted in a 20.8% decrease in $\dot{V}O_2$ max for trained subjects and only a 9.8% decrease for untrained subjects (66).

The decrease in $\dot{V}O_2$ max upon exposure to altitude was not the only physiological response that varied among the athletes. There also was a variable response in the size of the increase in $\dot{V}O_2$ max as the subjects stayed at altitude and continued to train. One study, lasting 28 days at 2,300 meters, found the $\dot{V}O_2$ max to increase from 1% to 8% over that time (94). Some found the $\dot{V}O_2$ max to gradually improve over a period of 10 to 28 days (6, 26, 28, 92), while others (33, 45) did not. In addition, when the subjects returned to sea level and were retested, some found the $\dot{V}O_2$ max to be higher than before they left (6, 26, 28), whereas others found no improvements (15, 36, 43). Why was there such variability in response?

There are several possibilities. If an athlete was not in peak condition before ascending to altitude, the combined stress of the exercise and altitude could increase the $\dot{V}O_2$ max over time while at altitude and show an additional gain upon return to sea level. Evidence exists both for (106) and against (1, 32, 121) the idea that the combination of altitude and exercise stress leads to greater changes in $\dot{V}O_2$ max than exercise stress alone. Another reason for the variability is related to the altitude at which the training was conducted. When runners trained at high (4,000 meters) altitude, the intensity of the runs (relative to sustained sea-level speeds) had to be reduced to complete a workout, due to the reduction in $\dot{V}O_2$ max that occurs at altitude. As a result, the runner might actually "detrain" while at altitude, and subsequent performance at sea level might not be as good as it was before going to altitude (15). Daniels and Oldridge (25) provided a way around this problem by having runners alternate training at altitude (7 to 14 days) and at sea level (5 to 11 days). Using an altitude of only 2,300 meters, the runners were still able to train at "race pace," and detraining did not occur. In fact, thirteen personal records were achieved by the athletes when they raced at sea level. For more on this, see Saunders, Pyne, and Gore's review on endurance

training at altitude in Suggested Readings. The focus on gaining the benefits of acclimation to altitude has resulted in a strategy in which the athlete lives at high altitude but trains at low altitude—without ever leaving low altitude. See The Winning Edge 24.1.

IN SUMMARY

- When athletes train at altitude, some experience a greater decline in $\dot{V}O_2$ max than others. This may be due to differences in the degree to which each athlete experiences a desaturation of hemoglobin. Remember, some athletes experience desaturation during maximal work at sea level.
- Some athletes show an increase in $\dot{V}O_2$ max while training at altitude, whereas others do not. This may be due to the degree to which the athlete was trained before going to altitude.
- In addition, some athletes show an improved $\dot{V}O_2$ max upon return to sea level, whereas others do not. Part of the reason may be the altitude at which they train. Those who train at high altitudes may actually "detrain" due to the fact that the quality of their workouts suffers at the high altitudes. To get around this problem, athletes can alternate low-altitude and sea-level exposures, or follow a "live high, train low" program.

The Quest for Everest

The most obvious tie between exercise and altitude is mountain climbing. The climber faces the stress of altitude, cold, radiation, and, of course, the work of climbing up steep slopes or sheer rock walls. A goal of some mountaineers has been to climb Mount Everest, at 8,848 meters, the highest mountain on earth. Figure 24.4 shows various attempts to climb Everest during the twentieth century (131). Special note should be made of Hillary and Tensing, who were the first to do it, and Messner and Habeler, who, to the amazement of all, did it without supplemental oxygen in 1978. See Messner in the Suggested Readings for complete details on how they accomplished this feat. This achievement brought scientists back to Everest in 1981 asking how this was possible. This section provides some background to this fascinating story.

In 1924, Norton's climbing team attempted to scale Everest without O_2 and almost succeeded—they stopped only 300 meters from the summit (84). This 1924 expedition was noteworthy because data were collected on the climbers and porters by physicians and scientists associated with the attempt. In addition, new questions have been raised about two of the climbers who died in their attempt to reach the summit (see A Closer Look 24.2). The story of this assault

THE WINNING EDGE 24.1

Live High, Train Low, or the Reverse!

There is great interest in the "live high, train low" strategy as a way of improving endurance performance. The "live high" refers to being exposed to a low PO_2 to obtain the unique benefits mentioned earlier, and "train low" refers to doing exercise at sea level (or a very low altitude) to not affect the intensity and/or duration of the workouts. However, support for this is mixed due to the influence of a wide variety of factors: subjects, length of study, intensity and volume of training, the altitude (be it simulated or real), and the length of stay at altitude (135). One study tried to shed some light on why there is such variability in response to this training strategy (22). Thirty-nine collegiate runners were divided into "responders" and "nonresponders" on the basis of changes in their 5,000-meter run time following training at a high-altitude training camp. All of the runners had lived "high" (2,500 m), but some had trained at 2,500 to 3,000 m (high-high group), some at 1,200 to 1,400 m (high-low group), and some had done low-intensity training at 2,500 to 3,000 m and interval work at low altitude (high-high-low). The responders were found to have an increase in plasma erythropoietin (EPO), red blood cell volume, and $\dot{V}O_2$ max, which provides a strong physiological connection to the increased performance in the 5,000-m run after altitude training. Interestingly, while the nonresponders had an increase in EPO, they did not have an increase in either red blood cell mass or $\dot{V}O_2$ max. Another difference between the responders and nonresponders was in their ability to maintain the quality of their workouts at altitude: nonresponders demonstrated a 9% reduction in interval-training velocity and a significantly lower $\dot{V}O_2$ during the intervals. There were two take-home messages from this study:

■ live at a high enough altitude to elicit an increase in red blood cell mass (due to an acute increase in EPO), and

■ train at a low enough altitude to maintain interval-training velocity. For runners who experience a significant desaturation of hemoglobin at sea level, even low-altitude training may be inconsistent with maintaining interval-training velocity.

It would seem that the physiology related to improvements in endurance performance following a live-high, train-low protocol is well described and accepted; however, that is not the case. Since the above study (22) was published, there has been a "point-counterpoint" debate on this issue (67), along with a series of letters to the editor in response to the debate (67), and an explosion of new research. Simply put, in contrast to the above link of altitude exposure to the increase in red blood cell mass, and then $\dot{V}O_2$ max and performance, other studies have shown that 6 weeks of intermittent hypoxia during training improved $\dot{V}O_2$ max and muscle oxidative potential and performance, without a change in red cell mass (30, 88, 139). A summary of potential mechanisms, other than red cell mass, linked to the improved performance following exposure to hypoxia was recently published (41). The focus in this review was on improved mitochondrial function and increased buffering capacity.

Given that intermittent hypobaric hypoxia (3 hrs/day, 5 days/wk at 4,000–5,500 m) for 4 weeks increased EPO, but did not increase red blood cell production or improve performance (42, 103), questions have been raised about what "dose" of altitude exposure is needed to generate a response. On the basis of several studies, it appears that 4 weeks of altitude exposure of ≥22 hrs/day at 2,000–2,500 meters is needed to elicit increases in red blood cell mass, $\dot{V}O_2$ max, and performance (125, 133). If a simulated altitude is used for fewer hours per day (12–16 hrs), a higher elevation (2,500–3,000 m) is needed. Clearly, such changes in $\dot{V}O_2$ max can have a favorable effect on athletic performances such as the marathon (21), so it is no surprise that the World Anti-Doping Agency (WADA) has examined the live-high, train-low approach to improving performance (because it results in changes in red blood cell mass similar to blood doping—see chapter 25). Interestingly, although WADA raised concerns from both an ethical standpoint and a violation of the "spirit of sport" criterion, it has not taken action at this time (132).

Although the live high, train low approach has been widely adopted, there is another school of thought that recommends a "live low, train high" approach, in which subjects train in hypoxia, but remain in normoxia the rest of the time. In this case the hypoxic environment exists only during exercise and is viewed as an option to avoid the negative impacts of prolonged exposure to high altitudes mentioned earlier. In general, $\dot{V}O_2$ max and blood parameters (e.g., hemoglobin concentration) are unchanged with this type of training. Further, Vogt and Hoppeler feel that it is difficult to draw strong conclusions regarding muscle adaptations due to this type of training because of differences in the training state of the subjects, the intensity and duration of the training, and the simulated altitude used (121). However, there is some limited evidence that when an athlete must perform at altitude, this type of training is beneficial. Given the small potential gains (~1%–2%) and the considerable costs, difficulties and potential risks (however small (7)), associated with either living high and training low or the reverse, only elite endurance athletes should consider these types of training strategies (110). See Millet et al. in the Suggested Readings for how the various hypoxic training methods can be combined.

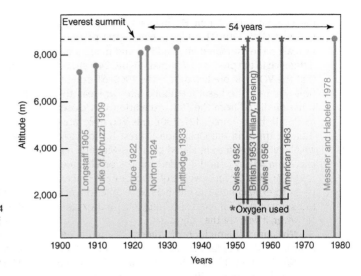

Figure 24.4 The highest altitudes attained by climbers in the twentieth century. In 1924 the climbers ascended within 300 meters of the summit without supplemental oxygen. It took another 54 years to climb those last 300 meters.

is good reading for those interested in mountain climbing and provides evidence of the keen powers of observation of the scientists. Major Hingston noted the respiratory distress associated with climbing to such heights, stating that at 5,800 meters (19,000 feet) "the very slightest exertion, such as the tying of a bootlace, the opening of a ration box, the getting into a sleeping bag, was associated with marked respiratory distress." At 8,200 meters (27,000 feet) one climber "had to take seven, eight, or ten complete respirations for every single step forward. And even at that slow rate of progress he had to rest for a minute or two every twenty or thirty yards" (84). Pugh, who made observations during a 1960–61 expedition to Everest, believed that fatigue of the respiratory muscles may be the primary factor limiting such

endeavors at extreme altitudes (95). Further, Pugh's observations of the decreases in $\dot{V}O_2$ max at the extreme altitudes suggested that $\dot{V}O_2$ max would be just above basal metabolism at the summit, making the task an unlikely one at best. How then did Messner and Habeler climb Everest without supplemental O_2?

This was one of the primary questions addressed by the 1981 expedition to Everest. As mentioned earlier, $\dot{V}O_2$ max decreases with altitude due to the lower barometric pressure, which causes a lower PO_2 and a desaturation of hemoglobin. In effect, the $\dot{V}O_2$ max at the summit of Everest was predicated on the observed rate of decrease in $\dot{V}O_2$ max at lower altitudes and then extrapolated to the barometric pressure at the top of the mountain. One of the first major findings of the 1981 expedition was that the barometric pressure at

A CLOSER LOOK 24.2

Mallory and Irvine—Did They Reach the Summit?

In the 1924 Everest expedition, two of the climbers, Norton and Somervell, left camp at 8,220 m (27,000 feet) to challenge the summit without supplemental oxygen. Somervell had to stop due to the cold air aggravating his frostbitten throat, but Norton continued on until he reached 8,580 m (28,314 feet)—a record for those not using supplemental oxygen that lasted for 54 years. A few days later, George L. Mallory and Andrew C. Irvine made an attempt with oxygen, but they never returned. Given that they were last

seen on the way to the summit, questions were raised about whether they had made it, and died on the way down. The 1999 Mallory and Irvine Research Expedition attempted to answer this question by finding their remains, and perhaps, some evidence that they might have achieved their goal. They knew that both climbers had cameras, and they were hoping to find photographic evidence to put this question to rest. The team did find Mallory's body at 27,000 feet, but unfortunately, could not find a camera.

After burying Mallory, they looked for additional evidence to try to determine where he fell from, to land where he did. One of his oxygen bottles placed him in a position consistent with a move to the summit; however, there was not enough evidence to conclude that the two climbers had achieved their goal. Nor was there enough to prove that they had not. The mystery continues (50). See Johnson, Hemmleb, and Simonson in the Suggested Readings for more on this adventure.

the summit was 17 mm Hg higher than previously believed (127, 130). This higher barometric pressure increased the estimated inspired PO_2 and made a big difference in the predicted $\dot{V}O_2$ max. Figure 24.5 shows that the $\dot{V}O_2$ max predicted from the 1960–61 expedition was near the basal metabolic rate, whereas the value predicted from the 1981 expedition was closer to 15 ml · kg^{-1} · min^{-1} (127, 130). This $\dot{V}O_2$ max value was confirmed in the Operation Everest II project in which subjects did a simulated ascent of Mount Everest over a 40-day period in a decompression chamber (25, 117). This $\dot{V}O_2$ max value of 15 ml · kg^{-1} · min^{-1} helps to explain how the climbers were able to reach the summit without the aid of supplemental oxygen. However, it was not the only reason.

The arterial saturation of hemoglobin is dependent upon the arterial PO_2, PCO_2, and pH (see chapter 10). A low PCO_2 and a high pH cause the oxygen hemoglobin curve to shift to the left, so that hemoglobin is more saturated under these conditions than under normal conditions. A person who can ventilate great volumes in response to hypoxia can exhale more CO_2 and cause the pH to become elevated. It has been shown that those who successfully deal with altitude have strong hypoxic ventilatory drives, allowing them to have a higher arterial PO_2 and oxygen saturation (113). In fact, when alveolar PCO_2 values were obtained at the top of Mount Everest in the 1981 expedition, the climbers had values much lower than expected (128). This ability to hyperventilate, coupled with the barometric pressure being higher than expected, resulted in higher arterial PO_2, and of course, $\dot{V}O_2$ max values. How high must your $\dot{V}O_2$ max be to climb Mount Everest?

Figure 24.5 shows that the climbers in the 1981 expedition had $\dot{V}O_2$ max values at sea level that were higher than those of the 1960–61 expedition. In fact,

several of the climbers had been competitive marathon runners (127), and, given the need to transport oxygen at these high altitudes to do work, having such a high $\dot{V}O_2$ max would appear to be a prerequisite to success in climbing without oxygen. Subsequent measurements on other mountaineers who had scaled 8,500 meters or more without oxygen confirmed this by showing them to possess primarily type I muscle fibers and to have an average $\dot{V}O_2$ max of 60 ± 6 ml · kg^{-1} · min^{-1} (85). However, there was one notable exception: One of the subjects in this study was Messner, who had climbed Mount Everest without oxygen; his $\dot{V}O_2$ max was 48.8 ml · kg^{-1} · min^{-1} (85). West et al. (129) provide food for thought in this regard: "It remains for someone to elucidate the evolutionary processes responsible for man being just able to reach the highest point on Earth while breathing ambient air." However, there is more to consider in climbing Mount Everest than a person's $\dot{V}O_2$ max.

It has been a common experience in mountain climbing, especially with prolonged exposure to high altitudes, for climbers to lose weight, secondary to a loss of appetite (63). Clearly, if a large portion of this weight loss were muscle, it would have a negative impact in the climber's ability to scale the mountain. Some research work from both simulated and real ascents of Mount Everest provides some insight into what changes are taking place in muscle and what may be responsible for those changes. In the Operation Everest II 40-day simulation of an ascent to Mount Everest, the subjects experienced a 25% reduction in the cross-sectional area of type I and type II muscle fibers, and a 14% reduction in muscle area (43, 70). These observations were supported by data from a real ascent that combined both heavy exercise and severe hypoxia (54, 58). What could have caused these changes? The Operation Everest II data on nutrition and body composition showed that caloric intake decreased 43% from 3,136 to 1,789 kcal/day over the course of the 40-day exposure to hypoxia. The subjects lost an average of 7.4 kg, with most of the weight from lean body mass, despite the availability of palatable food (105). The hypoxia itself was a sufficient stimulus to suppress the appetite and alter body composition. Whether such changes in muscle mass are linked directly to changes in $\dot{V}O_2$ max, they would clearly affect performance. (See A Closer Look 24.3 for how acute, versus chronic, exposure to altitude can affect the lactate response to exercise.)

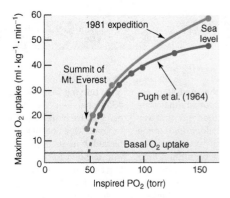

Figure 24.5   Plot of maximal oxygen uptake measured at a variety of altitudes, expressed as inspired PO_2 values. The 1964 data of Pugh et al. predicted the $\dot{V}O_2$ max to be equal to basal metabolic rate. The estimation based on the finding that the barometric pressure (and PO_2) was higher than expected at the summit shifts the estimate to about 15 ml · kg^{-1} · min^{-1}.

IN SUMMARY

- Climbers reached the summit of Mount Everest without oxygen in 1978. This surprised scientists who thought $\dot{V}O_2$ max would be just above resting $\dot{V}O_2$ at that altitude. They later found

A CLOSER LOOK 24.3

The Lactate Paradox

When a submaximal test is conducted at altitude, the heart rate, ventilation, and lactate responses are higher than what are measured at sea level. This is no surprise for the heart rate and ventilation responses, because there is less oxygen per liter of blood and air, respectively. The elevated lactate response is also not unexpected, the assumption being that the hypoxia of altitude provides additional stimulation of glycolysis. What is surprising is that when the same exercise is done after the subject has been acclimated to altitude for 3 or 4 weeks (chronic hypoxia), the lactate response is substantially reduced. This is the lactate paradox—that the same hypoxic stimulus in chronic hypoxia gives rise to a lower lactate response than observed when the subject is first exposed (acute hypoxia) to altitude (101).

A variety of studies have been done to try to uncover the causes of the reduced lactate response to exercise during chronic exposure to altitude. The results from some of these studies have shown that the lower lactate is not due to a greater oxidative capacity of the muscle, an improved capillary-to-fiber ratio, or an improvement in oxygen delivery (44, 101). Instead, the reduction in lactate seems to be associated with a lower plasma epinephrine concentration which, as we know from chapter 5, would provide less stimulation of glycogenolysis via β-adrenergic receptor stimulation (78, 101). Evidence supporting this proposition comes from a study in which propranolol (a β-adrenergic receptor blocking drug) was shown to reduce the lactate response to acute hypoxia to a level

seen only after chronic hypoxia (101). However, the changes in epinephrine with acclimatization to altitude cannot entirely explain the lower lactate response (78). The lower lactate response may also be due to muscular adaptations resulting in tighter metabolic control such that the ADP concentration does not increase as much during exercise; this results in less stimulation of glycolysis (44). Consequently, the lactate paradox may be the result of both hormonal (epinephrine) and intracellular (lower [ADP]) adaptations that occur with chronic exposure to hypoxia. The most recent attempt to explain the lactate paradox is found in a "viewpoint" by Noakes (82), with commentaries by other authors and Noakes' rebuttal (83). This explanation focuses on the brain's need to protect oxygen delivery to itself by limiting muscle recruitment when exercise is done under chronic exposure to hypoxia. If the brain limits the recruitment of muscle fibers, less carbohydrate is metabolized and less lactate will be produced. However, commentaries (23) from various authors, including the authors of the principal paper cited by Noakes, argued against that hypothesis.

In contrast to the above, a study by van Hall et al. (119), published in 2001, suggested that the lactate paradox was simply a time-dependent phenomenon, being present during the early weeks of acclimatization and disappearing thereafter. Two years later, Pronk et al. (91) challenged this conclusion. They measured the lactate response to the same absolute work load on ascent to altitude and at 2, 4, 6, and 8 weeks to track changes in the

response over time at altitude. They observed the expected increase in the blood lactate response to exercise upon ascent to altitude, and the now-classic decrease in the blood lactate response with continued exposure to altitude. They also confirmed the link of the lactate response to changes in plasma catecholamines. They concluded that there was no evidence of a reversal of the lactate paradox with continued altitude exposure. Lundby and van Hall's response (69) to this study, and Pronk's counterresponse (90), make interesting reading, but indicate how much the two are apart.

To further complicate matters, in a 2009 study from van Hall's group (120), lowlanders who were taken to 4,100 m altitude had the same elevated lactate response during exercise upon acute exposure to that altitude, and after 2 weeks and 8 weeks of acclimatization (compared to sea level). They showed that the muscle lactate concentration was the same at exhaustion across all conditions, from sea level to 8 weeks of chronic hypoxia. Further, the epinephrine and norepinephrine concentrations were increased above sea level values in acute hypoxia, and were further increased after weeks of acclimation, signifying a normal sympathetic nervous system response to exercise. Last, the ADP concentration in muscle was not different across conditions. These finding are obviously at odds with the Pronk et al. study (91) and other proponents of the lactate paradox. Although the pros and cons have already been debated (123, 126), we are sure to hear more in the years ahead.

that the barometric pressure was higher than they previously had thought and that the estimated $\dot{V}O_2$ max was about 15 ml · kg^{-1} · min^{-1} at this altitude.

- Those who are successful at these high altitudes have a great capacity to hyperventilate. This drives down the PCO_2 and the [H$^+$] in

blood, and allows more oxygen to bind with hemoglobin at the same arterial PO_2.

- Finally, those who are successful at climbing to extreme altitudes must contend with the loss of appetite that results in a reduction in body weight and in the cross-sectional area of type I and type II muscle fibers.

HEAT

Chapter 12 described the changes in body temperature with exercise, how heat loss mechanisms are activated, and the benefits of acclimation to heat. This section extends that discussion by considering the prevention of thermal injuries during exercise.

Hyperthermia

Our core temperature (37° C) is within a few degrees of a value (45° C) that could lead to death (see chapter 12). Given that, and the fact that distance running races, triathlons, fitness programs, and football games occur during the warmer part of the year, the potential for heat injury, **hyperthermia**, is increased (13, 46, 61). Heat injury is not an all-or-none affair, but includes a series of stages that need to be recognized and attended to in order to prevent a progression from the least to the most serious (60). Table 24.3 summarizes each stage, identifying signs, symptoms, and the immediate care that should be provided (19). The most rapid and preferred way to reduce body temperature of those with heat stroke is by cold water immersion (5, 20). Although it is important to recognize and deal with these problems, it is better to prevent them from happening.

Figure 24.6 shows the major factors related to heat injury. Each one independently influences susceptibility to heat injury:

TABLE 24.3   Heat-Related Problems and Their Treatment

Heat Illness	Signs and Symptoms	Immediate Care
Heat syncope—fainting or excessive loss of strength because of excessive heat	Headache Nausea	Normal intake of fluids.
Heat cramps—spasmodic muscular contractions caused by exertion in extreme heat	Muscle cramping (calf is very common location) Multiple cramping (very serious)	Isolated cramps: Apply pressure to the cramp and release, stretch muscle slowly and gently, apply gentle massage, and ice. Hydrate by drinking lots of water. Multiple cramps: Danger of heatstroke; treat as heat exhaustion.
Heat exhaustion—collapse with or without loss of consciousness, suffered in conditions of heat and high humidity, largely resulting from the loss of fluid and salt by sweating	Profuse sweating Cold, clammy skin Normal or slightly elevated temperature Pale Dizzy Weak, rapid pulse Shallow breathing Nausea Headache Loss of consciousness Thirst	Move individual out of the sun to a well-ventilated area. Place in shock position, with feet elevated 12 to 18 in. (31–46 cm); prevent heat loss or gain. Gently massage the extremities. Apply gentle ROM movement to the extremities. Force consumption of fluids. Reassure the individual. Monitor body temperature and other vital signs. Refer to a physician.
Heatstroke—final stage of heat exhaustion in which the thermoregulatory system shuts down to conserve depleted fluid levels	Generally no perspiration Dry skin Very hot Temperature as high as 106 °F (41.1° C) Skin color bright red or flushed (dark-pigmented individuals will have ashen skin) Rapid, strong pulse Labored breathing Change in behavior Unresponsive	Treat as an extreme medical emergency. Transport to hospital quickly. Remove as much clothing as possible without exposing the individual. Cool quickly, starting at the head and continuing down the body; use any means possible (fan, hose down, pack in ice). Wrap in cold, wet sheets for transport. Treat for shock; if breathing is labored, place in a semi-reclining position.

From: Carver S. 2007. Injury prevention and treatment. In: *Fitness Professional's Handbook*, edited by Howley E, and Franks B. Champaign: Human Kinetics, p. 375–397. [Permission needed]

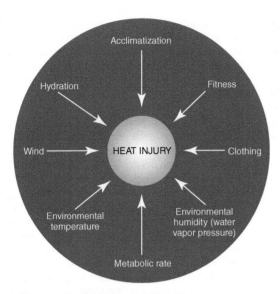

Figure 24.6   Factors affecting heat injury.

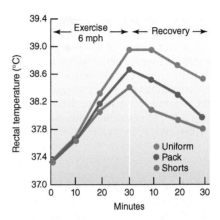

Figure 24.7   The effect of different types of uniforms on the body temperature response to treadmill running.

Fitness   A high level of fitness is related to a lower risk of heat injury (40). Fit subjects can tolerate more work in the heat (29), acclimate faster (13), and sweat more (11). However, very fit individuals can still develop exercise-related heat stroke (5).

Acclimation   Exercise in the heat for 10 to 14 days, either at low intensity (<50% $\dot{V}O_2$ max) and long duration (60–100 min) or at moderate intensity (75% $\dot{V}O_2$ max) and short duration (30–35 min), accomplish the following (5, 13, 57, 68):

- increases plasma volume and capacity to sweat,
- increases $\dot{V}O_2$ max, maximal cardiac output, and power output at the LT,
- lowers body temperature and heart rate responses to exercise,
- reduces salt loss in sweat and the chance of sodium depletion, and
- increases aerobic exercise performance.

This acclimation process is the best protection against exercise-related heat stroke and heat exhaustion (5).

Hydration   Inadequate hydration reduces sweat rate and increases the chance of heat injury (109, 111, 112). Chapter 23 discussed the procedures for fluid replacement. Generally, there are no differences among water, electrolyte drinks, or carbohydrate-electrolyte drinks in replacing body water during exercise (18, 24, 136).

Environmental   Temperature   Convection and radiation heat-loss mechanisms are dependent on a temperature gradient from skin to environment. Exercising in temperatures greater than skin temperatures

results in a heat gain. Evaporation of sweat must then compensate if body temperature is to remain at a safe value. See the later discussion on the use of the Wet Bulb Globe Temperature as a guide to reducing the risk of heat injury.

Clothing   Expose as much skin surface as possible to encourage evaporation. Choose materials, such as cotton, that will "wick" sweat to the surface for evaporation. Materials impermeable to water will increase the risk of heat injury. Figure 24.7 shows the influence of different uniforms on the body temperature response to treadmill running (73). Because many exercise-related heat injuries occur during the first four days of American football practice, attention to limiting clothing as well as attending to acclimation and hydration is advised (5).

Humidity (Water Vapor Pressure)   Evaporation of sweat is dependent on the water vapor pressure gradient between skin and environment. In warm/hot environments, the relative humidity is a good index of the water vapor pressure, with a lower relative humidity facilitating evaporation. See the later discussion on the use of the Wet Bulb Globe Temperature as a guide to reducing the risk of heat injury.

Metabolic Rate   Given that core temperature is proportional to work rate, metabolic heat production plays an important role in the overall heat load the body experiences during exercise. Decreasing the work rate decreases this heat load, as well as the strain on the physiological systems that must deal with it.

Wind   Wind places more air molecules into contact with the skin and can influence heat loss in two ways. If a temperature gradient for heat loss exists between the skin and the air, wind will increase the rate of heat loss by convection. In a similar manner, wind increases the rate of evaporation, assuming the air can accept moisture.

Even the time of day is a consideration when it comes to exercise performance during heat exposure. With its typical diurnal variation, core temperature is lower and the body's heat storage capacity is higher in the morning, compared to the afternoon, when resting core temperature is elevated (98). When male cyclists rode to exhaustion at 65% $\dot{V}O_2$ max in a warm environment (35° C, 60% RH), time to exhaustion was longer in the morning trial (45.8 min) compared to the afternoon trial (40.5 min). Core temperature was lower in the morning trial for the first 25 minutes, but was not different at exhaustion (52). The results suggested that the greater heat storage capacity contributed to the difference.

For a practical guide on the prevention and treatment of heat-related illness, see Howe and Boden in the Suggested Readings.

Implications for Fitness The person exercising for fitness needs to be educated about all of the previously listed factors. Suggestions might include:

■ providing information on heat illness symptoms: cramps, lightheadedness, and so on,

■ exercising in the cooler part of the day to avoid heat gain from the sun or structures heated by the sun,

■ gradually increasing exposure to high heat/ humidity to safely acclimatize,

■ drinking water before, during, and after exercise and weighing in each day to monitor hydration,

■ wearing only shorts and a tank top to expose as much skin as possible,

■ taking heart rate measurements several times during the activity and reducing exercise intensity to stay in the target heart rate (THR) zone.

The latter recommendation is most important. The heart rate is a sensitive indicator of dehydration, environmental heat load, and acclimation. Variation in any of these factors will modify the heart rate response to any fixed, submaximal exercise. It is therefore important for fitness participants to monitor heart rate on a regular basis and to slow down to stay within the THR zone. Age is sometimes raised as a predisposing factor related to heat injury, but that may not be the case after you account for the factors mentioned previously. We would like to direct the interested reader to a brief and clearly written review of this topic by Kenney and Munce in the Suggested Readings.

Implications for Performance Heat injury has been a concern in athletics for decades. Initially, the

vast majority of attention was focused on football because of the large number of heat-related deaths associated with that sport (14). Emphasis on preseason conditioning to improve fitness and promote acclimation, drinking water during practice and games, and weighing in each day to monitor hydration resulted in a steady reduction of heat-related deaths throughout the early 1990s. However, since that time there has been an increase in the number of heat-related deaths in football, especially at the high school level. In fact, among U.S. high school athletes, heat illness is the leading cause of death and disability (39). There is a need to return to the vigilance and practices that resulted in the low death rates of the early 1990s. It might be added that during the time that the number of heat-related deaths in football players was decreasing, there was an increase in the number of deaths in another athletic activity—long-distance road races (46, 62). In response to this problem, and on the basis of sound research, the American College of Sports Medicine developed a Position Stand on the Prevention of Thermal Injuries During Distance Running (3), parts of which have been recently updated (5). The elements recommended in this position statement are consistent with what we previously presented:

Medical Director

■ A sports medicine physician should work with the race director to enhance safety and coordinate first-aid measures.

Race Organization

■ Minimize environmental heat load by planning races for the cooler months, and at a time of day (before 8:00 A.M. or after 6:00 P.M.) to reduce solar heat gain.

■ Use an environmental heat stress index (see the next section, "Environmental Heat Stress") to help make decisions about whether to run a race.

■ Have a water station every 2 to 3 km; encourage runners to drink 150 to 300 milliliters of water every 15 minutes.

■ Clearly identify the race monitors and have them look for those who might be in trouble due to heat injury.

■ Have traffic control for safety.

■ Use radio communication throughout the race course.

Medical Support

■ Medical director coordinates ambulance service with local hospitals and has the authority to evaluate or stop runners who appear to be in trouble.

■ Medical director coordinates medical facilities at race site to provide first aid.

Competitor Education

- Provide information about factors related to heat illness that were discussed previously.
- Encourage the "buddy system" (see chapter 17). The primary focus in these recommendations is on safety.

Environmental Heat Stress The previous discussion mentioned high temperature and relative humidity as factors increasing the risk of heat injuries. To quantify the overall heat stress associated with any environment, a Wet Bulb Globe Temperature (**WBGT**) guide was developed (3). This overall heat stress index is composed of the following measurements:

Dry Bulb Temperature (T_{db})

- Ordinary measure of air temperature taken in the shade

Black Globe Temperature (T_g)

- Measure of the radiant heat load measured in direct sunlight

Wet Bulb Temperature (T_{wb})

- Measurement of air temperature with a thermometer whose mercury bulb is covered with a wet cotton wick. This measure is sensitive to the relative humidity (water vapor pressure) and provides an index of the ability to evaporate sweat.

The formula used to calculate the WBGT index shows the importance of this latter wet bulb temperature in determining heat stress (3):

$$WBGT = 0.7\,T_{wb} + 0.2\,T_g + 0.1\,T_{db}$$

The risk of exertional heat stroke (EHS) is classified as follows (5, 102):

■ WBGT ≤50.0° F (≤10.0° C)	Risk of hypothermia; EHS can occur
■ WBGT 50−65° F (10−18.3° C)	Low risk of both hypothermia and hyperthermia; EHS can occur
■ WBGT 65.1−72.0° F (18.4−22.2° C)	Caution: risk of heat illness increases; high-risk persons monitored or not compete
■ WBGT 72.1−78.0° F (22.3−25.6° C)	Extreme caution; risk of hyperthermia increased for all
■ WBGT 78.1−82.0° F (25.7−27.8° C)	Extreme caution; high risk for unfit, non-acclimatized
■ WBGT ≥82.1° F (≥27.9° C)	Extreme risk of hyperthermia; cancel or postpone

In addition to environmental factors contributing to the risk of heat injury, there is no question about their impact on performance. For example, the fastest marathons are run at environmental temperatures of 10.6–12.8°C for men and 11.6–13.6°C for women; times are systematically slower with higher environmental temperatures (30, 31). Not surprisingly, precooling the body prior to exercise in the heat improves performance; however, practical recommendations on how to do this are just being developed (97). In a recent study, both a standard whole-body immersion in 10°C water for 10 minutes and a new approach using a combination of consuming 14 g/kg of an ice slurry sports drink while wearing iced towels were effective in lowering core temperature prior to a cycling time trial in hot and humid conditions. However, the new approach of doing both internal and external cooling was more effective from a performance standpoint (107).

- Heat injury is influenced by environmental factors such as temperature, water vapor pressure, acclimation, hydration, clothing, and metabolic rate. The fitness participant should be educated about the signs and symptoms of heat injury, the importance of drinking water before, during, and after the activity, gradually becoming acclimated to the heat, exercising in the cooler part of the day, dressing appropriately, and checking the HR on a regular basis.
- Road races conducted in times of elevated heat and humidity need to reflect the coordinated wisdom of the race director and medical director to minimize heat and other injuries. Concerns include running the race at the correct time of the day and season of the year, frequent water stops, traffic control, race monitors to identify and stop those in trouble, and communication between race monitors, medical director, ambulance services, and hospitals.
- The heat stress index includes dry bulb, wet bulb, and globe temperatures. The wet bulb temperature, which is a good indicator of the water vapor pressure, is more important than the other two in determining overall heat stress.

COLD

Altitude and heat stress are not the only environmental factors having an impact on performance. A WBGT of 10° C or less is associated with hypothermia. **Hypothermia** results when heat loss from the body exceeds heat production and is defined, clinically, as a core temperature below 35° C (95° F), which is a drop of about 2° C (3.5° F) below normal body temperature (4).

Cold air facilitates this process in more ways than are readily apparent. First, and most obvious, when air temperature is less than skin temperature, a gradient for heat loss exists for convection, and physiological mechanisms involving peripheral vasoconstriction and shivering come into play to counter this gradient. Second, and less obvious, cold air has a low water vapor pressure, which encourages the evaporation of moisture from the skin to further cool the body. The combined effects can be deadly, as witnessed in Pugh's report of three deaths during a "walking" competition over a 45-mile distance (93).

Hypothermia can range in severity from mild to severe (4):

- Mild hypothermia
  - 35° C (95° F)—maximal shivering
  - 34° C (93.2° F)—amnesia, poor judgment
- Moderate hypothermia
  - 33° C (91.4° F)—ataxia, apathy
  - 31° C (87.8° F)—shivering ceases, pupils dilate
  - 29° C (85.2° F)—unconscious
- Severe hypothermia
  - 28° C (82.4° F)—ventricular fibrillation
  - 26° C (78.8° F)—no response to pain
  - 24° C (75.2° F)—hypotension, bradycardia
  - 19° C (66.2° F)—EEG silence
  - 13.7° C (56.7° F)—lowest temperature for adult survival

Figure 24.8 shows the factors related to hypothermia. These include environmental factors such as temperature, water vapor pressure, wind, and whether air or water is involved; insulating factors such as clothing and subcutaneous fat; the characteristics of the individuals involved (e.g., age and gender); and the capacity for sustained heat production, including fuels available. We will now comment on each of these relative to hypothermia. For a thorough presentation on this topic, see the American College of Sports Medicine's Position Stand (4) and the National Athletic Trainers' Association position statement (17).

Environmental Factors

Heat loss mechanisms introduced in chapter 12 included conduction, convection, radiation, and evaporation. Given that hypothermia is the result of higher heat loss than heat production, understanding how these mechanisms are involved will facilitate a discussion of how to deal with this problem.

Conduction, convection, and radiation are dependent on a temperature gradient between skin and environment; the larger the gradient, the greater the rate of heat loss. What is surprising is that the environmental temperature does not have to be below freezing to cause hypothermia. In effect, other environmental factors interact with temperature to create the dangerous condition by facilitating heat loss—namely, wind and water.

Wind Chill Index   The rate of heat loss at any given temperature is directly influenced by the wind speed. Wind increases the number of cold air molecules coming into contact with the skin so that heat loss is accelerated. The **wind chill index** indicates what the "effective" temperature is for any combination of temperature and wind speed. Siple and Passel (115) developed a formula for predicting how fast heat would be lost at different wind speeds and temperatures:

$$\text{Wind chill (kcal} \cdot \text{m}^{-2} \cdot \text{h}^{-1}) = [\sqrt{WV \times 100} + 10.45 - WV] \times (33 - T_A)$$

where WV = wind velocity (m · sec^{-1}); 10.45 is a constant; 33 is 33° C, which is taken as the skin temperature; and T_A = ambient dry bulb temperature in °C. Siple and Passel estimated how long it would take for exposed flesh to freeze and tabulated the levels of "danger" associated with combinations of wind speed and temperature.

This formula (38), which had been used for many years, was thought to overestimate the effect of increasing wind speed on tissue freezing and underestimated the effect of decreasing temperature (27). The following wind chill formula has been adopted by the National Weather Service (http://www.crh.noaa.gov/dtx/New_Wind_Chill.htm):

$$\text{Wind chill (°F)} = 35.74 + 0.6215 \, (T) - 35.75 \, (V^{0.16}) + 0.4275T \, (V^{0.16})$$

where wind speed (V) is in mph, and temperature (T) is in °F.

Table 24.4 provides the calculated wind chill temperatures for a variety of wind speeds and temperatures, along with estimates of the time it would take for frostbite to occur. Keep in mind that if you are running, riding, or cross-country skiing into the wind, you

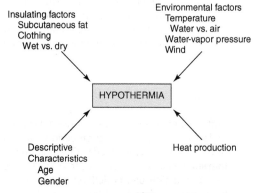

Figure 24.8   Factors affecting hypothermia.

TABLE 24.4 Wind Chill Chart

		Temperature (°F)																
	Calm	40	35	30	25	20	15	10	5	0	−5	−10	−15	−20	−25	−30	−35	−40	−45
Wind (MPH)	5	36	31	25	19	13	7	1	−5	−11	−16	−22	−28	−34	−40	−46	−52	−57	−63
	10	34	27	21	15	9	3	−4	−10	−16	−22	−28	−35	−41	−47	−53	−59	−66	−72
	15	32	25	19	13	6	0	−7	−13	−19	−26	−32	−39	−45	−51	−58	−64	−71	−77
	20	30	24	17	11	4	−2	−9	−15	−22	−29	−35	−42	−48	−55	−61	−68	−74	−81
	25	29	23	16	9	3	−4	−11	−17	−24	−31	−37	−44	−51	−58	−64	−71	−78	−84
	30	28	22	15	8	1	−5	−12	−19	−26	−33	−39	−46	−53	−60	−67	−73	−80	−87
	35	28	21	14	7	0	−7	−14	−21	−27	−34	−41	−48	−55	−62	−69	−76	−82	−89
	40	27	20	13	6	−1	−8	−15	−22	−29	−36	−43	−50	−57	−64	−71	−78	−84	−91
	45	26	19	12	5	−2	−9	−16	−23	−30	−37	−44	−51	−58	−65	−72	−79	−86	−93
	50	26	19	12	4	−3	−10	−17	−24	−31	−38	−45	−52	−60	−67	−74	−81	−88	−95
	55	25	18	11	4	−3	−11	−18	−25	−32	−39	−46	−54	−61	−68	−75	−82	−89	−97
	60	25	17	10	3	−4	−11	−19	−26	−33	−40	−48	−55	−62	−69	−76	−84	−91	−98

Frostbite Times ▢ 30 minutes ▢ 10 minutes ▢ 5 minutes

Wind Chill (°F) = 35.74 + 0.6215T − 35.75 $(V^{0.16})$ + 0.4275 $(V^{0.16})$

Where T = Air Temperature (°F)   V = Wind Speed (mph)

(Effective 11/01/01)

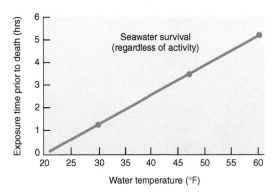

Figure 24.9 The effect of different water temperatures on survival of shipwrecked individuals.

must add your speed to the wind speed to evaluate the full impact of the wind chill. For example, cycling at 20 mph into calm air at 0° F is equivalent to a wind chill temperature of −22° F. However, it is clear that wind is not the only factor that can increase the rate of heat loss at any given temperature.

Water   The thermal conductivity of water is about twenty-five times greater than that of air, so you can lose heat twenty-five times faster in water compared to air of the same temperature (55). Figure 24.9 shows death can occur in only a few hours when a person is shipwrecked in cold water. Unlike air, water offers little or no insulation at the skin-water interface, so heat is rapidly lost from the body. Given that movement in such cold water would increase heat loss from the arms and legs, the recommendation is to stay as still as possible in long-term immersions (4, 55).

IN SUMMARY

- Hypothermia is influenced by natural and added insulation, environmental temperature, vapor pressure, wind, water immersion, and heat production.
- The wind chill index describes how wind lowers the effective temperature at the skin such that convective heat loss is greater than what it would be in calm air at that same temperature.
- Water causes heat to be lost by convection twenty-five times faster than it would be by exposure to air of the same temperature.

Insulating Factors

The rate at which heat is lost from the body is inversely related to the insulation between the body and the environment. The insulating quality is related to the thickness of subcutaneous fat, the ability of clothing to trap air, and whether the clothing is wet or dry.

Subcutaneous Fat   An excellent indicator of total body insulation per unit surface area (through which heat is lost) is the average subcutaneous fat thickness (49). Pugh and Edholm's (94) observation that a "fat" man was able to swim for 7 hours in 16° C water with no change in body temperature, whereas a "thin" man had to leave the water in 30 minutes with a core temperature of 34.5° C, supports this statement. Long-distance swimmers tend to be fatter than short-course swimmers. The higher body fatness does more than help maintain body temperature; fatter swimmers are more buoyant, requiring less energy to swim at any set speed (53). In addition, body fatness plays a role in the onset and magnitude of the shivering response to cold exposure (see later discussion in the "Heat Production" section).

Clothing   Clothing can extend our natural subcutaneous fat insulation to allow us to sustain very cold environments. The insulation quality of clothing is given in **clo** units, where 1 clo is the insulation needed at rest (1 MET) to maintain core temperature when the environment is 21° C, the RH = 50%, and the air movement is 6 m · min⁻¹ (12). Still air next to the body has a clo rating of 0.8. As the air temperature falls, clothing with a higher clo value must be worn to maintain core temperature, because the gradient between skin and environment increases (86). Figure 24.10 shows the insulation needed at different energy expenditures across a broad range of temperatures from −60 to +80° F (12). It is clear that as heat production increases,

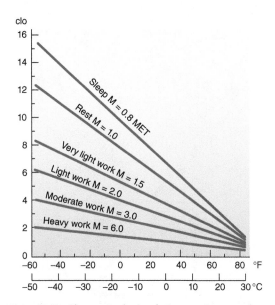

Figure 24.10 Changes in the insulation requirement of clothing (plus air) with increasing rates of energy expenditure over environmental temperatures of −50 to +30° C.

insulation must decrease to maintain core temperature. By wearing clothing in layers, insulation can be removed piece by piece, because less insulation is needed to maintain core temperature. By following these steps, sweating, which can rob the clothing of its insulating value, will be minimized. A practical example of how clothing helps maintain body temperature (and comfort) can be seen in the following study. Heat loss from the head increases linearly from $+32°$ C to $-21°$ C, with about half of the entire heat production being lost through the head when the temperature is $-4°$ C. Wearing a simple "helmet" with a clo rating of 3.5 allows an individual to stay out indefinitely at $0°$ C (37).

Clothing offers insulation by trapping air, a poor conductor of heat. If the clothing becomes wet, the insulating quality decreases because the water can now conduct heat away from the body at a faster rate (55). A primary goal, then, is to avoid wetness, due either to sweat or to weather. This problem is exacerbated by the cold environment's very low water vapor pressure. Recall from chapter 12 that the water vapor pressure in the environment is the primary factor influencing evaporation and that at low environmental temperatures the water vapor pressure is low even when the relative humidity is high. Think of a time when you finished playing a game indoors and stepped outside into cold, damp weather to cool off. You noticed "steam" coming off your body; how is this possible when the RH is near 100%? The water vapor pressure is high at the skin surface, since the skin temperature is elevated; so, a gradient for water vapor pressure exists. You will cool off very fast under these circumstances. This is why cold, wet, windy environments carry an extra risk of hypothermia. The wind not only provides for greater convective heat loss as described in the wind chill chart, but it also accelerates evaporation (47).

Heat Production

Figure 24.10 shows that the amount of insulation needed to maintain core temperature decreases as energy expenditure increases. This is also true for our "natural" insulation, subcutaneous fat. McArdle et al. (79) showed that when fat men (27.6% fat) were immersed for 1 hour in $20°$ C, $24°$ C, and $28°$ C water, the resting $\dot{V}O_2$ and core temperature did not change compared to values measured in air. In thinner men (<16.8% fat), the $\dot{V}O_2$ increased to counter the rapid loss of heat; however, the core temperature still decreased. When these same subjects did exercise in the cold water, requiring a $\dot{V}O_2$ of 1.7 L $\cdot$ min^{-1}, the fall in body temperature was either prevented or retarded (80), showing the importance of high rates of heat production in preventing hypothermia. More recent studies support these observations, showing

an earlier onset and greater magnitude of shivering in lean subjects when exposed to cold air (118). Similar findings have been reported for fit subjects (8).

Fuel Use Shivering can increase oxygen consumption to 1000 ml/min during resting immersion in cold water, and like moderate exercise of the same intensity, fat is a primary fuel to support shivering in well-fed individuals (4). However, it is clear that inadequate carbohydrate stores may lead to hypoglycemia, which can impact one's ability to shiver. Further, bursts of shivering lead to greater muscle glycogen depletion. Consequently, having adequate carbohydrate stores is important to reduce the risk for hypothermia (4). Given the importance of body fatness and body type in the metabolic response to cold exposure, are there differences due to gender and age?

Descriptive Characteristics

Subject characteristics, such as gender and age, influence the metabolic and body temperature responses to cold exposure.

Gender Sex differences in response to cold water exposure are linked to a woman's higher body fatness, thicker subcutaneous layer, less lean mass, and higher surface area-to-mass ratio, compared to men of the same weight and age. At rest, women show a faster reduction in body temperature than do men, even when subcutaneous fat thickness is the same. In contrast, when exercise is done in cold water, women and men of the same body fatness have similar decreases in body temperature. Consequently, any gender differences in core temperature responses to cold exposure can be explained primarily on the basis of differences in body composition and anthropometry. It must be added that amenorrheic women cannot maintain core temperature during exercise in the cold as well as eumenorrheic women can (4).

Age In general, individuals over 60 years may be less tolerant to cold exposures than younger individuals because the ability of older individuals to vasocontrict skin blood vessels and conserve heat is reduced. They also have less thermal sensitivity. That is, their response to a decrease in temperature is reduced, allowing time for greater heat loss. In contrast to adults, children have a larger surface area-to-mass ratio and less subcutaneous fat. This results in a faster fall in core temperature on cold water exposure and a greater risk of hypothermia. Similar to the gender differences (or lack thereof) mentioned above, 11- to 12-year-old boys with the same subcutaneous fat as men had the same core temperature response when doing exercise in cold air (4). See A Look Back—Important People in Science for an individual who had

A LOOK BACK—IMPORTANT PEOPLE IN SCIENCE

L. G. C. E. Pugh Furthered Our Understanding of How to Survive and Function Well in Extreme Environments

In this chapter that deals with the effect of cold, heat, and altitude on performance, we thought it would be appropriate to highlight an individual who had a major impact on our understanding of the physiology involved in adapting to adverse environments: **Lewis Griffith Cresswell Evans (L.G.C.E.) Pugh, M.D.**

L.G.C.E. Pugh was born in 1909 in England. He attended New College, Oxford, and completed his B.A. in 1931. He then studied natural sciences during 1931–33 and medicine until 1938, at which time he received his B.M and M.A. degrees. He was a competitive downhill and cross-country skier and qualified for England's 1936 Winter Olympics. In 1939 he entered the army as a medical officer and served in Europe and the Middle East. In 1943, he was sent to the Mountain Warfare Training Centre in Lebanon to

select, train, and evaluate troops for mountain warfare. There he became involved in the systematic study of the interaction of altitude, environmental temperature, nutrition, clothing, and fitness on human performance, and he developed training manuals based on his work. Following the war he was involved in British navy research expeditions to the Arctic, and in 1950 he accepted a position in the Medical Research Council's Division in Human Physiology to study the effects of extreme environments.

Dr. Pugh was a major participant in several high-altitude expeditions during the 1950s and 1960s. The first, in 1952, gave him insight into what kinds of clothing, nutrition, hydration, and oxygen were required for humans to function at extreme altitudes. His work is recognized as being crucial to the success of the 1953 British expedition to Mt. Everest in which Edmund Hillary and Tenzing Norgay were the first to reach the summit. In the late 1950s he

joined Edmund Hillary for an Antarctic expedition in which he studied human tolerance to extreme cold; it was also during this time that the two planned to return to Everest. Dr. Pugh was the principal scientist in the 1960–61 Scientific and Mountaineering Expedition to Everest that provided ground-breaking, and yet fundamental, information about how humans adapt to chronic exposure to high altitude. In addition, in the late 1960s he was involved in helping athletes prepare for the Olympic Games which were to take place in Mexico City at an altitude of ~2,300 m. His life's work revolved around understanding how humans adapt to exercise in extreme environments and his findings are as relevant today as they were 60 years ago. He died in 1994.

Sources: Peter H. Hansen. Pugh, (Lewis) Griffith Cresswell Evans (1909–1994), physiologist and mountaineer. *Oxford Dictionary of National Biography.* University of California, San Diego. Mandeville Special Collections Library, Geisel Library. *The Register of L. G. C. E. Pugh Papers 1940–1986.*

a major impact on our understanding of the physiology of how humans adapt to extreme environments.

IN SUMMARY

- Subcutaneous fat is the primary "natural" insulation and is very effective in preventing rapid heat loss when a person is exposed to cold water.
- Clothing extends this insulation, and the insulation value of clothing is described in clo units, where a value of 1 describes what is needed to maintain core temperature while sitting in a room set at 21° C and 50% RH with an air movement of 6 m · sec^{-1}.
- The amount of insulation needed to maintain core temperature is less when one exercises because the metabolic heat production helps maintain the core temperature. Clothing should be worn in layers when exercising so one can shed one insulating layer at a time as body temperature increases.
- Heat production increases on exposure to cold, with an inverse relationship between the

increase in $\dot{V}O_2$ and body fatness. Women cool faster than men when exposed to cold water, exhibiting a longer delay in the onset of shivering and a lower $\dot{V}O_2$, despite a greater stimulus to shiver.

Dealing with Hypothermia

As body temperature falls, the person's ability to carry out coordinated movements is reduced, speech is slurred, and judgment is impaired. As mentioned earlier, people can die from hypothermia, and the condition must be dealt with when it occurs. The following steps on how to do this are taken from the National Athletic Trainers' Association position statement on cold injuries (17):

- **Mild hypothermia**
  - Remove wet or damp clothing.
  - Insulate the person with warm dry clothing or blankets, covering the head.
  - Move person to warm environment with shelter from wind and rain.

- When rewarming, apply heat only to the trunk and other areas of heat transfer (axilla, chest wall, groin).
- Provide warm, nonalcoholic fluids and food containing 6–8% carbohydrate.

■ **Moderate/severe hypothermia**
- Determine if CPR is necessary and activate emergency medical system.
- Remove wet or damp clothing.
- Insulate the person with warm dry clothing or blankets, covering the head.
- Move person to warm environment with shelter from wind and rain.
- When rewarming, apply heat only to the trunk and other areas of heat transfer (axilla, chest wall, groin).
- If physician is not present, initiate rewarming strategies immediately and continue during transport.
- During treatment/transit, continue to monitor vital signs and be prepared for airway management.

IN SUMMARY

- For mild hypothermia get the person out of the wind, rain, and cold; remove wet clothing and put on dry clothing; for rewarming, apply heat only to the trunk and other areas of heat transfer; and provide warm drinks and food.
- For moderate/severe hypothermia do as above, check vital signs, activate emergency medical system, and transport.

AIR POLLUTION

Air pollution includes a variety of gases and particulates that are products of the combustion of fossil fuels. The "smog" that results when these pollutants are in high concentration can have a detrimental effect on health and performance. The gases can affect performance by decreasing the capacity to transport oxygen, increasing airway resistance, and altering the perception of effort required when the eyes "burn" and the chest "hurts." A study on traffic policemen, who are routinely exposed to a full range of pollutants throughout their workday, makes the point. Although their physiological responses were normal at rest, during an exercise test about one-third of the policemen experienced ECG changes and elevated blood pressure responses, with the vast majority of those individuals also experiencing a desaturation of hemoglobin (122). In addition, children living in an air-

polluted environment had significantly lower $\dot{V}O_2$ max values compared to those living in areas with better air quality (137).

The physiological responses to these pollutants are related to the amount or "dose" received. The major factors determining the dose are the concentration of the pollutant, the duration of the exposure to the pollutant, and the volume of air inhaled. This last factor increases during exercise and is one reason why physical activity should be curtailed during times of peak pollution levels (34). The following discussion focuses on the major air pollutants: particulate matter, ozone, sulfur dioxide, and carbon monoxide.

Particulate Matter

The air is full of microscopic and submicroscopic particles, many of which can be tied to motor vehicles (especially diesels) and industrial sources. Over the past 10 years, more attention has been focused on the very small particles because of their potential to promote pulmonary infection and actually cross the epithelium to enter the circulation (35). Fine particle pollution causes an elevation in blood pressure in those with pre-existing cardiovascular disease and may contribute to an increased risk of cardiac mortality and morbidity (114, 138). The mechanisms by which this occurs include a decreased capacity of the blood vessels to dilate and a reduction in fibrinolytic activity (81). Finally, evidence exists that these particles cause systemic oxidative stress with damage to DNA (9), and that antioxidant supplements may moderate this effect, especially in those with vitamin deficiencies (104).

Ozone

The ozone we breathe is generated by the reaction of UV light and emissions from internal combustion engines. While a single, 2-hour exposure to a high ozone concentration, 0.75 part per million (ppm), decreases $\dot{V}O_2$ max, recent studies show that a 6- to 12-hour exposure to a concentration of only 0.12 ppm (the U.S. air quality standard) decreases lung function and increases respiratory symptoms. Further, in amateur cyclists who practiced and raced in air containing varying concentrations of ozone, the decrease in pulmonary function following activity was directly related to the ozone concentration (10). Interestingly, an adaptation to ozone exposure can occur, with subjects showing a diminished response to subsequent exposures during the "ozone season." However, concern about long-term lung health suggests that it would be prudent to avoid heavy exercise during the time of day when ozone and other pollutants are elevated (34).

Sulfur Dioxide

Sulfur dioxide (SO_2) is produced by smelters, refineries, and electrical utilities that use fossil fuel for energy generation. SO_2 does not affect lung function in normal subjects, but it causes bronchoconstriction in asthmatics. These latter responses are influenced by the temperature and humidity of the inspired air, as mentioned in chapter 17. Nose breathing is encouraged to "scrub" the SO_2, and drugs like cromolyn sodium and β_2-agonists can partially block the asthmatic's response to SO_2 (34).

Carbon Monoxide

Carbon monoxide (CO) is derived from the burning of fossil fuel, coal, oil, gasoline, and wood, as well as from cigarette smoke. Carbon monoxide can bind to hemoglobin to form carboxyhemoglobin (HbCO) and decrease the capacity for oxygen transport. This has the potential to affect the physiological responses to submaximal exercise (51) and $\dot{V}O_2$ max, as does altitude. The carbon monoxide concentration [HbCO] in blood is generally less than 1% in nonsmokers, but may be as high as 10% in smokers (99). Horvath et al. (56) found that the critical concentration of HbCO needed to decrease $\dot{V}O_2$ max was 4.3%. Figure 24.11 shows the relationship between the blood HbCO concentration and the decrease in $\dot{V}O_2$ max; beyond 4.3% HbCO, $\dot{V}O_2$ max decreases 1% for each 1% increase in HbCO (100).

In contrast, when one performs light work, at about 40% $\dot{V}O_2$ max, the [HbCO] can be as high as 15% before endurance is affected. The cardiovascular system has the capacity to compensate with a larger cardiac output when the HbO_2 concentration is reduced during submaximal work (56, 99, 100). Because it takes 2 to 4 hours to remove half the CO from the blood after the exposure has been removed, CO can have a lasting effect on performances (34).

Unfortunately, it is difficult to predict what the actual [HbCO] will be in any given environment. One must consider the previous exposure to the pollutant, as well as the length of time and rate of ventilation associated with the current exposure. As a result, Raven (99) provides the following guidelines for exercising in an area with air pollution:

- Reduce exposure to the pollutant prior to exercise, because the physiological effects are time- and dose-dependent.
- Stay away from areas where you might receive a "bolus" dose of CO: smoking areas, high-traffic areas, urban environments.
- Do not schedule activities around the times when pollutants are at their highest levels (7–10 A.M. and 4–7 P.M.) due to traffic.

The **Air Quality Index (AQI)** is a measure of the quality of the air for five major air pollutants regulated by the Clean Air Act: ground-level ozone, particulate matter, carbon monoxide, sulfur dioxide, and nitrogen dioxide. Figure 24.12 shows a color-coded chart of the AIQ, with the interpretation of what the numerical values mean. Information on the AIQ is generally provided in a local community's weather forecast and should be suited to the individual—some will experience symptoms at lower levels of pollution than others (16).

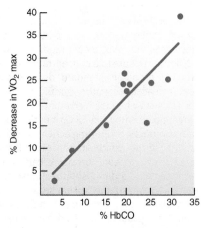

Figure 24.11 The effect of the concentration of carbon monoxide in the blood on the change in $\dot{V}O_2$ max.

- Air pollution can affect performance. Exposure to ozone decreases $\dot{V}O_2$ max and respiratory function, and sulfur dioxide causes bronchoconstriction in asthmatics.
- Carbon monoxide binds to hemoglobin and reduces oxygen transport.
- To prevent problems associated with pollution of any type, reduce exposure time; stay away from "bolus" amounts of the pollutant; and schedule activity at the least polluted part of the day.
- The Air Quality Index should be monitored to determine if conditions are safe for exercising outdoors.

Air Quality Index Levels of Health Concern	Numerical Value	Meaning
Good	0 to 50	Air quality is considered satisfactory, and air pollution poses little or no risk
Moderate	51 to 100	Air quality is acceptable; however, for some pollutants there may be a moderate health concern for a very small number of people who are unusually sensitive to air pollution.
Unhealthy for Sensitive Groups	101 to 150	Members of sensitive groups may experience health effects. The general public is not likely to be affected.
Unhealthy	151 to 200	Everyone may begin to experience health effects; members of sensitive groups may experience more serious health effects.
Very Unhealthy	201 to 300	Health alert: everyone may experience more serious health effects
Hazardous	301 to 500	Health warnings of emergency conditions. The entire population is more likely to be affected.

Figure 24.12 The Air Quality Index (AQI)—A Guide to Air Quality and Your Health. AIRNow website. Available at: http://www.airnow.gov/index.cfm?action=aqibasics.aqi

STUDY QUESTIONS

1. Describe the changes in barometric pressure, PO_2, and air density with increasing altitude.
2. Why is sprint performance not affected by altitude?
3. Explain why maximal aerobic power decreases at altitude and what effect this has on performance in long-distance races.
4. Graphically describe the effect of altitude on the HR and ventilation responses to submaximal work and provide recommendations for fitness participants who occasionally exercise at altitude.
5. Describe the process by which an individual adapts to altitude, and contrast the adaptation of the permanent residents of high altitude with that of the lowlander who arrives there as an adult.
6. While training at altitude can be beneficial, how could someone "detrain"? How can you work around this problem?
7. It was formerly believed that a person could not climb Mount Everest without oxygen because the estimated

$\dot{V}O_2$ max at altitude was close to basal metabolic rate. When two climbers accomplished the feat in 1978, scientists had to determine how this was possible. What were the primary reasons allowing the climb to take place without oxygen?
8. List and describe the factors related to heat injury.
9. What is the heat stress index, and why is the wet bulb temperature weighed so heavily in the formula?
10. List the factors related to hypothermia.
11. Explain what the wind chill index is relative to convective heat loss.
12. What is a clo unit, and why is the insulation requirement less when you exercise?
13. What would you do if a person had hypothermia?
14. Explain how carbon monoxide can influence $\dot{V}O_2$ max and endurance performance.
15. What steps would you follow to minimize the effect of pollution on performance?

SUGGESTED READINGS

Howe, A. S., and B. P. Boden. 2007. Heat-related illness in athletes. *American Journal of Sports Medicine* 35:1384–95.

Johnson, L., J. Hemmleb, and E. Simonson. 1999. *The Ghosts of Everest*. Seattle, WA: Mountaineers Books. (Detailed account of the expedition that found Mallory's body.)

Kenney, W. L., and T. A. Munce. 2003. Invited review: aging and human temperature regulation. *Journal of Applied Physiology* 95:598–603.

Messner, R. 1999. *Everest: Expedition to the Ultimate*. Seattle, WA: Mountaineers Books. (A story of the first trip to the summit by Messner and Habeler without oxygen.)

Millet, G. P., B. Roels, L. Schmitt, X. Woorons, and J. P. Richalet. 2010. Combining hypoxic methods for peak performance. *Sports Medicine*. 40:1–25.

Saunders, P. U., D. B. Pyne, and C. J. Gore. 2009. Endurance training at altitude. *High Altitude Medicine & Biology* 10:135–48.

REFERENCES

1. **Adams WC, Bernauer EM, Dill DB, and Bomar JB, Jr.** Effects of equivalent sea-level and altitude training on $\dot{V}O_2$ max and running performance. *Journal of Applied Physiology* 39: 262–266, 1975.
2. **Alexander JK, Hartley LH, Modelski M, and Grover RF.** Reduction of stroke volume during

exercise in man following ascent to 3,100 m altitude. *Journal of Applied Physiology* 23: 849–858, 1967.
3. **American College of Sports Medicine.** Position stand: heat and cold illnesses during distance running. *Medicine and Science in Sports and Exercise* 28: i–x, 1996.

4. **American College of Sports Medicine.** Position stand: prevention of cold injuries during exercise. *Medicine and Science in Sports and Exercise* 38: 2012–2029, 2006.

5. **American College of Sports Medicine.** Position stand. Exertional heat illness during training and competition. *Medicine and Science in Sports and Exercise* 39: 556–572, 2007.

6. **Balke B, Nagle FJ, and Daniels J.** Altitude and maximum performance in work and sports activity. *JAMA* 194: 646–649, 1965.

7. **Bassovitch O.** Intermittent hypoxia training: risks versus benefits. A biomedical engineering point of view. *European Journal of Applied Physiology* 110: 659–660, 2010.

8. **Bittel JH, Nonotte-Varly C, Livecchi-Gonnot GH, Savourey GL, and Hanniquet AM.** Physical fitness and thermoregulatory reactions in a cold environment in men. *Journal of Applied Physiology* 65: 1984–1989, 1988.

9. **Brauner EV, Forchhammer L, Moller P, Simonsen J, Glasius M, Wahlin P, Raaschou-Nielsen O, and Loft S.** Exposure to ultrafine particles from ambient air and oxidative stress-induced DNA damage. *Environmental Health Perspectives* 115: 1177–1182, 2007.

10. **Brunekreef B, Hoek G, Breugelmans O, and Leentvaar M.** Respiratory effects of low-level photochemical air pollution in amateur cyclists. *American Journal of Respiratory and Critical Care Medicine* 150: 962–966, 1994.

11. **Buono MJ, and Sjoholm NT.** Effect of physical training on peripheral sweat production. *Journal of Applied Physiology* 65: 811–814, 1988.

12. **Burton A, and Edholm O.** *Man in a Cold Environment.* London: Edward Arnold, 1955.

13. **Buskirk E, and Bass D.** Climate and exercise. In: *Science and Medicine of Exercise and Sport,* edited by Johnson W, and Buskirk E. New York: Harper & Row, 1974, p. 190–205.

14. **Buskirk E, and Grasley W.** Heat injury and conduct of athletics. In: *Science and Medicine of Exercise and Sport,* edited by Johnson W, and Buskirk E. New York: Harper & Row, 1974, p. 206–210.

15. **Buskirk ER, Kollias J, Akers RF, Prokop EK, and Reategui EP.** Maximal performance at altitude and on return from altitude in conditioned runners. *Journal of Applied Physiology* 23: 259–266, 1967.

16. **Campbell ME, Li Q, Gingrich SE, Macfarlane RG, and Cheng S.** Should people be physically active outdoors on smog alert days? *Canadian Journal of Public Health* 96: 24–28, 2005.

17. **Cappaert TA, Stone JA, Castellani JW, Krause BA, Smith D, and Stephens BA.** National Athletic Trainers' Association postion statement: environmental cold injuries. *Journal of Athletic Training* 43: 640–658, 2008.

18. **Carter JE, and Gisolfi CV.** Fluid replacement during and after exercise in the heat. *Medicine and Science in Sports and Exercise* 21: 532–539, 1989.

19. **Carver S.** Injury prevention and treatment. In: *Fitness Professional's Handbook,* edited by Howley E, and Franks B. Champaign: Human Kinetics, 2007, p. 375–397.

20. **Casa DJ, McDermott BP, Lee EC, Yeargin SW, Armstrong LE, and Maresh CM.** Cold water immersion: the gold standard for exertional heatstroke treatment. *Exercise and Sport Sciences Reviews* 35: 141–149, 2007.

21. **Chapman R, and Levine BD.** Altitude training for the marathon. *Sports Medicine (Auckland, NZ)* 37: 392–395, 2007.

22. **Chapman RF, Stray-Gundersen J, and Levine BD.** Individual variation in response to altitude training. *Journal of Applied Physiology* 85: 1448–1456, 1998.

23. **Commentaries on lactate paradox.** Commentaries on viewpoint: evidence that reduced skeletal muscle recruitment explains the lactate paradox during exercise at high altitude. *Journal of Applied Physiology* 106: 739–744, 2009.

24. **Costill DL, Cote R, Miller E, Miller T, and Wynder S.** Water and electrolyte replacement during repeated days of work in the heat. *Aviation, Space, and Environmental Medicine* 46: 795–800, 1975.

25. **Cymerman A, Reeves JT, Sutton JR, Rock PB, Groves BM, Malconian MK, Young PM, Wagner PD, and Houston CS.** Operation Everest II: maximal oxygen uptake at extreme altitude. *Journal of Applied Physiology* 66: 2446–2453, 1989.

26. **Daniels J, and Oldridge N.** The effects of alternate exposure to altitude and sea level on world-class middle-distance runners. *Medicine and Science in Sports* 2: 107–112, 1970.

27. **Danielsson U.** Windchill and the risk of tissue freezing. *Journal of Applied Physiology* 81: 2666–2673, 1996.

28. **Dill DB, and Adams WC.** Maximal oxygen uptake at sea level and at 3,090-m altitude in high school champion runners. *Journal of Applied Physiology* 30: 854–859, 1971.

29. **Drinkwater BL, Denton JE, Kupprat IC, Talag TS, and Horvath SM.** Aerobic power as a factor in women's response to work in hot environments. *Journal of Applied Physiology* 41: 815–821, 1976.

30. **Dufour SP, Ponsot E, Zoll J, Doutreleau S, Lonsdorfer-Wolf E, Geny B, Lampert E, Fluck M, Hoppeler H, Billat V, Mettauer B, Richard R, and Lonsdorfer J.** Exercise training in normobaric hypoxia in endurance runners. I. Improvement in aerobic performance capacity. *Journal of Applied Physiology* 100: 1238–1248, 2006.

31. **Ely MR, Cheuvront SN, and Montain SJ.** Neither cloud cover nor low solar loads are associated with fast marathon performance. *Medicine and Science in Sports and Exercise* 39: 2029–2035, 2007.

32. **Engfred K, Kjaer M, Secher NH, Friedman DB, Hanel B, Nielsen OJ, Bach FW, Galbo H, and Levine BD.** Hypoxia and training-induced adaptation of hormonal responses to exercise in humans. *European Journal of Applied Physiology and Occupational Physiology* 68: 303–309, 1994.

33. **Faulkner JA, Kollias J, Favour CB, Buskirk ER, and Balke B.** Maximum aerobic capacity and running performance at altitude. *Journal of Applied Physiology* 24: 685–691, 1968.

34. **Folinsbee L.** Discussion: exercise and the environment. In: *Exercise, Fitness, and Health,* edited by Bouchard C, Shephard R, Stevens T, Sutton J, and McPherson B. Champaign: Human Kinetics, 1990, p. 179–183.

35. **Frampton M.** Effects of exposure to ultrafine carbon particles in healthy subjects and subjects with asthma. *Research Report–Health Effects Institute* 126: 1–63, 2004.

36. **Frisancho AR, Martinez C, Velasquez T, Sanchez J, and Montoye H.** Influence of developmental adaptation on aerobic capacity at high altitude. *Journal of Applied Physiology* 34: 176–180, 1973.

37. **Froese G, and Burton AC.** Heat losses from the human head. *Journal of Applied Physiology* 10: 235–241, 1957.

38. **Gates D.** *Man and His Environment: Climate.* New York: Harper & Row, 1972.

39. **Gilchrist J, Murphy M, Comstock RD, Collins C, McIlvain N, and Yard E.** Heat illness among high school athletes-United States, 2005–2009. *Morbidity and Mortality Weekly Report* 59: 1009–1013, 2010.

40. **Gisolfi CV, and Cohen JS.** Relationships among training, heat acclimation, and heat tolerance in men and women: the controversy revisited. *Medicine and Science in Sports* 11: 56–59, 1979.

41. **Gore CJ, Clark SA, and Saunders PU.** Nonhematological mechanisms of improved sea-level performance after hypoxic exposure. *Medicine and Science in Sports and Exercise* 39: 1600–1609, 2007.

42. **Gore CJ, Rodriguez FA, Truijens MJ, Townsend NE, Stray-Gundersen J, and Levine BD.** Increased serum erythropoietin but not red cell production after 4 wk of intermittent hypobaric hypoxia (4,000–5,500 m). *Journal of Applied Physiology* 101: 1386–1393, 2006.

43. **Green HJ, Sutton JR, Cymerman A, Young PM, and Houston CS.** Operation Everest II: adaptations in human skeletal muscle. *Journal of Applied Physiology* 66: 2454–2461, 1989.

44. **Green HJ, Sutton JR, Wolfel EE, Reeves JT, Butterfield GE, and Brooks GA.** Altitude acclimatization and energy metabolic adaptations in skeletal muscle during exercise. *Journal of Applied Physiology* 73: 2701–2708, 1992.

45. **Grover RF, Reeves JT, Grover EB, and Leathers JE.** Muscular exercise in young men native to 3,100 m altitude. *Journal of Applied Physiology* 22: 555–564, 1967.

46. **Hanson PG, and Zimmerman SW.** Exertional heatstroke in novice runners. *JAMA* 242: 154–157, 1979.

47. **Hardy J, and Bard P.** Body temperature regulation. In: *Medical Physiology*, edited by Mount-Castle V. St. Louis: C. V. Mosby, 1974, p. 1305–1342.

48. **Hartley LH, Vogel JA, and Cruz JC.** Reduction of maximal exercise heart rate at altitude and its reversal with atropine. *Journal of Applied Physiology* 36: 362–365, 1974.

49. **Hayward MG, and Keatinge WR.** Roles of subcutaneous fat and thermoregulatory reflexes in determining ability to stabilize body temperature in water. *The Journal of Physiology* 320: 229–251, 1981.

50. **Hemmleb J, and Johnson L.** Discovery on Everest. *Climbing* 188: 98–190, 1999.

51. **Hirsch GL, Sue DY, Wasserman K, Robinson TE, and Hansen JE.** Immediate effects of cigarette smoking on cardiorespiratory responses to exercise. *Journal of Applied Physiology* 58: 1975–1981, 1985.

52. **Hobson RM, Clapp EL, Watson P, and Maughan RJ.** Exercise capacity in the heat is greater in the morning than in the evening in man. *Medicine and Science in Sports and Exercise* 41: 174–180, 2009.

53. **Holmer I.** Physiology of swimming man. In: *Exercise and Sport Sciences Reviews*, edited by Hutton R, and Miller D. Salt Lake City: Franklin Institute, 1979.

54. **Hoppeler H, Kleinert E, Schlegel C, Claassen H, Howald H, Kayar SR, and Cerretelli P.** Morphological adaptations of human skeletal muscle to chronic hypoxia. *International Journal of Sports Medicine* 11 Suppl 1: S3–9, 1990.

55. **Horvath SM.** Exercise in a cold environment. In: *Exercise and Sport Sciences Reviews*, edited by Miller D. Salt Lake: Franklin Institute, 1981, p. 221–263.

56. **Horvath SM, Raven PB, Dahms TE, and Gray DJ.** Maximal aerobic capacity at different levels of carboxyhemoglobin. *Journal of Applied Physiology* 38: 300–303, 1975.

57. **Houmard JA, Costill DL, Davis JA, Mitchell JB, Pascoe DD, and Robergs RA.** The influence of exercise intensity on heat acclimation in trained subjects. *Medicine and Science in Sports and Exercise* 22: 615–620, 1990.

58. **Howald H, Pette D, Simoneau JA, Uber A, Hoppeler H, and Cerretelli P.** Effect of chronic hypoxia on muscle enzyme activities. *International Journal of Sports Medicine* 11 Suppl 1: S10–14, 1990.

59. **Howley E.** Effect of altitude on physical performance. In: *Encyclopedia of Physical Education, Fitness, and Sports: Training, Environment, Nutrition, and Fitness*, edited by Stull G, and Cureton T. Salt Lake: Brighton, 1980, p. 177–187.

60. **Hubbard R, and LE A.** Hyperthermia: new thoughts on an old problem. *The Physician and Sportsmedicine* 17: 97–113, 1989.

61. **Hughson RL, Green HJ, Houston ME, Thomson JA, MacLean DR, and Sutton JR.** Heat injuries in Canadian mass participation runs. *Canadian Medical Association Journal* 122: 1141–1144, 1980.

62. **Hurtado A.** Animals in high altitudes: resident man. In: *Handbook of Physiology: Section 4-Adaptation to the Environment*, edited by Dill D. Washington, DC: American Physiological Society, 1964.

63. **Kayser B.** Nutrition and energetics of exercise at altitude. Theory and possible practical implications. *Sports Medicine (Auckland, NZ)* 17: 309–323, 1994.

64. **Kollias J, and Buskirk E.** Exercise and altitude. In: *Science and Medicine of Exercise and Sport*, edited by Johnson W, and Buskirk E. New York: Harper & Row, 1974.

65. **Kollias J, Buskirk ER, Akers RF, Prokop EK, Baker PT, and Picon-Reategui E.** Work capacity of long-time residents and newcomers to altitude. *Journal of Applied Physiology* 24: 792–799, 1968.

66. **Lawler J, Powers SK, and Thompson D.** Linear relationship between $\dot{V}O_2$ max and $\dot{V}O_2$ max decrement during exposure to acute hypoxia. *Journal of Applied Physiology* 64: 1486–1492, 1988.

67. **Levine BD, and Stray-Gundersen J.** Point: positive effects of intermittent hypoxia (live high: train low) on exercise performance are mediated primarily by augmented red cell volume. *Journal of Applied Physiology* 99: 2053–2055, 2005.

68. **Lorenzo S, Halliwill JR, Sawka MN, and Minson CT.** Heat acclimation improves exercise performance. *Journal of Applied Physiology* 109: 1140–1147, 2010.

69. **Lundby C, and van Hall G.** Lactate metabolism at high altitude. *High Altitude Medicine & Biology* 5: 195–196; author reply 197–198, 2004.

70. **MacDougall JD, Green HJ, Sutton JR, Coates G, Cymerman A, Young P, and Houston CS.** Operation Everest II: structural adaptations in skeletal muscle in response to extreme simulated altitude. *Acta Physiologica Scandinavica* 142: 421–427, 1991.

71. **Marconi C, Marzorati M, Grassi B, Basnyat B, Colombini A, Kayser B, and Cerretelli P.** Second generation Tibetan lowlanders acclimatize to high altitude more quickly than Caucasians. *The Journal of Physiology* 556: 661–671, 2004.

72. **Martin D, and O'Kroy J.** Effects of acute hypoxia on the $\dot{V}O_2$ max of trained and untrained subjects. *Journal of Sports Sciences* 11: 37–42, 1993.

73. **Mathews DK, Fox EL, and Tanzi D.** Physiological responses during exercise and recovery in a football uniform. *Journal of Applied Physiology* 26: 611–615, 1969.

74. **Mazess RB.** Cardiorespiratory characteristics and adaptation to high altitudes. *American Journal of Physical Anthropology* 32: 267–278, 1970.

75. **Mazess RB.** Exercise performance at high altitude in Peru. *Federation Proceedings* 28: 1301–1306, 1969.

76. **Mazess RB.** Exercise performance of Indian and white high altitude residents. *Human Biology: an International Record of Research* 41: 494–518, 1969.

77. **Mazzeo RS.** Physiological responses to exercise at altitude—an update. *Sports Medicine* 38: 1–8, 2008.

78. **Mazzeo RS, Brooks GA, Butterfield GE, Cymerman A, Roberts AC, Selland M, Wolfel EE, and Reeves JT.** Beta-adrenergic blockade does not prevent the lactate response to exercise after acclimatization to high altitude. *Journal of Applied Physiology* 76: 610–615, 1994.

79. **McArdle WD, Magel JR, Gergley TJ, Spina RJ, and Toner MM.** Thermal adjustment to cold-water exposure in resting men and women. *Journal of Applied Physiology* 56: 1565–1571, 1984.

80. **McArdle WD, Magel JR, Spina RJ, Gergley TJ, and Toner MM.** Thermal adjustment to cold-water exposure in exercising men and women. *Journal of Applied Physiology* 56: 1572–1577, 1984.

81. **Mills NL, Tornqvist H, Robinson SD, Gonzalez M, Darnley K, MacNee W, Boon NA, Donaldson K, Blomberg A, Sandstrom T, and Newby DE.** Diesel exhaust inhalation causes vascular dysfunction and impaired endogenous fibrinolysis. *Circulation* 112: 3930–3936, 2005.

82. **Noakes TD.** Evidence that reduced skeletal muscle recruitment explains the lactate paradox during exercise at high altitude. *Journal of Applied Physiology* 106: 737–738, 2009.

83. **Noakes TD.** Last word on viewpoint: evidence that reduced skeletal muscle recruitment explains the lactate paradox during exercise at high altitude. *Journal of Applied Physiology* 106: 745, 2009.

84. **Norton E.** *The Fight for Everest: 1924.* New York: Longmans, Green, 1925.

85. **Oelz O, Howald H, Di Prampero PE, Hoppeler H, Claassen H, Jenni R, Buhlmann A, Ferretti G, Bruckner JC, Veicsteinas A, et al.** Physiological profile of world-class high-altitude climbers. *Journal of Applied Physiology* 60: 1734–1742, 1986.

86. **Pascoe DD, Shanley LA, and Smith EW.** Clothing and exercise. I: biophysics of heat transfer between the individual, clothing and environment. *Sports Medicine (Auckland, NZ)* 18: 38–54, 1994.

87. **Peronnet F, Thibault G, and Cousineau DL.** A theoretical analysis of the effect of altitude on running performance. *Journal of Applied Physiology* 70: 399–404, 1991.

88. **Ponsot E, Dufour SP, Zoll J, Doutrelau S, N'Guessan B, Geny B, Hoppeler H, Lampert E, Mettauer B, Ventura-Clapier R, and Richard R.** Exercise training in normobaric hypoxia in endurance runners. II. Improvement of mitochondrial properties in skeletal muscle. *Journal of Applied Physiology* 100: 1249–1257, 2006.

89. **Powers SK, Martin D, and Dodd S.** Exercise-induced hypoxaemia in elite endurance athletes. Incidence, causes and impact on $\dot{V}O_2$ max. *Sports Medicine (Auckland, NZ)* 16: 14–22, 1993.

90. **Pronk M.** Lactate metabolism at high altitude: a reply. *High Altitude Medicine and Biology* 5: 197–198, 2004.

91. **Pronk M, Tiemessen I, Hupperets MD, Kennedy BP, Powell FL, Hopkins SR, and Wagner PD.** Persistence of the lactate paradox over 8 weeks at 3,800 m. *High Altitude Medicine & Biology* 4: 431–443, 2003.

92. **Pugh L.** Athletes at altitude. *Journal of Physiology (London)* 192: 619–646, 1967.

93. **Pugh LG.** Deaths from exposure on Four Inns Walking Competition, March 14–15, 1964. *Lancet* 1: 1210–1212, 1964.

94. **Pugh LG, and Edholm OG.** The physiology of channel swimmers. *Lancet* 269: 761–768, 1955.

95. **Pugh LG, Gill MB, Lahiri S, Milledge JS, Ward MP, and West JB.** Muscular exercise at great altitudes. *Journal of Applied Physiology* 19: 431–440, 1964.

96. **Quinn MD.** The effects of wind and altitude in the 400-m sprint. *Journal of Sports Sciences* 22: 1073–1081, 2004.

97. **Quod MJ, Martin DT, and Laursen PB.** Cooling athletes before competition in the heat: comparison of techniques and practical considerations. *Sports Medicine (Auckland, NZ)* 36: 671–682, 2006.

98. **Racinais S.** Different effects of heat exposure upon exercise performance in the morning and afternoon. *Scandanavian Journal of Medicine & Science in Sports* 20 Suppl. 3: 80–89, 2010.

99. **Raven P.** Effects of air pollution on physical performance. In: *Encyclopedia of Physical Education, Fitness, and Sports: Training, Environment, Nutrition, and Fitness*, edited by Stull G, and Cureton T. Salt Lake: Brighton, 1980, p. 201–216.

100. **Raven PB, Drinkwater BL, Ruhling RO, Bolduan N, Taguchi S, Gliner J, and Horvath SM.** Effect of carbon monoxide and peroxyacetyl nitrate on man's maximal aerobic capacity. *Journal of Applied Physiology* 36: 288–293, 1974.

101. **Reeves JT, Wolfel EE, Green HJ, Mazzeo RS, Young AJ, Sutton JR, and Brooks GA.** Oxygen transport during exercise at altitude and the lactate paradox: lessons from Operation Everest II and Pikes Peak. *Exercise and Sport Sciences Reviews* 20: 275–296, 1992.

102. **Roberts WO.** Heat and cold: what does the environment do to marathon injury? *Sports Medicine (Auckland, NZ)* 37: 400–403, 2007.

103. **Rodriguez FA, Truijens MJ, Townsend NE, Stray-Gundersen J, Gore CJ, and Levine BD.** Performance of runners and swimmers after four weeks of intermittent hypobaric hypoxic exposure plus sea level training. *Journal of Applied Physiology* 103: 1523–1535, 2007.

104. **Romieu I, Castro-Giner F, Kunzli N, and Sunyer J.** Air pollution, oxidative stress and dietary supplementation: a review. *Eur Respir J* 31: 179–197, 2008.

105. **Rose MS, Houston CS, Fulco CS, Coates G, Sutton JR, and Cymerman A.** Operation Everest. II: Nutrition and body composition. *Journal of Applied Physiology* 65: 2545–2551, 1988.

106. **Roskamm H, Landry F, Samek L, Schlager M, Weidemann H, and Reindell H.** Effects of a standardized ergometer training program at three different altitudes. *Journal of Applied Physiology* 27: 840–847, 1969.

107. **Ross MR, Garvican LA, Jeacocke NA, Laursen PB, Abbiss CR, Martin DT, and Burke LM.** Novel precooling strategy enhances time trial cycling in the heat. *Medicine and Science in Sports and Exercise* 43: 123–133, 2011.

108. **Rupert JL, and Hochachka PW.** Genetic approaches to understanding human adaptation to altitude in the Andes. *The Journal of Experimental Biology* 204: 3151–3160, 2001.

109. **Saltin B.** Circulatory response to submaximal and maximal exercise after thermal dehydration. *Journal of Applied Physiology* 19: 1125–1132, 1964.

110. **Saunders PU, Pyne DB, and Gore CJ.** Endurance training at altitude. *High Altitude Medicine & Biology* 10: 135–148, 2009.

111. **Sawka MN, Francesconi RP, Young AJ, and Pandolf KB.** Influence of hydration level and body fluids on exercise performance in the heat. *JAMA* 252: 1165–1169, 1984.

112. **Sawka MN, Young AJ, Francesconi RP, Muza SR, and Pandolf KB.** Thermoregulatory and blood responses during exercise at graded hypohydration levels. *Journal of Applied Physiology* 59: 1394–1401, 1985.

113. **Schoene RB, Lahiri S, Hackett PH, Peters RM, Jr., Milledge JS, Pizzo CJ, Sarnquist FH, Boyer SJ, Graber DJ, Maret KH, et al.** Relationship of hypoxic ventilatory response to exercise performance on Mount Everest. *Journal of Applied Physiology* 56: 1478–1483, 1984.

114. **Sharman JE, Cockcroft JR, and Coombes JS.** Cardiovascular implications of exposure to traffic air pollution during exercise. *QJM* 97: 637–643, 2004.

115. **Siple P, and Passel C.** Measurements of dry atmospheric cooling in subfreezing temperatures. *Proceedings of the American Philosophical Society* 89: 177–199, 1945.

116. **Strohl KP.** Lessons in hypoxic adaptations from high-altitude populations. *Sleep Breath* 12: 115–121, 2008.

117. **Sutton JR, Reeves JT, Wagner PD, Groves BM, Cymerman A, Malconian MK, Rock PB, Young PM, Walter SD, and Houston CS.** Operation Everest II: oxygen transport during exercise at extreme simulated altitude. *Journal of Applied Physiology* 64: 1309–1321, 1988.

118. **Tikuisis P, Bell DG, and Jacobs I.** Shivering onset, metabolic response, and convective heat transfer during cold air exposure. *Journal of Applied Physiology* 70: 1996–2002, 1991.

119. **Van Hall G, Calbet JA, Sondergaard H, and Saltin B.** The re-establishment of the normal blood lactate response to exercise in humans after prolonged acclimatization to altitude. *The Journal of Physiology* 536: 963–975, 2001.

120. **Van Hall G, Lundby C, Araoz M, Calbet JAL, Sander M, and Saltin B.** The lactate paradox revisited in lowlanders during acclimatization to 4100 m and in high-altitude natives. *J Physiol* 587: 1117–1129, 2009.

121. **Vogt M, and Hoppeler H.** Is hypoxia training good for muscles and exercise performance? *Progress in Cardiovascular Diseases* 52: 525–533, 2010.

122. **Volpino P, Tomei F, La Valle C, Tomao E, Rosati MV, Ciarrocca M, De Sio S, Cangemi B, Vigliarolo R, and Fedele F.** Respiratory and cardiovascular function at rest and during exercise testing in a healthy working population: effects of outdoor traffic air pollution. *Occupational Medicine (Oxford, England)* 54: 475–482, 2004.

123. **Wagner PD, and Lundby C.** The lactate paradox: does acclimatization to high altitude affect blood lactate during exercise? *Medicine and Science in Sports and Exercise* 39: 749–755, 2007.

124. **Ward-Smith AJ.** The influence of aerodynamic and biomechanical factors on long jump performance. *Journal of Biomechanics* 16: 655–658, 1983.

125. **Wehrlin JP, Zuest P, Hallen J, and Marti B.** Live high-train low for 24 days increases hemoglobin mass and red cell volume in elite endurance athletes. *Journal of Applied Physiology* 100: 1938–1945, 2006.

126. **West JB.** Point: the lactate paradox does/does not occur during exercise at high altitude. *Journal of Applied Physiology* 102: 2398–2399, 2007.

127. **West JB, Boyer SJ, Graber DJ, Hackett PH, Maret KH, Milledge JS, Peters RM, Jr., Pizzo CJ, Samaja M, Sarnquist FH, et al.** Maximal exercise at extreme altitudes on Mount Everest. *Journal of Applied Physiology* 55: 688–698, 1983.

128. **West JB, Hackett PH, Maret KH, Milledge JS, Peters RM, Jr., Pizzo CJ, and Winslow RM.** Pulmonary gas exchange on the summit of Mount Everest. *Journal of Applied Physiology* 55: 678–687, 1983.

129. **West JB, Lahiri S, Gill MB, Milledge JS, Pugh LG, and Ward MP.** Arterial oxygen saturation during exercise at high altitude. *Journal of Applied Physiology* 17: 617–621, 1962.

130. **West JB, Lahiri S, Maret KH, Peters RM, Jr., and Pizzo CJ.** Barometric pressures at extreme altitudes on Mt. Everest: physiological significance. *Journal of Applied Physiology* 54: 1188–1194, 1983.

131. **West JB, and Wagner PD.** Predicted gas exchange on the summit of Mt. Everest. *Respiration Physiology* 42: 1–16, 1980.

132. **Wilber RL.** Application of altitude/hypoxic training by elite athletes. *Medicine and Science in Sports and Exercise* 39: 1610–1624, 2007.

133. **Wilber RL, Stray-Gundersen J, and Levine BD.** Effect of hypoxic "dose" on physiological responses and sea-level performance. *Medicine and Science in Sports and Exercise* 39: 1590–1599, 2007.

134. **Wilson MJ, Julian CG, and Roach RC.** Genomic analysis of high-altitude adapatation: innovations and implications. *Current Sports Medicine Reports* 10: 59–61, 2011.

135. **Wolski LA, McKenzie DC, and Wenger HA.** Altitude training for improvements in sea level performance. Is the scientific evidence of benefit? *Sports Medicine (Auckland, NZ)* 22: 251–263, 1996.

136. **Yaspelkis BB, III, and Ivy JL.** Effect of carbohydrate supplements and water on exercise metabolism in the heat. *Journal of Applied Physiology* 71: 680–687, 1991.

137. **Yu IT, Wong TW, and Liu HJ.** Impact of air pollution on cardiopulmonary fitness in schoolchildren. *Journal of Occupational and Environmental Medicine / American College of Occupational and Environmental Medicine* 46: 946–952, 2004.

138. **Zanobetti A, Canner MJ, Stone PH, Schwartz J, Sher D, Eagan-Bengston E, Gates KA, Hartley LH, Suh H, and Gold DR.** Ambient pollution and blood pressure in cardiac rehabilitation patients. *Circulation* 110: 2184–2189, 2004.

139. **Zoll J, Ponsot E, Dufour S, Doutreleau S, Ventura-Clapier R, Vogt M, Hoppeler H, Richard R, and Fluck M.** Exercise training in normobaric hypoxia in endurance runners. III. Muscular adjustments of selected gene transcripts. *Journal of Applied Physiology* 100: 1258–1266, 2006.

Training for Performance

■ Objectives

By studying this chapter, you should be able to do the following:

1. Design a sport-specific training program based on an analysis of the energy systems utilized by the activity.
2. Define the terms *overload*, *specificity*, and *reversibility*.
3. Compare and contrast the use of interval training and continuous training in the improvement of the maximal aerobic power in athletes.
4. Discuss the differences between training for anaerobic power and training for the improvement of strength.
5. Discuss the advantages and disadvantages of different equipment types in weight training.
6. Define delayed-onset muscle soreness (DOMS). List the factors that contribute to its development.
7. Discuss the use of static and ballistic stretching to improve flexibility.
8. Discuss the differences between conditioning goals during (1) the off-season, (2) the preseason, and (3) in-season.
9. List and discuss several common training errors.

■ Outline

■ Key Terms

delayed-onset muscle soreness (DOMS)
dynamic stretching
hyperplasia
hypertrophy
overtraining
progressive resistance exercise (PRE)
proprioceptive neuromuscular facilitation (PNF)
repetition
rest interval
set
static stretching
tapering
variable-resistance exercise
work interval

Traditionally, coaches and trainers have planned conditioning programs for their teams by following regimens used by teams that have successful win-loss records. This type of reasoning is not sound because win-loss records alone do not scientifically validate the conditioning programs used by the successful teams. In fact, the successful team might be victorious by virtue of its superior athletes and not its outstanding conditioning program. Without question, the planning of an effective athletic conditioning program can best be achieved by the application of proven physiological training principles. Optimizing training programs for athletes is important because failure to properly condition an athletic team results in a poor performance and often defeat. This chapter presents an overview of how to apply scientific principles to the development of an athletic conditioning program.

TRAINING PRINCIPLES

The overall objective of a sport conditioning program is to improve performance. Depending upon the specific sport, this can be achieved by increasing the muscle's ability to generate force and power, improving muscular efficiency, and/or improving muscular endurance (8, 70). Recall that throughout this book (e.g., chapters 3, 4, and 20), emphasis has been placed on the fact that dissimilar sport activities use different metabolic pathways or "energy systems" to produce the ATP needed for movement. An understanding of exercise metabolism is important to the coach or trainer because the design of a conditioning program to optimize athletic performance requires knowledge of the principal energy systems utilized by the sport. Consider a few examples. The performance of a 60-meter dash uses the ATP-PC system almost exclusively to produce the needed ATP. In contrast, a marathon runner depends on aerobic metabolism to provide the energy needed to complete the race. However, most sport activities use multiple energy pathways. For instance, soccer uses a combination of metabolic pathways to provide the needed ATP. Knowledge of the relative anaerobic-aerobic contributions to ATP production during an activity is the cornerstone of planning a conditioning program. A well-designed conditioning program allocates the appropriate amount of aerobic and anaerobic conditioning time to match the energy demand of the sport. For instance, if an activity derives 40% of its ATP from anaerobic pathways and 60% from aerobic pathways (e.g., 1,500-meter run), the training program should be divided 40%/60% between anaerobic/aerobic training (8). Table 21.1 contains a list of various sports and an estimation of their predominant energy systems. The

TABLE 21.1	The Predominant Energy Systems for Selected Sports		
	% ATP CONTRIBUTION BY ENERGY SYSTEM		
Sport/ Activity	ATP-PC	Glycolysis	Aerobic
Baseball	80	15	5
Basketball	80	10	10
Field hockey	60	20	20
Football	90	10	—
Golf (swing)	100	—	—
Gymnastics	90	10	—
Ice hockey:			
Forwards/ defense	80	20	—
Goalie	95	5	—
Rowing	20	30	50
Soccer:			
Goalie/wings/ strikers	80	20	—
Halfbacks	60	20	20
Swimming:			
Diving	98	2	—
50 meters	95	5	—
100 meters	80	15	—
200 meters	30	65	5
400 meters	20	40	40
1,500 meters	10	20	70
Tennis	70	20	10
Track and field:			
100/200 meters	98	2	—
Field events	90	10	—
400 meters	40	55	5
800 meters	10	60	30
1,500 meters	5	35	60
5,000 meters	2	28	70
Marathon	—	2	98
Volleyball	90	10	—
Wrestling	45	55	—

From E. L. Fox and D. K. Mathews, *Interval Training: Conditioning for Sports and General Fitness.* Copyright © 1974 Saunders College Publishing, Orlando FL. Reprinted by permission of the author.

coach or trainer can use this information to allocate the appropriate amount of time to training each energy system.

This discussion does not necessarily imply that power athletes (e.g., sprinters) should not perform aerobic training. On the contrary, aerobic activity during the preseason to strengthen tendons and ligaments is generally recommended for all athletes (90).

Overload, Specificity, and Reversibility

The terms *overload*, *specificity*, and *reversibility* were introduced in chapter 13 and are repeated here only briefly. Recall that an organ system (e.g., cardiovascular, skeletal muscle, etc.) increases its capacity in response to a training overload. That is, the training program must stress the system above the level to which it is accustomed. While a training overload is required to achieve improvements in performance, too much overload can result in overtraining. **Overtraining** is defined as an accumulation of training stress that impairs an athlete's ability to perform training sessions and results in long-term decrements of performance (45). Overtraining is commonly associated with both physiological and psychological symptoms (e.g., chronic fatigue, mood disturbance, etc.). Recovery from overtraining can restore performance capacity but may require several weeks or months of reduced exercise training. A related term, *overreaching*, is also commonly used in the exercise training literature. The definition of overreaching is an accumulation of training stress that results in a short-term decrement in performance capacity with/without reaching the physiological signs and symptoms of overtraining (45). As you can see, these two terms are very similar and it has been argued that overreaching and overtraining studies should be viewed with caution because it is difficult to distinguish between these two terms (45). Therefore, this chapter will refer to an extreme accumulation of training stress as overtraining, and the term overreaching will not be used (23, 24, 86).

The concept of specificity refers not only to the specific muscles involved in a particular movement, but also to the energy systems that provide the ATP required to complete the movement under competitive conditions. Therefore, training programs need to deal with specificity by using not only those muscle groups engaged during competition, but also the energy systems that will be providing the ATP. For instance, specific training for a sprinter would involve running high-intensity dashes. Similarly, specific training for a marathoner would involve long, slow-paced runs in which virtually all the ATP needed by the working muscles would be derived from aerobic metabolism.

When an athlete stops training, the training effect is quickly lost (reversibility). Studies have demonstrated that within 2 weeks after the cessation of training, significant reductions in $\dot{V}O_2$ max can occur (23, 24). A classic study by Saltin and colleagues (86) demonstrated that after 20 days of bed rest, a group of subjects showed a 25% reduction in $\dot{V}O_2$ max and maximal cardiac output. These dramatic decrements in working capacity as a result of inactivity clearly demonstrate the rapid reversibility of training.

Influence of Gender and Initial Fitness Level

At one time, it was believed that conditioning programs for women had special requirements that differed from those used to train men. Today, however, much evidence exists to demonstrate that men and women respond to training programs in a similar fashion (7, 89). Therefore, the same general approach to physiological conditioning can be used in planning programs for men and women. This does not mean that men and women should perform identical exercise training sessions (e.g., same volume and intensity). Indeed, individual training programs should be designed appropriately to match the level of fitness and maturation of the athlete, regardless of gender. Individual "exercise prescriptions" is an important concern in the design of training programs and is discussed in further detail in the next several paragraphs.

It is a common observation that individuals differ greatly in the degree to which their performance benefits from training programs. Many factors contribute to the observed individual variations in the training response. One of the most important influences is the athlete's beginning level of fitness. In general, the amount of training improvement is always greater in those who are less conditioned at the beginning of the training program. It has been demonstrated that sedentary, middle-aged men with heart disease may improve their $\dot{V}O_2$ max by as much as 50%, whereas the same training program in normal, active adults improves $\dot{V}O_2$ max by only 10% to 20% (51). Similarly, conditioned athletes may improve their level of conditioning by only 3% to 5% following an increase in training intensity. However, this 3% to 5% improvement in the trained athlete may be the difference between winning an Olympic gold medal and failing to place in the event.

Influence of Genetics

As discussed in chapter 13, it is clear that genetics plays an important role in how an individual responds to a training program (4, 10, 48, 83). For instance, a person with a high genetic endowment for endurance sports responds differently to endurance training than one with a markedly different genetic profile. Indeed, recent research has provided genetic clues as to why some individuals are "high responders" to training and improve their fitness levels quickly to a greater extent than "low responders" (10). For this reason, and the fact that athletes begin conditioning programs at different levels of fitness, training programs should be individualized. It is unrealistic to expect each athlete on the team to perform the same amount of work or to exercise at the same work rate during training sessions.

Note that while training can greatly improve performance, there is no substitute for genetically inherited athletic talent if the individual is to compete at a world-class level. For example, there is a limit to how much training can improve aerobic power. Therefore, those individuals with a low genetic endowment for aerobic power cannot, under any training program, increase their $\dot{V}O_2$ max to world-class levels. Åstrand and Rodahl (8) have commented that if you want to become a world-class athlete, you must choose your parents wisely.

Similar to aerobic exercise, research indicates that genetics plays a key role in determining the performance level that can be achieved in anaerobic sports (e.g., sprinting in track and field) (13, 67). Indeed, it is well known that training can only improve anaerobic performance to a small degree. The primary reason is that the type of skeletal muscle fiber that is best suited for anaerobic performance (i.e., fast fibers, type IIx) is determined early in development, and the relative percentage of muscle fiber types does not vary widely over the lifetime. Therefore, anaerobic capacity appears to be largely genetically determined because the percentage of fast/anaerobic fibers is a primary determinant of anaerobic capacity.

IN SUMMARY

- The general objective of sport conditioning is to improve performance by increasing muscle force/power output, improving muscular efficiency, and/or improving muscle endurance.
- A conditioning program should allocate the appropriate amount of training time to match the aerobic and anaerobic energy demands of the sport.
- Muscles respond to training as a result of a progressive overload. When an athlete stops training, a rapid decline in fitness occurs due to detraining (reversibility).
- In general, men and women respond to conditioning in a similar fashion. The amount of training improvement is always greater in those individuals who are less conditioned at the onset of the training program.

COMPONENTS OF A TRAINING SESSION: WARM-UP, WORKOUT, AND COOL DOWN

Every training session should consist of three components: (1) warm-up, (2) workout, and (3) cool down. This idea was first introduced in chapter 16 and is mentioned only briefly here. The warm-up prior to a training workout has several important objectives. First, warm-up exercises increase cardiac output and blood flow to the skeletal muscles to be used during the training session. Second, the warm-up activity results in an increase in muscle temperature, which elevates muscle enzyme activity. Third, preliminary exercise affords the athlete an opportunity to perform stretching exercises. The duration of the warm-up may be from 5 to 20 minutes, depending on environmental conditions and the nature of the training activity. Although limited data exist, a recent review concludes that a proper warm-up may reduce the possibility of muscle injury due to pulls or strains (33, 94) and may also improve physical performance (34). Nonetheless, additional research is needed to definitively demonstrate whether a warm-up can deter exercise-induced injuries.

Immediately following the training session, a period of low-intensity "cool-down" exercises should be performed. The principal objective of a cool down is to return "pooled" blood from the exercised skeletal muscles back to the central circulation. Similar to the warm-up, the length of the cool down may vary from 10 to 30 minutes, depending on environmental conditions, the age and fitness level of the individual, and the nature of the training session.

IN SUMMARY

- Every training session should consist of a warm-up period, a workout session, and a cool-down period.
- Although limited data exist, it is believed that a warm-up reduces the risk of muscle and/or tendon injury during exercise.

TRAINING TO IMPROVE AEROBIC POWER

Recall from chapter 13 that endurance training improves $\dot{V}O_2$ max by increasing both maximal cardiac output and the a-$\bar{v}$ O_2 difference (i.e., increasing the muscle's ability to extract O_2). Therefore, a training program designed to improve maximal aerobic power must overload the circulatory system and stress the oxidative capacities of skeletal muscles as well. As in all training regimens, specificity is critical. The athlete should stress the specific muscles to be used in his or her sport. In other words, runners should train by running, cyclists should train on the bicycle, swimmers should swim, and so forth.

There are three principal aerobic training methods used by athletes: (1) interval training, (2) long, slow distance (low-intensity), and (3) high-intensity, continuous exercise. Controversy exists as to which of these training methods results in the greatest improvement in $\dot{V}O_2$ max. Indeed, there does not appear to be a magic training formula for all athletes to follow. However, evidence suggests that training intensity is the most important factor in improving $\dot{V}O_2$ max (50, 76, 77, 81). Nonetheless, from a psychological standpoint, it would appear that a mixing of all three methods would provide the needed variety to prevent the athlete from becoming bored with a single and rather monotonous training program.

Note that improvement of $\dot{V}O_2$ max is only one variable related to endurance. Recall from chapter 20 that although a high $\dot{V}O_2$ max is important for success in endurance events, both movement economy and the lactate threshold are also important variables. Therefore, training to improve endurance performance should not only be geared toward the improvement of $\dot{V}O_2$ max, but should also increase the lactate threshold and improve running economy. A brief discussion of various training methods used to improve endurance performance follows.

Interval Training

Interval training involves the performance of repeated exercise bouts, with brief recovery periods in between. The length and intensity of the **work interval** depends on what the athlete is trying to accomplish. For instance, a longer work interval requires a greater involvement of aerobic energy production, whereas a shorter, more intense interval provides greater participation of anaerobic metabolism. Therefore, interval training that is designed to improve $\dot{V}O_2$ max should generally utilize intervals longer than 60 seconds to maximize the involvement of aerobic ATP production. Further, it is generally believed that high-intensity intervals are more effective in improving aerobic power, and perhaps the lactate threshold, than low-intensity intervals (29, 31, 59). These improvements may be due to the recruitment of fast-twitch (types IIa and IIx) fibers during this type of high-intensity exercise.

One obvious advantage of interval training over continuous running is that this method of training provides a means of performing large amounts of high-intensity exercise in a short time. Further, this training method offers two ways of providing a training overload. For example, the interval training prescription can be modified to provide "overload" in terms of increasing either the total number of exercise intervals performed or the intensity of the work interval. Adjustments to either of these factors allow the coach or athlete to alter the workout plan to accomplish specific training goals. How does one design an interval workout? A complete discussion of the theory and rationale of designing an interval

training program to improve athletic performance is beyond the scope of this chapter; therefore, only an overview of interval training will be provided here. In planning an interval training session, the following variables need to be considered: (1) length of the work interval, (2) intensity of the effort, (3) duration of the rest interval, (4) number of interval sets, and (5) the number of work repetitions. The length of the work interval refers to the distance to be covered during the work effort. In training to improve aerobic power, the work interval should generally last longer than 60 seconds. The intensity of the work effort during interval training can be monitored from a 10-second HR count upon completion of the interval (i.e., 10 sec HR count × 6 = HR per min). In general, exercise HRs should reach 85% to 100% of the maximal HR during interval training. The time between work efforts is termed the **rest interval** and consists of light activity such as walking. The length of the rest interval is generally expressed as a ratio of the duration of the work interval. For example, if the work interval for running 400 meters was 75 seconds, a rest interval of 75 seconds would result in a 1:1 ratio of work to rest. Generally, the rest interval should be at least as long as the work interval (8). In planning an interval training program for athletes who are not already highly trained, a work:rest ratio of 1:3 or 1:2 seems preferable. As a general rule, the HR should drop to approximately 120 beats · min^{-1} near the end of the recovery interval (8).

A **set** is a specified number of work efforts performed as a unit. For instance, a set may consist of 8 × 400-meter runs with a prescribed rest interval between each run. The term **repetition** is the number of work efforts within one set. In the example just given, 8 × 400-meter run repetitions constituted one set. The number of repetitions and sets performed per workout depends on the purpose of the particular training session and the fitness levels of the athletes involved. For more details on interval training, see reference (62).

Long, Slow-Distance Exercise

The use of long, slow-distance (LSD) runs (or cycle rides, long swims, etc.) became a popular means of training for endurance events in the 1970s (21). In general, this method of training involves performing exercise at a low intensity (i.e., 57% $\dot{V}O_2$ max or approximately 70% of max HR) for durations that are generally greater in length than the normal competition distance. Although it seems reasonable that this type of training is a useful means of preparing an athlete to compete in long endurance competitions (marathon running), evidence suggests that short-term, high-intensity exercise is superior to long-term, low-intensity exercise in improving $\dot{V}O_2$ max (50, 51).

One of the historical reasons that researchers have used training sessions of long duration is the common belief that improvements in endurance are proportional to the volume of training performed. Indeed, many coaches and athletes believe that improvements in athletic performance are directly related to how much work was performed during training, and that athletes can reach their potential only by doing long-duration exercise bouts. Evidence by Costill and colleagues (22) contradicts this belief. These workers demonstrated that athletes training 1.5 hours per day performed as well as athletes training 3 hours per day. In fact, the athletes who trained 3 hours per day performed more poorly in some events than the group training 1.5 hours per day. This study illustrates the point that "more" is not always better in endurance training. Therefore, coaches and athletes should carefully consider the volume of training required to reach maximal benefits from long, slow-distance exercise.

High-Intensity, Continuous Exercise

Again, research suggests that continuous, high-intensity exercise is an outstanding means of improving $\dot{V}O_2$ max and the lactate threshold in athletes (25, 27, 30, 40, 50). Although the exercise intensity that promotes the greatest improvement in $\dot{V}O_2$ max may vary from athlete to athlete, it is commonly believed that exercise intensities between 90–100% $\dot{V}O_2$ max are optimal (see figure 21.1) (76). Nonetheless, evidence also indicates that a work rate that is equal to or slightly above the lactate threshold provides improvement in maximum aerobic power (76, 81, 88).

How does the athlete quantify their exercise intensity during a training session? A precise quantification of training intensity during exercise is complicated, but the measurement of exercise heart rate can be used as an estimate of an athlete's relative training

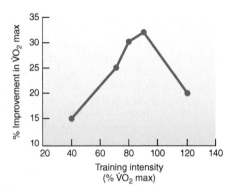

Figure 21.1 Relationship between training intensity and percent improvement in $\dot{V}O_2$ max. Data from references (30, 35, and 59).

intensity. An example of a heart rate-based training intensity scale to prescribe and monitor training of endurance athletes is presented in table 21.2. Obviously, standardizing exercise intensity based on heart rate alone has limitations and fails to account for individual variation among athletes in the relationship between heart rate and blood lactate concentration. Nonetheless, the advantage of this type of intensity scale is the simplicity because athletes can easily measure their heart rates during exercise using electronic heart rate monitors. For more details on using heart rate to monitor training intensity see Seiler (2010) in the Suggested Readings.

Altitude Training Improves Exercise Performance at Sea Level

For many years, endurance athletes believed that living and training at high altitude enhances performance compared to living and training at sea level (69). However, this may not always be true because athletes cannot perform as much high-intensity

---

TABLE 21.2 Example of a Five-Zone Intensity Scale to Prescribe and Monitor Exercise

Training in Athletes
A practical variable to monitor exercise intensity is heart rate expressed as a percent max heart rate. Note that the exercise intensity zones presented in this table are arbitrary, beginning with a relatively low-intensity zone (zone 1) and ending with a high-intensity zone (zone 5). Data are modified from reference (88).

Intensity Zone	% Heart Rate Max	%$\dot{V}O_2$ max	Blood Lactate Levels (mmol · L⁻¹)	Typical Training Duration in Zone
1	60–71	50–65	0.8–1.5	1–3 hours
2	72–82	66–80	1.5–2.5	1–2 hours
3	83–87	81–87	2.6–4.0	30–90 min
4	88–92	88–93	4.1–6.0	10–40 min
5	93–100	94–100	>6.1	5–10 min

A LOOK BACK—IMPORTANT PEOPLE IN SCIENCE

Dr. Benjamin Levine Is a Pioneer in the Physiology of Training Adaptation

Dr. Benjamin Levine earned his B.S. degree at Brown University and his medical degree from Harvard University. He completed his residency training in internal medicine and cardiology at Stanford University and the University of Texas. Dr. Levine is currently a professor at the University of Texas-Southwestern Medical Center and directs the Institute for Exercise and Environmental Medicine. This institute is a multidisciplinary, integrative physiology research center designed to explore the mechanisms that limit human performance in both health and disease.

Dr. Levine's research has greatly advanced our understanding of the physiology of training adaptation. In this regard, one of Dr. Levine's major contributions is his work on the benefits of altitude training for endurance

athletes. Here's the story: For more than 50 years, endurance athletes have used high-altitude training (altitudes >6,000 feet above sea level) in an effort to improve sea-level performance. The rationale for this practice is that both altitude adaptation and hypoxic exercise training have been proposed to improve $\dot{V}O_2$ max and exercise performance. However, hypoxic exercise impairs the athlete's ability to perform high-intensity exercise; therefore, training at altitude may limit exercise-training adaptation. To study this issue, Dr. Levine and his colleague, Dr. James Stray-Gundersen, performed several landmark studies investigating the impact of living and training at high altitude on endurance performance. Their work led to the development of the altitude training modality known as "Live-High, Train-Low." Their studies show that athletes living at high altitudes but performing

their training at lower altitudes exhibited improved endurance performance gains compared to athletes who live and train at high altitudes. The Levine/Stray-Gundersen concept of "Live-High, Train-Low" has become the model by which many endurance athletes use altitude training in preparation for major competitions.

In addition to his work on high-altitude training, Dr. Levine has made many other major contributions to our understanding of the physiological adaptations to endurance exercise training. Indeed, his work has greatly improved our knowledge about the cardiovascular adaptation to exercise and the impact of deconditioning (i.e., bed rest and space flight) on the cardiovascular system. Dr. Levine's work has resulted in more than 150 scientific publications, and many of these papers are widely cited in the research literature.

---

exercise training at altitude compared to sea level. Therefore, by performing less training, a form of detraining could actually occur while living and training at altitude. So, how can athletes design a training program to optimize the physiological benefits of living at altitude without the potentially negative de-training effects?

This altitude-training riddle was solved when researchers developed the altitude training modality known as "Live-High, Train-Low" (63) (see A Look Back—Important People in Science). This training program requires the athlete to spend many hours a day resting and sleeping at altitude, but the athlete performs exercise training sessions at a much lower altitude. This approach affords the athlete the benefit of altitude acclimatization, and by training at a low altitude, the athlete's ability to perform intense training sessions is not hampered by high altitude. This type of altitude training program has been shown to provide significant performance gains compared to training and living at sea level (63).

The physiological adaptation responsible for the endurance performance gains achieved from altitude training remains controversial. Nonetheless, it appears that one of the major advantages is that

residing at high altitude increases the red blood cell volume, and therefore the oxygen transport capacity of the blood is increased due to a greater hemoglobin concentration (64, 91). For more on altitude adaptation and the Live-High, Train-Low concept, see chapter 24 and Mazzeo (2008) in the References at the end of this chapter (69).

IN SUMMARY

- Historically, training to improve maximal aerobic power has used three methods: (1) interval training, (2) long, slow-distance, and (3) high-intensity, continuous exercise.
- Although controversy exists as to which of the training methods results in the greatest improvement in $\dot{V}O_2$ max, growing evidence suggests that it is intensity and not duration that is the most important factor in improving $\dot{V}O_2$ max.
- The Live-High, Train-Low altitude training program provides significant endurance performance gains compared to training and living at sea level.

INJURIES AND ENDURANCE TRAINING

An important question associated with any type of endurance training is what type of training program presents the lowest risk of injury to the athlete. At present, a clear answer to this question is not available. However, a review of exercise-training-induced injuries suggests that the majority of training injuries are a result of overtraining (e.g., overuse injuries) and occur in the knee (57, 75). The overuse injury can come from either short-term, high-intensity exercise or long-term, low-intensity exercise (75). A commonsense guideline to avoid overuse injuries is to avoid large increases in training volume or intensity. Perhaps the most useful general rule for increasing the training load is the "ten percent rule" (75). In short, the ten percent rule suggests that training intensity or duration should not be increased more than 10% per week to avoid an overtraining injury. For example, a runner running 50 miles per week could increase his/her weekly distance to 55 miles (10% of 50 = 5) the following week.

In addition to overtraining, several other exercise-induced injury risk factors have been identified (75). Among these factors are musculotendonous imbalance of strength and/or flexibility, footwear problems (i.e., excessive wear), anatomical malalignment, poor running surface, and disease (e.g., arthritis, old fracture, etc.) (14).

Note that gender is not an injury risk factor for endurance training (75). Similar to male athletes, it appears that most of the leg injuries in female runners are the result of overtraining (75). This may be especially true for poorly conditioned women beginning training programs.

IN SUMMARY

- The majority of training injuries are a result of overtraining (e.g., overuse injuries) and can come from either short-term, high-intensity exercise or prolonged, low-intensity exercise.
- A useful rule for increasing the training load is the "ten percent rule." The ten percent rule states that training intensity or duration should not be increased more than 10% per week to avoid an overtraining injury.

TRAINING TO IMPROVE ANAEROBIC POWER

Athletic events lasting fewer than 60 seconds depend largely on anaerobic production of the necessary energy. In general, training to improve anaerobic power centers around the need to enhance either the ATP-PC system or anaerobic glycolysis (lactate system) (74). However, some activities require major contributions of both of these anaerobic metabolic pathways to provide the necessary ATP for competition (see table 21.1). Moreover, many activities require ATP production from both aerobic and anaerobic sources. For example, running an 800-meter race is typically performed at a power output that exceeds $\dot{V}O_2$ max by ~30%. Therefore, energy to perform this type of sporting event requires both aerobic and anaerobic energy production.

Anaerobic training is commonly defined as exercise that is performed at intensities above $\dot{V}O_2$ max where the primary aim is to stimulate anaerobic energy production (55). High intensity anaerobic training lasting 2–10 seconds is often termed *speed training*, whereas the term *speed endurance training* is commonly used to describe all forms of anaerobic training lasting longer than 10 seconds (55). Identical to aerobic endurance training, it is critical that the anaerobic training program use the specific muscle groups that are required by the athlete during competition.

Training to Improve the ATP–PC System

Sports such as football, weight lifting, and short dashes in track (100 meters) depend on the ATP-PC system to provide the bulk of the energy needed for competition. Therefore, optimal performance requires a training program that will maximize ATP production via the ATP-PC pathway.

Training to improve the ATP-PC system involves a special type of interval training. To maximally stress the ATP-PC metabolic pathway, short, high-intensity intervals (5 to 10 seconds' duration) using the muscles utilized in competition are ideal. Because of the short durations of this type of interval, limited lactate is produced and recovery is rapid. The rest interval may range between 30 and 60 seconds, depending on the fitness levels of the athletes. For example, a training program for football players might involve repeated 30-yard dashes (with several directional changes), with a 30-second rest period between efforts. The number of repetitions per set would be determined by the athletes' fitness levels, environmental factors, and perhaps other considerations.

Training to Improve the Glycolytic System

After approximately 10 seconds of a maximal effort, there is a growing dependence on energy production from anaerobic glycolysis (32). To improve the capacity of this energy pathway, the athlete must overload

ASK THE EXPERT 21.1

Training to Improve Anaerobic Performance: Questions and Answers with Dr. Michael Hogan

Michael Hogan, Ph.D.,
Professor in the Department of Medicine at the University of California–San Diego, is an internationally known exercise physiologist whose research focuses on delivery and utilization of oxygen in skeletal muscle. Dr. Hogan has published more than 100 research articles and his work is widely cited in the scientific literature. Further, he has been a leader in numerous scientific organizations, including the American College of Sports Medicine and the American Physiological Society. In addition to being an internationally known scientist, Dr. Hogan continues to be an active competitor in the pole vault. As a collegiate athlete, Dr. Hogan was a four-year letterman in track and field and a school record holder in the pole vault at the University of Notre Dame. In the years following his graduation from college, Dr. Hogan has continued to train and compete in the pole vault and has recently excelled in both national and international age-group championships in this event. In this box feature, Dr. Hogan answers questions related to training to improve anaerobic power.

QUESTION: In designing a training program to improve anaerobic power, should weekly training sessions be planned on a "hard-easy" cycle?

ANSWER: Absolutely! This is possibly even more critical in anaerobic power training versus aerobic training. The reason for this is that to improve anaerobic capacity, extremely high-intensity exercise needs to be conducted to totally activate the type IIx fibers within the muscle. Recall from chapter 7 that due to the size principle, type IIx muscle fibers are the last fibers recruited during the muscle activation process. An important component of anaerobic training is to work during the "hard" cycle at an extremely high intensity that subsequently results in increasing muscle fiber size, so that muscle power is increased. A key concern is the duration of the "hard-easy" cycles, as each individual athlete will be very different in how much high-intensity exercise can be endured before the athlete "breaks down" and injury ensues. Knowing the proper balance of "hard-easy" is the difference between an Olympic gold medal and an injured athlete.

QUESTION: In sports or athletic events (e.g., 200-meter dash) that require energy from both the ATP-PC system and glycolysis, is it possible to design a training program to improve energy production from each of these bioenergetic systems?

ANSWER: Yes, these bioenergetic systems can be improved, although not to the degree that adaptation to endurance training (i.e., cardiovascular and oxidative enzyme changes) can be accomplished with aerobic training. The key to anaerobic performance that requires high ATP turnover rates for a short period of time (~30 seconds) is to have as much capacity in the glycolytic and ATP-PC systems and to minimize the factors that lead to fatigue in these short, high-intensity exercise bouts. Studies have demonstrated that glycolytic enzymes can be increased in all fiber-types by high-intensity training, so that more ATP can be generated anaerobically when necessary. Anaerobic training will also slightly improve aerobic capacity of the muscle, which can be important in that any aerobic generation of ATP will result in "sparing" of the ATP-PC and a lower rate of lactate production. Anaerobic training will also improve the speed at which phosphocreatine (PC) can be degraded, so that a faster ATP turnover is possible. It is unclear whether PC levels are affected by training, however creatine supplementation may increase resting levels of PC, thereby potentially improving anaerobic performance.

QUESTION: Recently, much interest has focused upon high-intensity training as a means of improving both anaerobic and aerobic power. Please define high-intensity training and discuss the evidence that this type of training can improve both anaerobic and aerobic bioenergetic systems.

ANSWER: Growing evidence indicates that high-intensity training (HIT), which is characterized by brief repeated bursts of intense exercise (e.g., 30–60 seconds of exercise at 100–120% $\dot{V}O_2$ max), can significantly improve not only anaerobic bioenergetic pathways but maximal aerobic power as well. This has surprised some scientists because, historically, it has been believed that HIT would improve only anaerobic power. Nonetheless, it is now clear that HIT can induce many adaptations in muscle normally associated with traditional endurance exercise training, including increased mitochondrial volume and improved endurance performance.

the "system" via short-term, high-intensity efforts. In general, high-intensity intervals of 20 to 60 seconds' duration are useful in overloading this metabolic pathway.

This type of anaerobic training is both physically and psychologically demanding and thus requires a high commitment on the part of the athlete. Further, this type of training may drastically reduce muscle glycogen stores. For these reasons, athletes often alternate hard-interval training days and light training sessions. For more details on training for improved anaerobic performance, see Ask the Expert 21.1 and Iaia and Bangsbo (2010) in the Suggested Readings.

■ Training to improve anaerobic power involves a special type of interval training. In general, the intervals are of short duration and consist of high-intensity exercise (near-maximal effort).

TRAINING TO IMPROVE MUSCULAR STRENGTH

The goal of a strength-training program is to increase the maximum amount of force and power that can be generated by a particular muscle group. In general, any muscle that is regularly exercised at a high intensity (i.e., intensity near its maximum force-generating capacity) will become stronger. Strength-training exercises can be classified into three categories: (1) isometric or static, (2) dynamic or isotonic (includes variable-resistance exercise), and (3) isokinetic. Recall that isometric exercise is the application of force without joint movement, and that dynamic exercise involves force application with joint movement (see chapters 8 and 20). **Variable-resistance exercise** is the term used to describe exercise performed on machines such as Nautilus equipment, which provide a variable amount of resistance during the course of a dynamic contraction. Isokinetic exercise is the exertion of force at a constant speed. Although isometric exercise has been shown to improve strength, isotonic and isokinetic strength training are generally preferred in the preparation of athletes because isometric training does not increase strength over the full range of motion—only at the specific joint angle maintained during training.

What physiological adaptations occur as a result of strength training? This issue was discussed in chapter 13 and will be addressed only briefly here. One of the obvious and perhaps most important physiological changes that occurs following a strength-training program is the increase in muscle mass. Recall from chapter 8 that the amount of force that can be generated by a muscle group is proportional to the cross-sectional area of the muscle (56). Therefore, larger muscles exert greater force than smaller muscles. As discussed in chapter 13, most of the increase in muscle size via resistance training is due to **hypertrophy** (an increase in muscle fiber diameter due to an increase in myofibrils) (2, 3, 87, 89). Nonetheless, research in animals suggests that muscles also increase their size in response to strength training by **hyperplasia** (increase in the number of muscle fibers) (42–44, 58, 87). Although this issue remains controversial, it appears that most of the increase in muscle size due to strength training occurs via hypertrophy (87).

Progressive Resistance Exercise

The most common form of strength training is weight lifting using free weights or various types of weight machines (i.e., dynamic or isokinetic training). To improve strength, weight training must employ the overload principle by periodically increasing the amount of weight (resistance) used in a particular exercise. This method of strength training was first described in 1948 by Delorme and Watkins and is called **progressive resistance exercise (PRE).** Since this early work, numerous other systems of training to improve muscular strength have been proposed, but the concept of PRE is the basis for most weight-training programs.

Resistance training workouts are prescribed around the exercise intensity and the volume of exercise performed. The exercise intensity of resistance training is expressed in terms of the repetitions maximum (RM), where 1 RM is the greatest weight that can be lifted one time using good form. The volume of resistance training is established by the number or repetitions (reps) and sets that are performed. Sets are the number of times a specific exercise is performed, and reps are the number of times a movement is repeated within a set.

General Strength-Training Principles

Muscles increase in strength by being forced to contract at relatively high tensions. If muscles are not overloaded, no improvement in strength occurs. The first application of the overload principle was used by the famous Olympic wrestler, *Milo of Crotona* (500 B.C.). Milo incorporated overload in his training routine by carrying a bull calf on his back each day until the animal reached maturity. Since the days of Milo, athletes have applied the principle of overload to training by lifting heavy objects.

The perfect training regimen for optimal improvement of strength remains controversial. Indeed, there does not appear to be a magic formula for strength training that meets the needs of everyone (1). Therefore, the exercise prescription for strength training should be tailored to the individual. However, a general guideline for a strength-training prescription is as follows: In general, the recommended intensity of training is eight to twelve maximal repetitions (RM) and practiced in multiple sets (1). Rest days between workouts seem critical for optimal strength improvement (1). Therefore, a training schedule of 2–4 days per week is recommended for novice or immediate individuals (1). For advanced weight training, a frequency of 4–6 days per week is recommended when using split routines (i.e., training one to three muscle groups per training session) (1).

A common belief among coaches and athletes is that strength increases in direct proportion to the volume of training (i.e., number of sets performed). Although a physiological link exists between training volume and strength gains, the optimal number of sets to improve strength continues to be debated. Nonetheless, two recent reviews conclude that multiple sets (i.e., 2 or more sets) of resistance exercise results in greater hypertrophy and strength gains compared to one set alone (60, 61). It appears likely that the optimal number of sets for maximal improvement of muscular strength may vary among subjects of different ages and fitness levels (1). Further, it is clear that weight-training programs incorporating extremely high training volumes (e.g., >10 sets) are not required for optimal strength gains (38, 80).

Similar to other training methods, strength training should involve those muscles used in competition. Indeed, strength-training exercises should stress the muscles in the same movement pattern used during the athletic competition. For instance, a shot-putter should perform exercises that strengthen the specific muscles of the arm, chest, back, and legs that are involved in "putting the shot."

A final concern in the design of strength-training programs for sport performance is that the speed of muscle shortening during training should be similar to those speeds used during the event. For example, many sports require a high velocity of movement. Studies have shown that strength-training programs using high-velocity movements in a sport-specific movement pattern produce superior gains in strength/power-oriented sports. Table 21.3 provides an overview of resistance training guidelines for training programs to

TABLE 21.3	**Resistance Training Guidelines for Training Programs That Emphasize Maximal Strength or Muscular Endurance. Data are from reference (1).**			
Frequency per Week	Number of Sets per Exercise	Number of Repetitions per Set	Intensity (Percentage of 1-RM)	Rest Interval Between Sets
Resistance Training Programs to Maximize Strength Gains				
Novice Trainer				
2–3 total body sessions	1–3	8–12	60–70%	2–3 minutes
Intermediate Trainer				
3 total body sessions 4 split routines	Multiple (>2 sets)	8–12	60–70%	2–3 minutes
Advanced trainer				
4–6 split routines	Multiple (>2 sets)	1–12	80–100% in a periodized program	2–3 minutes
Frequency per Week	Number of Sets per Exercise	Number of Repetitions per Set	Intensity (Percentage of 1-RM)	Rest Interval Between Sets
Resistance Training Programs to Emphasize Muscular Endurance				
Novice trainer				
2–3 total body sessions	Multiple (>2 sets)	10–15	Low (e.g. 30–50%)	1 minute
Intermediate Trainer				
3 total body sessions 4 split routines	Multiple (>2 sets)	10–15	Low (e.g., 30–50%)	1 minute
Advanced Trainer				
4–6 split routines	Multiple (>2 sets)	10–25	Range from 30–60%	1 minute for 10–15 reps 1–2 minutes for 15–25 reps

Note the following definitions: Novice trainer—less than one year of experience with resistance training; Intermediate trainer—2–3 years of experience with resistance training; advanced trainer ≥ 3 years of experience with resistance training; split routine—body is divided into different areas with each trained in a separate training session.

THE WINNING EDGE 21.1

Periodization of Strength Training

Resistance training workouts are structured around the exercise intensity and "sets" and "reps." Further, when working with athletic populations interested in maximal performance, a strength coach may also specify the rest periods between exercises and sets, the type of muscle action (eccentric or concentric), the number of training sessions per week, and the training volume (the total number of reps done in a workout). Periodized strength training uses these variables (and more) to develop workouts to achieve optimal gains in strength, power, motor performance,

and/or hypertrophy over the course of a season, year, or athletic career (1). Periodization describes a systematic process in which the volume and intensity of training are varied over time. For example, in "linear periodization," the individual is progressed from high volume/low intensity to low volume/high intensity over a specified time period (e.g., months). Are periodized resistance training programs better than nonperiodized programs?

A recent literature review (a meta-analysis) indicates that periodized programs are more effective in promoting

maximal strength than nonperiodized programs for men and women of all age groups and individuals with varying backgrounds in resistance training (i.e., novice or athletes) (84). Consistent with the overload principle, periodization-induced additions to volume, intensity, and frequency resulted in improved strength gains. Several types of periodization have been formulated and are discussed in the American College of Sports Medicine *Position Stand on Progression Models in Resistance Training for Healthy Adults* located in the Suggested Readings.

emphasize gains in maximal strength or muscular endurance. For a complete overview of progression models of strength training see the ACSM position stand (2009) in the Suggested Readings. Further, see the Winning Edge 21.1 for information on Periodization of Strength Training to improve strength gains.

Free Weights Versus Machines

Over the past several years, much controversy has centered around the question of whether training with free weights (barbells) or various types of weight machines (Nautilus, etc.) produces the greater strength gains in athletes. It is clear that both free weights and machines are effective at improving strength. Research shows that free-weight training leads to greater strength improvements in free-weight tests, whereas machine training results in greater strength performance on machine tests (1). When a neutral testing device is used to measure strength, strength improvement from free weights and machines are similar (1, 66). A recent review published by the American College of Sports Medicine concludes that each training mode has some advantages. For example, weight machines are regarded as safer to use, easy to learn, and they allow performance of some exercises that are difficult to achieve with free weights (e.g., knee extension) (1). Advantages of training with free weights include the fact that lifting free weights forces the athlete to control both balance and stabilizing factors. This type of training is useful because most sports require the

athlete to maintain balance and body stability during competition (90). Table 21.4 summarizes some of the advantages and disadvantages of strength training using isometric, dynamic (free weights, Nautilus, etc.), and isokinetic machines.

Concurrent Strength- and Endurance-Training Programs

Strength and endurance training are often done concurrently by athletes and fitness enthusiasts. As discussed in chapter 13, some evidence indicates that performing combined strength- and endurance-training programs may antagonize the strength gains achieved by weight training alone (28, 47, 49, 85). However, whether the combination of weight and endurance training impedes strength gains probably depends on several factors, including the training state of the subjects, the volume and frequency of training, and the way the two training methods are integrated (85). In this regard, Sale (85) has demonstrated that athletes who perform concurrent strength- and endurance-training programs on the same day show a reduction in strength gains compared to athletes performing strength training alone. However, athletes who perform concurrent strength- and endurance-training programs on separate days gain strength as rapidly as athletes performing strength training only (15, 71). Therefore, the current recommendation for the training of power athletes is that the athlete should perform strength- and endurance-training programs on separate days.

TABLE 21.4 Summary of Potential Advantages and Disadvantages of Weight-Training Programs Using Various Types of Equipment

Program	Equipment	Advantages	Disadvantages
Isometric	Variety of home-designed devices	Minimal cost; less time required	Not directly applicable to most sport activities; may become boring; progress is difficult to monitor
Dynamic	Free weights	Low cost; specialized exercises may be designed to simulate a particular sport movement; progress easy to monitor	Injury potential due to dropping weights; increase in workout time due to time required to change weights
Dynamic	Commercial weight machines (i.e., Life Fitness®)	Generally safe; progress easy to monitor; small amount of time required to change weight	Does not permit specialized exercise; high cost
Variable resistance	Commercial devices (e.g., Nautilus®)	Has a cam system that provides a variable resistance that changes to match the joint's ability to produce force over the range of motion; progress easy to monitor; safety	High cost; limited specialized exercises
Isokinetic	Commercial isokinetic devices (e.g., Cybex®)	Allows development of maximal resistance over full range of motion; exercises can be performed at a variety of speeds	High cost; limited specialized exercises

Modified from reference (8).

Gender Differences in Response to Strength Training

It is well established that when absolute strength (i.e., total amount of force applied) is compared in untrained men and women, men are typically stronger. This difference is greatest in the upper body, where men are approximately 50% stronger than women, whereas men are only 30% stronger than women in the lower body (78). This apparent sex difference in strength is eliminated when force production in men and women is compared on the basis of the cross-sectional area of muscle. Figure 21.2 illustrates this point. Notice that as the cross-sectional area of muscle increases (x-axis), the arm flexor strength (y-axis) increases in a linear fashion and is independent of sex. That is, human muscle can generate 3 to 4 kg of force per cm^2 of muscle cross-section regardless of whether the muscle belongs to a male or a female (56).

An often-asked question is "Do women gain strength as rapidly as men when training with weights?" In an effort to answer this question, Wilmore (93) compared the strength change between a group of untrained men and women before and after 10 weeks of isotonic weight training. The results revealed that no differences existed between sexes in the percentage of strength gained during the training period (see figure 21.3). Similar findings have been reported in other studies, and they demonstrate that untrained men and women

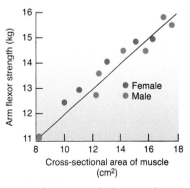

Figure 21.2 Arm flexor strength of men and women graphed as a function of muscle cross-sectional area.

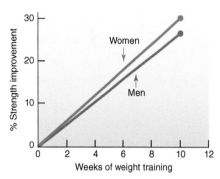

Figure 21.3 Strength changes in men and women as a result of a 10-week strength-training program.

respond similarly to weight training (52, 62, 79). However, the aforementioned studies are considered short-term training periods and may not reflect what occurs over long-term training. For instance, it is generally believed that men exhibit a greater degree of muscular hypertrophy than women as a result of long-term weight training. This gender difference in muscular hypertrophy appears to be related to the fact that men have twenty to thirty times higher blood levels of testosterone (52).

Muscle Soreness

It is a common experience for novice weight trainers and sometimes even veteran strength athletes to notice a **delayed-onset muscle soreness (DOMS)** that appears 24 to 48 hours after strenuous exercise. The search for an answer to the question of "What causes DOMS?" has extended over many years. A number of possible explanations have been proposed, including a buildup of lactate in muscle, muscle spasms, and torn muscle and connective tissue. It is clear that lactate does not cause this type of soreness. Based on present evidence, it appears that DOMS is due to tissue injury caused by excessive mechanical force exerted upon muscle and connective tissue (6, 16, 18, 35). Perhaps the strongest data to support this viewpoint come from electron microscopy studies in which electron micrographs taken of muscles suffering from DOMS reveal microscopic tears in these muscle fibers (36).

How does DOMS occur, and what is the physiological explanation for DOMS? Complete answers to these questions are not currently available (for reviews, see references (6, 17, 82)). However, current evidence suggests that DOMS occurs in the following manner (6, 82): (1) strenuous muscular contractions (especially eccentric contractions) result in structural

damage in muscle (i.e., disruption of sarcomeres); (2) membrane damage occurs, including damage to the membranes of the sarcoplasmic reticulum; (3) calcium leaks out of the sarcoplasmic reticulum and collects in the mitochondria, which inhibits ATP production; (4) the buildup of calcium also activates enzymes (proteases), which degrade cellular proteins, including contractile proteins (41); (5) membrane damage combines with a breakdown of muscle proteins and results in an inflammatory process, which includes an increase in prostaglandins/histamine production and production of free radicals (19); and finally (6) the accumulation of histamines and edema surrounding muscle fibers stimulates free nerve endings (pain receptors), which results in the sensation of pain in the muscle (see figure 21.4).

How does one avoid being a victim of DOMS following exercise? It appears that DOMS occurs most frequently following intense exercise using muscles that are unaccustomed to being worked (17, 21). Further, eccentric exercise (i.e., lengthening contractions)

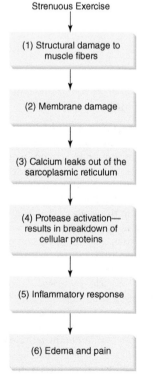

Figure 21.4 Proposed model to explain the occurrence of delayed-onset muscle soreness (DOMS) resulting from strenuous muscular exercise.

appears to cause greater suffering from DOMS than does concentric work. Therefore, a general recommendation for the avoidance of DOMS is to slowly begin a specific exercise during the first five to ten training sessions. This pattern of slow progression allows the exercised muscles to "adapt" to the exercise stress and therefore reduces the incidence or severity of DOMS (see Research Focus 21.1). For more information on DOMS, see Ask the Expert 21.2 and Proske and Allen (2005) in the References (82).

IN SUMMARY

- Improvement in muscular strength can be achieved via progressive overload by using either isometric, isotonic, or isokinetic exercise. Isotonic or isokinetic training seems preferable to isometric exercise in developing strength gains in athletes, because isometric strength gains occur only at the specific joint angles that are held during isometric training.
- Although untrained men exhibit greater absolute strength than untrained females, there do not appear to be gender differences in strength gains during a short-term weight-training program.
- Delayed-onset muscle soreness (DOMS) is thought to occur due to microscopic tears in muscle fibers or connective tissue. This results in cellular degradation and an inflammatory response, which results in pain within 24 to 48 hours after strenuous exercise.

TRAINING TO IMPROVE FLEXIBILITY

Historically, it has been believed that improvement of flexibility via stretching reduces the risk of exercise-induced injury. Nonetheless, at present, limited evidence exists to support the concept that stretching prevents injuries during exercise and participation in many sports (5, 46, 73). Further, a general consensus is that stretching in addition to warm-up does not reduce the risk of overuse injuries(73).

Although improved flexibility may not reduce the risk of exercise-induced injury, the ability to move joints through a full range of motion is important in many sports. Indeed, loss of flexibility can result in a reduction of movement efficiency. Therefore, many athletic trainers and coaches recommend regular stretching exercises to improve flexibility and perhaps optimize the efficiency of movement.

There are two general stretching techniques in use today: (1) **static stretching** (continuously holding a stretch position), and (2) **dynamic stretching** (sometimes referred to as ballistic stretching if movements are not controlled). Although both techniques result in an improvement in flexibility, static stretching is considered to be superior to dynamic stretching because (1) there is less chance of injury (9), (2) static stretching causes less muscle spindle activity when compared to dynamic stretching, and (3) there is less chance of muscle soreness. Stimulation of muscle spindles during dynamic stretching can produce a stretch reflex and therefore result in muscular contraction. This type of muscular contraction counteracts the desired lengthening of the muscle and may increase the chance of injury.

Research has shown that 30 minutes of static stretching exercises performed twice per week will improve flexibility within 5 weeks (26). It is recommended that the stretch position be held for 10 seconds at the beginning of a flexibility program and increased to 60 seconds after several training sessions. Each stretch position should be repeated three to five times, with the number increased up to ten repetitions. Overload is applied by increasing the range of motion during the stretch position and increasing the amount of time the stretch position is held.

Preceding a static stretch with an isometric contraction of the muscle group to be stretched is an effective means of improving muscle relaxation and may enhance the development of flexibility (12, 92). This stretching technique is called **proprioceptive neuromuscular facilitation (PNF).** The procedure generally requires two people and is performed as follows (65): A training partner moves the target limb passively through its range of motion; after reaching the end point of the range of motion, the target muscle is isometrically contracted (against the partner) for 6 to 10 seconds. The target muscle is then relaxed and is again stretched by the partner to a greater range of motion. The physiological rationale for the use of PNF stretching is that muscular relaxation follows an isometric contraction because the contraction stimulates the Golgi tendon organs, which inhibit contraction during the subsequent stretching exercise.

IN SUMMARY

- Limited evidence exists to support the notion that improved joint mobility (flexibility) reduces the incidence of exercise-induced injury.
- Stretching exercises are often recommended to improve flexibility and optimize the efficiency of movement.
- Improvement in flexibility can be achieved via static or dynamic stretching, with static stretching being the preferred technique.

RESEARCH FOCUS 21.1

Protection Against Exercise-Induced Muscle Soreness: The Repeated Bout Effect

Performing a bout of unfamiliar exercise often results in muscle injury and delayed-onset muscle soreness (DOMS). This is particularly true when the bout of unfamiliar exercise involves eccentric actions. Interestingly, following recovery from DOMS, a subsequent bout of the same exercise results in minimal symptoms of muscle injury and soreness; this is called the "repeated bout effect" (72). This protective effect of prior exercise has been recognized for more than 40 years. Although many theories have been proposed to explain the repeated bout effect, the specific mechanism responsible for this exercise-induced protection is unknown and continues to be debated. In general, three primary theories have been proposed to explain the repeated bout effect: (1) neural theory, (2) connective tissue theory, and (3) cellular theory (72).

The neural theory proposes that the exercise-induced muscle injury occurs in a relatively small number of active type II (fast) fibers. In the subsequent exercise bout, a change occurs in the pattern of recruitment of muscle fibers to increase motor unit activation to recruit a larger number of muscle fibers. This results in the contractile stress being distributed over a larger number of fibers. Hence, there is a reduction in stress within individual fibers, and no muscle injury occurs during subsequent exercise bouts.

The connective tissue theory argues that muscle damage due to the initial exercise bout results in an increase in connective tissue to provide more protection to the muscle during the stress of exercise. This increased connective tissue is postulated to be responsible for the repeated bout effect.

Finally, the cellular theory predicts that exercise-induced muscle damage results in the synthesis of new proteins (e.g., stress proteins, cytoskeletal proteins, etc.) that improve the integrity of the muscle fiber. The synthesis of these "protective proteins" reduces the strain on the muscle fiber and protects the muscle from exercise-induced injury.

Which of these theories best explains the repeated bout effect is unknown. It seems unlikely that one theory can explain all the various observations associated with the repeated bout effect. Thus, it is possible that the repeated bout effect occurs through the interaction of various neural, connective tissue, and cellular factors that respond to the specific type of exercise-induced muscle injury (72). This idea is summarized in figure 21.5.

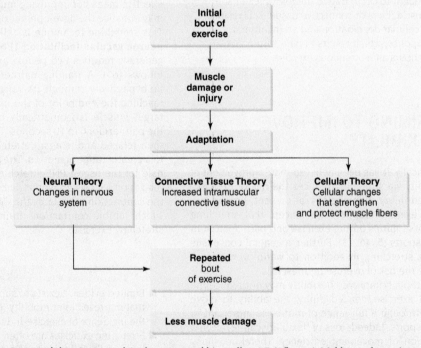

FIGURE 21.5 Proposed theories to explain the "repeated bout effect." Briefly, an initial bout of exercise results in muscle injury. This muscular injury results in a physiological adaptation, which occurs via changes in the nervous system, muscle connective tissue, and/or cellular changes within muscle fibers. One or all of these adaptations serve to protect the muscle from injury during a subsequent bout of exercise. Figure redrawn from McHugh et al. (83).

ASK THE EXPERT 21.2

Exercise-Induced Muscle Soreness:
Questions and Answers with Dr. Priscilla Clarkson

Priscilla M. Clarkson is a Professor of Exercise Science and Associate Dean for the School of Public Health and Health Sciences at the University of Massachusetts–Amherst. She has served as President of the American College of Sports Medicine (ACSM) and has received numerous academic awards, including the National ACSM Citation Award, the New England ACSM Honor Award, the Excellence in Education Award from the Gatorade Sport Science Institute, and the University of Massachusetts Chancellor's Medal.

Professor Clarkson has published more than 100 scientific research articles and has given numerous national and international scientific presentations. The major focus of her research is exercise-induced muscle soreness and damage. In this box feature, she responds to three applied questions related to exercise and muscle soreness.

QUESTION: Several popular fitness publications have suggested that the use of nonsteroidal anti-inflammatory drugs (e.g., ibuprofen) following an intense exercise bout will reduce exercise-induced muscle soreness. Is this concept supported by the research literature?

ANSWER: Studies that have examined the effects of nonsteroidal anti-inflammatory drugs (NSAIDs) on the reduction of muscle soreness after exercise have produced inconsistent results. There are many reasons to explain these inconsistent findings, including the different types and intensities of exercises used to induce soreness, different types of NSAIDs used, and different doses of the NSAID. Another important reason for the lack of consistent results is that the amount of reduction in soreness by the NSAIDs is small, generally less than 15%. On a scale of 1–10 (with 10 being very, very sore), a person who scores an 8 would be expected to see a reduction of soreness to about a 7. This is a small reduction relative to the large inter-

subject variability in the soreness response to the exercise. In other words, some individuals will experience a high degree of soreness while others experience little soreness in response to the same exercise stimulus. Therefore, to detect small differences in soreness due to a treatment, a large population of subjects needs to be tested. Published studies on the effects of NSAIDs on muscle soreness have used sample sizes that are likely too small to provide conclusive evidence.

A key question is whether NSAIDs should even be considered as a treatment to reduce muscle soreness. NSAIDs, like all drugs, have side effects. Given that NSAIDs will only reduce muscle soreness by a small amount and the long-term consequences of NSAID use on muscle recovery are not known, it may be unwise to risk experiencing side effects for so little benefit. Moreover, soreness will dissipate in a couple of days anyway with no intervention. Unless the muscle pain is unbearable, NSAIDs should be used with discretion.

QUESTION: Animal studies suggest that estrogen may protect skeletal muscle from stress-induced injury. This has led to the speculation that women may be protected from exercise-induced muscle injury. Do the studies performed in your laboratory suggest that compared to men, women are less susceptible to exercise-induced muscle damage?

ANSWER: The data from animal models clearly show that estrogen serves a protective role against contraction-induced muscle injury. When these data were first published, it was assumed that women would show less injury in response to eccentric exercise compared with men, because of the higher estrogen levels in women. However, our laboratory examined differences in the development of muscle soreness

and losses in muscle force and range of motion (common indirect indicators of muscle damage) in a large group of men and women both immediately after and during several days following exercise. We found that the men and women experienced a similar degree of soreness and strength loss. However, women actually showed a greater loss in range of motion. Clearly, estrogen does not play the same role in women as has been seen in the animal models of exercise-induced muscle injury.

QUESTION: Some authors have postulated that supplementation with oral creatine could reduce exercise-induced muscle injury by protecting muscle membranes. Research in your laboratory has directly addressed this issue in humans. Based on your data, does creatine supplementation protect skeletal muscle against exercise-induced injury?

ANSWER: To determine whether creatine supplementation would protect against eccentric contraction-induced injury, we had subjects ingest either 20 g creatine or a placebo for 5 days. This dosage has been shown to increase creatine levels in skeletal muscle. After the 5-day supplementation period, subjects performed fifty maximal, eccentric contractions of the elbow flexors. The results indicated that the development of soreness and muscle injury did not differ between the groups. Therefore, these results indicate that creatine supplementation offers no obvious protection against this type of exercise damage to muscle. Any protection offered by an increased amount of creatine in the muscle may be no match for the strain induced by the severe exercise that the subjects performed. Whether using a less-strenuous exercise would have shown any benefits of creatine awaits further study.

YEAR-ROUND CONDITIONING FOR ATHLETES

It is common for today's athletes to engage in year-round conditioning exercises. This is necessary to prevent gain of excessive body fat and to prevent extreme physical detraining between competitive seasons. The training periods of athletes can be divided into three phases: (1) off-season training, (2) pre-season training, and (3) in-season training, and can incorporate the periodization techniques discussed earlier in this chapter (see The Winning Edge 21.1). A brief description of each training period follows.

Off-Season Conditioning

In general, the objectives of off-season conditioning programs are to (1) prevent excessive fat weight gain, (2) maintain muscular strength or endurance, (3) maintain ligament and bone integrity, and (4) maintain a reasonable skill level in the athlete's specific sport. Obviously, the exact nature of the off-season conditioning program will vary from sport to sport. For example, a football player would spend considerably more time performing strength-training exercises than would a distance runner. Conversely, the runner would incorporate more running into an off-season conditioning program than would the football player. Hence, specific exercises should be selected on the basis of the sport's demands.

No matter what the sport, it is critical that an off-season conditioning program provide variety for the athlete. Further, off-season conditioning programs generally use a training regimen that is composed of low-intensity, high-volume work. This combination of low-intensity training and variety may prevent the occurrence of "overtraining syndromes" and the development of psychological staleness. Figure 21.6 contains a list of some recommended training activities for off-season conditioning.

Off-season conditioning allows athletes to concentrate on fitness areas where they may be weak.

Therefore, it is important that off-season programs be designed for the individual. For instance, a basketball player may lack leg strength and power and therefore have a limited vertical jump. An off-season conditioning program allows this athlete to engage in specific strength-training activities that will improve leg power and enhance vertical jumping capacity.

Preseason Conditioning

The principal objective of preseason conditioning (e.g., 8 to 12 weeks prior to competition) is to increase to a maximum the capacities of the predominant energy systems used in a particular sport. In the transition from off-season conditioning to preseason conditioning, there is a gradual shift from low-intensity, high-volume exercise to high-intensity, low-volume exercise. As in all phases of a training cycle, the program should be sport specific.

In general, the types of exercise performed during preseason conditioning are similar to those used during off-season conditioning (figure 21.6). The principal difference between off-season and preseason conditioning is the intensity of the conditioning effort. During preseason conditioning, the athlete applies a progressive overload by increasing the intensity of workouts, whereas off-season conditioning involves high-volume, low-intensity workouts.

In-Season Conditioning

The general goal of in-season conditioning for most sports is to maintain the fitness level achieved during the preseason training program. For instance, in a sport such as football, in which there is a relatively long competitive season, the athlete must be able to maintain strength and endurance during the entire season. A complicating factor in planning an in-season conditioning program for many team sports is that the season may not have a clear-cut ending. That is, at the end of the regular season, playoff games may extend the season an additional several weeks. Therefore, it is difficult in these types of sports to plan a climax in the conditioning program, and so there is the need for a maintenance training program.

Suggested Activities for the Various Phases of A Year-Round Training Program		
Off-Season	Preseason	In-Season
Weight training	Weight training	Maintenance program
Running	Running	
Skill practice →	Skill practice →	
Participation in other sports	Learning strategies (increased intensity)	

Figure 21.6 Recommended activities for the various phases of year-round training.

- Year-round conditioning programs for athletes include an off-season program, a preseason program, and an in-season program.
- The general objectives of an off-season conditioning program are to prevent excessive fat weight gain, maintain muscular strength and endurance, maintain bone and ligament strength, and preserve a reasonable skill level in the athlete's specific sport.

COMMON TRAINING MISTAKES

Some of the most common training errors include (1) overtraining, (2) undertraining, (3) using exercises and work-rate intensities that are not sport specific, (4) failure to plan long-term training schedules to achieve specific goals, and (5) failure to taper training prior to a competition. Let's discuss each of these training errors briefly.

Overtraining may be a more significant problem than undertraining for several reasons. First, overtraining (workouts that are too long or too strenuous) may result in injury or reduce the athlete's resistance to disease (see chapter 6). Further, overtraining may result in a psychological staleness, which can be identified by a general lack of enthusiasm on the part of the athlete (72). The general symptoms of overtraining include (1) elevated heart rate and blood lactate levels at a fixed submaximal work rate, (2) loss in body weight due to a reduction in appetite, (3) chronic fatigue, (4) psychological staleness, (5) multiple colds or sore throats, and/or (6) a decrease in performance (see figure 21.7). An overtrained athlete may exhibit one or all of these symptoms (11, 37, 53). Therefore, it is critical that coaches and trainers recognize the classic symptoms of overtraining and be prepared to reduce their athletes' workloads when overtraining symptoms appear. Recall that specific training programs should be planned for athletes when possible to compensate for individual differences in genetic potential and fitness levels. This is an important point to remember when planning training programs for athletic conditioning.

For more details on overtraining, see Halson and Jeukendrup (2004) in the References (45).

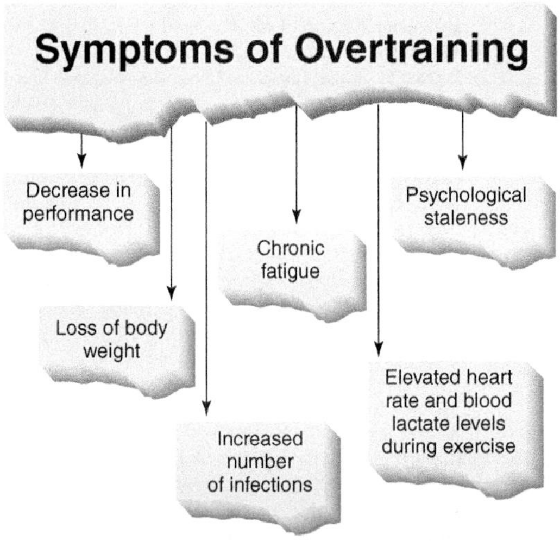

Another common mistake in the training of athletes is the failure to plan sport-specific training exercises. Often coaches or trainers fail to understand the importance of the law of specificity, and they develop training exercises that do not enhance the energy capacities of the skeletal muscles used in competition. This error can be avoided by achieving a broad understanding of the training principles discussed earlier in this chapter.

Further, coaches, trainers, and athletes should plan and record training schedules designed to achieve specific fitness objectives at various times during the year. Failure to plan a training strategy may result in the misuse of training time and ultimately result in inferior performance.

Finally, failure to reduce the intensity and volume of training prior to competition is also a common training error. Achieving a peak athletic performance requires a healthy blend of proper nutrition, training, and rest. Failure to reduce the training volume and/or intensity prior to competition results in inadequate rest and compromises performance. Therefore, in an effort to achieve peak performance, athletes should reduce their training load for several days prior to competition; this practice is called **tapering.** The goal of tapering is to provide time for muscles to resynthesize glycogen to maximal levels and to allow muscles to heal from training-induced damage. Although the optimum length of a taper period continues to be debated, a reduced training load of 3 to 21 days has been used successfully in both strength and endurance sports (54, 68). Indeed, runners and swimmers can reduce their training load by approximately 60% for up to 21 days without a reduction in performance (20, 39, 54).

Figure 21.7 Common symptoms of overtraining.

- Common mistakes in training include undertraining, overtraining, performing nonspecific exercises during training sessions, failing to carefully schedule a long-term training plan, and failing to taper training prior to a competition.
- Symptoms of overtraining include (1) elevated heart rate and blood lactate levels at a fixed submaximal work rate, (2) loss in body weight due to a reduction in appetite, (3) chronic fatigue, (4) psychological staleness, (5) increased number of infections, and/or (6) a decrease in performance.
- Tapering is the term applied to short-term reduction in training load prior to competition. Research has shown that tapering prior to a competition is useful in improving performance in both strength and endurance events.

STUDY QUESTIONS

1. Explain how knowledge of the energy systems used in a particular activity or sport might be useful in designing a sport-specific training program.
2. Provide an outline of the general principles of designing a training program for the following sports: (1) football, (2) soccer, (3) basketball, (4) volleyball, (5) distance running (5,000 meters), and (6) 200-meter dash (track).
3. Define the following terms as they relate to interval training: (1) work interval, (2) rest interval, (3) work-to-rest ratio, and (4) set.
4. How can interval training be used to improve both aerobic and anaerobic power?
5. List and discuss the three most common types of training programs used to improve $\dot{V}O_2$ max.
6. Discuss the practical and theoretical differences between an interval training program used to improve

the ATP-PC system and a program designed to improve the lactate system.
7. List the general principles of strength development.
8. Define the terms *isometric, isotonic, dynamic,* and *isokinetic.*
9. Outline the model to explain delayed-onset muscle soreness proposed by Armstrong.
10. Discuss the use of static and dynamic stretching to improve flexibility. Why is a high degree of flexibility not desired in all sports?
11. List and discuss the objectives of (1) off-season conditioning, (2) preseason conditioning, and (3) in-season conditioning.
12. What are some of the more common errors made in the training of athletes?

SUGGESTED READINGS

ACSM. 2009. American College of Sports Medicine position stand. Progression models in resistance training for healthy adults. *Med Sci Sports Exerc* 41:687–708.

Hawley, J. A. 2009. Molecular responses to strength and endurance training: Are they incompatible? *Appl Physiol Nutr Metab* 34:355–61.

Iaia, F. M., and J. Bangsbo. 2010. Speed endurance training is a powerful stimulus for physiological adaptations and performance improvements of athletes. *Scand J Med Sci Sports* 20 Suppl 2:11–23.

Fradkin, A. J., T. R. Zazryn, J. M. Smoglia. 2010. Effects of warming-up on physical performance: A systematic review with meta-analysis. *J Strength Cond Res* 24:140–48.

Krieger, J. W. 2010. Single vs. multiple sets of resistance exercise for muscle hypertrophy: A meta-analysis. *J Strength Cond Res* 24:1150–59.

McHugh, M. P., and C. H. Cosgrave. 2010. To stretch or not to stretch: The role of stretching in injury prevention and performance. *Scand J Med Sci Sports* 20:169–81.

Midgley, A. W., L. R. McNaughton, and A. M. Jones. 2007. Training to enhance the physiological determinants of long-distance running performance: Can valid recommendations be given to runners and coaches based on current scientific knowledge? *Sports Med* 37:857–80.

Midgley, A. W., L. R. McNaughton, and M. Wilkinson. 2006. Is there an optimal training intensity for enhancing the maximal oxygen uptake of distance runners?: Empirical research findings, current opinions, physiological rationale and practical recommendations. *Sports Med* 36:117–32.

Seiler, S. 2010. What is best practice for training intensity and duration distribution in endurance athletes? *Int J Sports Physiol Perform* 5:276–91.

REFERENCES

1. **ACSM.** American College of Sports Medicine position stand. Progression models in resistance training for healthy adults. *Med Sci Sports Exerc* 41: 687–708, 2009.
2. **Alway SE, Sale DG, and MacDougall JD.** Twitch contractile adaptations are not dependent on the intensity of isometric exercise in the human triceps surae. *Eur J Appl Physiol Occup Physiol* 60: 346–352, 1990.
3. **Alway SE, Stray-Gundersen J, Grumbt WH, and Gonyea WJ.** Muscle cross-sectional area and torque in resistance-trained subjects. *Eur J Appl Physiol Occup Physiol* 60: 86–90, 1990.
4. **Amir O, Amir R, Yamin C, Attias E, Eynon N, Sagiv M, Sagiv M, and Meckel Y.** The ACE deletion allele is associated with Israeli elite endurance athletes. *Exp Physiol* 92: 881–886, 2007.
5. **Andersen J.** Stretching before and after exercise: effect on muscle soreness and injury risk. *Journal of Athletic Training* 40: 218–220, 2005.
6. **Armstrong RB.** Mechanisms of exercise-induced delayed onset muscular soreness: a brief review. *Med Sci Sports Exerc* 16: 529–538, 1984.
7. **Astorino TA, Allen RP, Roberson DW, Jurancich M, Lewis R, McCarthy K, and Trost E.** Adaptations to high-intensity training are independent of gender. *Eur J Appl Physiol* 2010.
8. **Åstrand P, and Rodahl K.** *Textbook of Work Physiology.* New York: McGraw-Hill, 1986.

9. **Berger R.** *Applied Exercise Physiology.* Philadelphia: Lea & Febiger, 1982.
10. **Bouchard C, Sarzynski MA, Rice TK, Kraus WE, Church TS, Sung YJ, Rao DC, and Rankinen T.** Genomic predictors of maximal oxygen uptake response to standardized exercise training programs. *J Appl Physiol* 2010.
11. **Bowers R, and Fox E.** *Sports Physiology.* New York: McGraw-Hill, 1992.
12. **Burke E.** Physiological similar effects of similar training programs in males and females. *Research Quarterly* 48: 510–517, 1977.
13. **Calvo M, Rodas G, Vallejo M, Estruch A, Arcas A, Javierre C, Viscor G, and Ventura JL.** Heritability of explosive power and anaerobic capacity in humans. *Eur J Appl Physiol* 86: 218–225, 2002.
14. **Carvalho AC, Junior LC, Costa LO, and Lopes AD.** The association between runners' lower limb alignment with running-related injuries: a systematic review. *Br J Sports Med* 45: 339, 2011.
15. **Chilibeck PD, Syrotuik DG, and Bell GJ.** The effect of concurrent endurance and strength training on quantitative estimates of subsarcolemmal and intermyofibrillar mitochondria. *Int J Sports Med* 23: 33–39, 2002.
16. **Clarkson PM, Byrnes WC, McCormick KM, Turcotte LP, and White JS.** Muscle soreness and serum creatine kinase activity following isometric, eccentric, and concentric exercise. *Int J Sports Med* 7: 152–155, 1986.

17. **Clarkson PM, Nosaka K, and Braun B.** Muscle function after exercise-induced muscle damage and rapid adaptation. *Med Sci Sports Exerc* 24: 512–520, 1992.

18. **Clarkson PM, and Sayers SP.** Etiology of exercise-induced muscle damage. *Can J Appl Physiol* 24: 234–248, 1999.

19. **Close GL, Ashton T, McArdle A, and Maclaren DP.** The emerging role of free radicals in delayed onset muscle soreness and contraction-induced muscle injury. *Comp Biochem Physiol A Mol Integr Physiol* 142: 257–266, 2005.

20. **Costill D.** Effects of reduced training on muscular power in swimmers. *Physician and Sports Medicine* 13: 94–101, 1985.

21. **Costill DL, Coyle EF, Fink WF, Lesmes GR, and Witzmann FA.** Adaptations in skeletal muscle following strength training. *J Appl Physiol* 46: 96–99, 1979.

22. **Costill DL, Thomas R, Robergs RA, Pascoe D, Lambert C, Barr S, and Fink WJ.** Adaptations to swimming training: influence of training volume. *Med Sci Sports Exerc* 23: 371–377, 1991.

23. **Coyle EF, Martin WH, III, Bloomfield SA, Lowry OH, and Holloszy JO.** Effects of detraining on responses to submaximal exercise. *J Appl Physiol* 59: 853–859, 1985.

24. **Coyle EF, Martin WH, III, Sinacore DR, Joyner MJ, Hagberg JM, and Holloszy JO.** Time course of loss of adaptations after stopping prolonged intense endurance training. *J Appl Physiol* 57: 1857–1864, 1984.

25. **Davies CT, and Knibbs AV.** The training stimulus: the effects of intensity, duration and frequency of effort on maximum aerobic power output. *Int Z Angew Physiol* 29: 299–305, 1971.

26. **Deschenes M.** Short review: motor coding and motor unit recruitment pattern. *Journal of Applied Sport Science Research* 3: 33–39, 1989.

27. **Dudley GA, Abraham WM, and Terjung RL.** Influence of exercise intensity and duration on biochemical adaptations in skeletal muscle. *J Appl Physiol* 53: 844–850, 1982.

28. **Dudley GA, and Djamil R.** Incompatibility of endurance- and strength-training modes of exercise. *J Appl Physiol* 59: 1446–1451, 1985.

29. **Fox E, and Mathews D.** *Interval Training: Conditioning for Sports and General Fitness.* Philadelphia: W. B. Saunders, 1974.

30. **Fox EL, Bartels RL, Billings CE, Mathews DK, Bason R, and Webb WM.** Intensity and distance of interval training programs and changes in aerobic power. *Med Sci Sports* 5: 18–22, 1973.

31. **Fox EL, Bartels RL, Billings CE, O'Brien R, Bason R, and Mathews DK.** Frequency and duration of interval training programs and changes in aerobic power. *J Appl Physiol* 38: 481–484, 1975.

32. **Fox EL, Robinson S, and Wiegman DL.** Metabolic energy sources during continuous and interval running. *J Appl Physiol* 27: 174–178, 1969.

33. **Fradkin AJ, Gabbe BJ, and Cameron PA.** Does warming up prevent injury in sport? The evidence from randomised controlled trials? *J Sci Med Sport* 9: 214–220, 2006.

34. **Fradkin AJ, Zazryn TR, and Smoliga JM.** Effects of warming-up on physical performance: a systematic review with meta-analysis. *J Strength Cond Res* 24: 140–148, 2010.

35. **Friden J, and Lieber RL.** Structural and mechanical basis of exercise-induced muscle injury. *Med Sci Sports Exerc* 24: 521–530, 1992.

36. **Friden J, Sjöström M, and Ekblom B.** Myofibrillar damage following intense eccentric exercise in man. *Int J Sports Med* 4: 170–176, 1983.

37. **Fry RW, Grove JR, Morton AR, Zeroni PM, Gaudieri S, and Keast D.** Psychological and immunological correlates of acute overtraining. *Br J Sports Med* 28: 241–246, 1994.

38. **Galvao D, and Taafee D.** Single- vs. multiple-set resistance training: recent developments in the controversy. *Journal of Strength and Conditioning Research* 18: 660–667, 2004.

39. **Gibala MJ, MacDougall JD, and Sale DG.** The effects of tapering on strength performance in trained athletes. *Int J Sports Med* 15: 492–497, 1994.

40. **Gibbons E.** Effects of various training intensity levels on anaerobic threshold and aerobic capacity in females. *Journal of Sports Medicine and Physical Fitness* 23: 315–318, 1983.

41. **Gissel H, and Clausen T.** Excitation-induced Ca^{2+} influx and skeletal muscle cell damage. *Acta Physiol Scand* 171: 327–334, 2001.

42. **Gonyea W, Ericson GC, and Bonde-Petersen F.** Skeletal muscle fiber splitting induced by weight-lifting exercise in cats. *Acta Physiol Scand* 99: 105–109, 1977.

43. **Gonyea WJ.** Role of exercise in inducing increases in skeletal muscle fiber number. *J Appl Physiol* 48: 421–426, 1980.

44. **Gonyea WJ, Sale DG, Gonyea FB, and Mikesky A.** Exercise induced increases in muscle fiber number. *Eur J Appl Physiol Occup Physiol* 55: 137–141, 1986.

45. **Halson SL, and Jeukendrup AE.** Does overtraining exist? An analysis of overreaching and overtraining research. *Sports Med* 34: 967–981, 2004.

46. **Hart L.** Effect of stretching on sport injury risk: a review. *Clin J Sport Med* 15: 113, 2005.

47. **Hawley JA.** Molecular responses to strength and endurance training: are they incompatible? *Appl Physiol Nutr Metab* 34: 355–361, 2009.

48. **Henderson J, Withford-Cave JM, Duffy DL, Cole SJ, Sawyer NA, Gulbin JP, Hahn A, Trent RJ, and Yu B.** The EPAS1 gene influences the aerobic-anaerobic contribution in elite endurance athletes. *Hum Genet* 118: 416–423, 2005.

49. **Hickson RC.** Interference of strength development by simultaneously training for strength and endurance. *Eur J Appl Physiol Occup Physiol* 45: 255–263, 1980.

50. **Hickson RC, Bomze HA, and Holloszy JO.** Linear increase in aerobic power induced by a strenuous program of endurance exercise. *J Appl Physiol* 42: 372–376, 1977.

51. **Hickson RC, Hagberg JM, Ehsani AA, and Holloszy JO.** Time course of the adaptive responses of aerobic power and heart rate to training. *Med Sci Sports Exerc* 13: 17–20, 1981.

52. **Holloway JB, and Baechle TR.** Strength training for female athletes: a review of selected aspects. *Sports Med* 9: 216–228, 1990.

53. **Hooper SL, Mackinnon LT, Howard A, Gordon RD, and Bachmann AW.** Markers for monitoring overtraining and recovery. *Med Sci Sports Exerc* 27: 106–112, 1995.

54. **Houmard JA, Costill DL, Mitchell JB, Park SH, Hickner RC, and Roemmich JN.** Reduced training maintains performance in distance runners. *Int J Sports Med* 11: 46–52, 1990.

55. **Iaia FM, and Bangsbo J.** Speed endurance training is a powerful stimulus for physiological adaptations and performance improvements of athletes. *Scand J Med Sci Sports* 20 Suppl 2: 11–23, 2010.

56. **Ikai M, and Fukunaga T.** Calculation of muscle strength per unit cross-sectional area of human muscle by means of ultrasonic measurement. *Int Z Angew Physiol* 26: 26–32, 1968.

57. **Junior LC, Carvalho AC, Costa LO, and Lopes AD.** The prevalence of musculoskeletal injuries in runners: a systematic review. Br J Sports Med 45: 351–352, 2011.

58. **Kelley G.** Mechanical overload and skeletal muscle fiber hyperplasia: a meta-analysis. J Appl Physiol 81: 1584–1588, 1996.

59. **Knuttgen HG, Nordesjo LO, Ollander B, and Saltin B.** Physical conditioning through interval training with young male adults. Med Sci Sports 5: 220–226, 1973.

60. **Krieger JW.** Single versus multiple sets of resistance exercise: a meta-regression. J Strength Cond Res 23: 1890–1901, 2009.

61. **Krieger JW.** Single vs. multiple sets of resistance exercise for muscle hypertrophy: a meta-analysis. J Strength Cond Res 24: 1150–1159, 2010.

62. **Laursen PB, and Jenkins DG.** The scientific basis for high-intensity interval training: optimising training programmes and maximising performance in highly trained endurance athletes. Sports Med 32: 53–73, 2002.

63. **Levine BD, and Stray-Gundersen J.** Living high-training low: effect of moderate-altitude acclimatization with low-altitude training on performance. J Appl Physiol 83: 102–112, 1997.

64. **Levine BD, and Stray-Gundersen J.** Point: positive effects of intermittent hypoxia (live high: train low) on exercise performance are mediated primarily by augmented red cell volume. J Appl Physiol 99: 2053–2055, 2005.

65. **Liemohn W, and Sharpe G.** Muscular strength and endurance, flexibility, and low-back function. In: Health/Fitness Instructor's Handbook, edited by Howley E, and Frank D. Champaign: Human Kinetics, 1992, p. 179–196.

66. **Manning RJ, Graves JE, Carpenter DM, Leggett SH, and Pollock ML.** Constant vs variable resistance knee extension training. Med Sci Sports Exerc 22: 397–401, 1990.

67. **Maridaki M.** Heritability of neuromuscular performance and anaerobic power in preadolescent and adolescent girls. J Sports Med Phys Fitness 46: 540–547, 2006.

68. **Martin DT, Scifres JC, Zimmerman SD, and Wilkinson JG.** Effects of interval training and a taper on cycling performance and isokinetic leg strength. Int J Sports Med 15: 485–491, 1994.

69. **Mazzeo RS.** Physiological responses to exercise at altitude: an update. Sports Med 38: 1–8, 2008.

70. **McArdle W, Katch F, and Katch V.** Exercise Physiology: Energy, Nutrition, and Human Performance. Baltimore: Lippincott Williams & Wilkins, 1996.

71. **McCarthy JP, Pozniak MA, and Agre JC.** Neuromuscular adaptations to concurrent strength and endurance training. Med Sci Sports Exerc 34: 511–519, 2002.

72. **McHugh MP, Connolly DA, Eston RG, and Gleim GW.** Exercise-induced muscle damage and potential mechanisms for the repeated bout effect. Sports Med 27: 157–170, 1999.

73. **McHugh MP, and Cosgrave CH.** To stretch or not to stretch: the role of stretching in injury prevention and performance. Scand J Med Sci Sports 20: 169–181, 2010.

74. **Medbo JI, and Burgers S.** Effect of training on the anaerobic capacity. Med Sci Sports Exerc 22: 501–507, 1990.

75. **Micheli L.** Injuries and prolonged exercise. In: Prolonged Exercise, edited by Lamb D, and Murray R. Indianapolis: Benchmark Press, 1988, p. 393–407.

76. **Midgley AW, McNaughton LR, and Jones AM.** Training to enhance the physiological determinants of long-distance running performance: can valid recommendations be given to runners and coaches based on current scientific knowledge? Sports Med 37: 857–880, 2007.

77. **Midgley AW, McNaughton LR, and Wilkinson M.** Is there an optimal training intensity for enhancing the maximal oxygen uptake of distance runners?: empirical research findings, current opinions, physiological rationale and practical recommendations. Sports Med 36: 117–132, 2006.

78. **Morrow JR, Jr., and Hosler WW.** Strength comparisons in untrained men and trained women athletes. Med Sci Sports Exerc 13: 194–197, 1981.

79. **O'Shea J, and Wegner J.** Power weight training in the female athlete. Physician and Sports Medicine 9: 109–114, 1981.

80. **Peterson MD, Rhea MR, and Alvar BA.** Applications of the dose-response for muscular strength development: a review of meta-analytic efficacy and reliability for designing training prescription. J Strength Cond Res 19: 950–958, 2005.

81. **Priest JW, and Hagan RD.** The effects of maximum steady state pace training on running performance. Br J Sports Med 21: 18–21, 1987.

82. **Proske U, and Allen TJ.** Damage to skeletal muscle from eccentric exercise. Exerc Sport Sci Rev 33: 98–104, 2005.

83. **Rankinen T, Bray MS, Hagberg JM, Perusse L, Roth SM, Wolfarth B, and Bouchard C.** The human gene map for performance and health-related fitness phenotypes: the 2005 update. Med Sci Sports Exerc 38: 1863–1888, 2006.

84. **Rhea MR, and Alderman BL.** A meta-analysis of periodized versus nonperiodized strength and power training programs. Res Q Exerc Sport 75: 413–422, 2004.

85. **Sale DG, Jacobs I, MacDougall JD, and Garner S.** Comparison of two regimens of concurrent strength and endurance training. Med Sci Sports Exerc 22: 348–356, 1990.

86. **Saltin B, Blomqvist G, Mitchell JH, Johnson RL, Jr., Wildenthal K, and Chapman CB.** Response to exercise after bed rest and after training. Circulation 38: VII 1–78, 1968.

87. **Schoenfeld BJ.** Squatting kinematics and kinetics and their application to exercise performance. J Strength Cond Res 24: 3497–3506, 2010.

88. **Seiler S.** What is best practice for training intensity and duration distribution in endurance athletes? Int J Sports Physiol Perform 5: 276–291, 2010.

89. **Staron RS, Malicky ES, Leonardi MJ, Falkel JE, Hagerman FC, and Dudley GA.** Muscle hypertrophy and fast fiber type conversions in heavy resistance-trained women. Eur J Appl Physiol Occup Physiol 60: 71–79, 1990.

90. **Stone M, and O'Bryant H.** Weight Training: A Scientific Approach. Minneapolis: Burgess, 1986.

91. **Wehrlin JP, Zuest P, Hallen J, and Marti B.** Live high-train low for 24 days increases hemoglobin mass and red cell volume in elite endurance athletes. J Appl Physiol 100: 1938–1945, 2006.

92. **Wilmore J, and Costill D.** Training for Sport and Activity. New York: McGraw-Hill, 1993.

93. **Wilmore JH.** Alterations in strength, body composition and anthropometric measurements consequent to a 10-week weight training program. Med Sci Sports 6: 133–138, 1974.

94. **Woods K, Bishop P, and Jones E.** Warm-up and stretching in the prevention of muscular injury. Sports Med 37: 1089–1099, 2007.